PAUL ENSOM'S fascination with minerals, rocks and fossils goes back to his childhood. After leaving school he landed a job as an Assistant Curator in the Department of Palaeontology at the British Museum (Natural History) (1972-74). From there he went to Leicester University (1974-77) where he obtained a BSc (Hons) 2.1, in Combined Studies, contriving to make geology by far the biggest component! He remained at Leicester to obtain the Certificate in Museum Studies (1977-78), after which he was appointed Assistant Curator at the Dorset County Museum, Dorset (1978-1989), turning down the opportunity to embark on a PhD. While there he developed a particular love of Dorset geology and a special interest in the Purbeck Limestone Group. He supervised the excavation of two dinosaur track sites, in the process discovering new micro-vertebrate bearing strata. This in turn led to the discovery of several new species of amphibian and mammal and the first recovery of the eggshell of reptiles, including dinosaurs in the Purbeck strata. He has sub-edited geological articles for the *Proceedings of the Dorset Natural History & Archaeological Society* from 1981-89, and 2006 to date.

He left Dorset to become the Yorkshire Museum's Keeper of Geology (1989-97), home of a large and historically important geological collection. Thanks to parental holidays, he was already familiar with parts of this huge county and its fascinating geology. While in York he was responsible for the installation of two geology galleries. The first was 'Time Climb', which utilised a stairwell and an ex National Coal Board drilling rig to reveal what was below 'our feet'. The second, 'Hunters and the Hunted', was a display examining the relationship between the large marine reptiles and the abundant invertebrates which had once occupied seas across parts of the County. He is a keen supporter of the public understanding of science, and while based in Yorkshire organised two Fossil Roadshows, a four day 'Geoevents', and in 1992 he initiated and co-ordinated the 'Yorkshire Geology Month' which involved organisations and individuals from across 'greater Yorkshire'. He was a member of the Council of the Yorkshire Geological Society from 1992-1995 and again from 1996-1997. In 2000, after leaving the County, he was awarded the prestigious John Phillips Medal by the Yorkshire Geological Society for his contribution to Yorkshire geology, through his work at the Yorkshire Museum.

In 1997 he was appointed Head of Collections in the Department of Palaeontology, Natural History Museum, where his career had begun. He resigned in 2005, becoming a freelance museum consultant and geologist.

He has written and contributed to over 130 publications, many connected with Dorset's geology. He co-authored a *Bibliography of Dorset Geology* (1989), and wrote 'Discover Dorset' – *Geology* (1998). He continues to work and publish on the Purbeck Limestone Group amongst other things.

FOLLOWING PAGES
Crake Dale near Langtoft on the Wolds. A sharply incised dry valley, characteristic of these Chalk uplands (Chapter 12).

Yorkshire Geology

PAUL ENSOM

THE DOVECOTE PRESS

To my long-suffering and generous parents,
Donald and Sonia Ensom,
who in 1965 first introduced me to Yorkshire,
and over many years, did so much to encourage my
interest in geology.

First published in 2009 by The Dovecote Press Ltd
Stanbridge, Wimborne Minster, Dorset BH21 4JD

ISBN 978-1-904-34964-8
© Paul Ensom 2009

Designed by The Dovecote Press
Printed and bound by KHL Printing, Singapore

All papers used by The Dovecote Press are natural,
recyclable products made from wood grown in
sustainable, well-managed forests

A CIP catalogue record for this book is available
from the British Library

1 3 5 7 9 8 6 4 2

OPPOSITE PAGE *Goredale Scar (A view of Gordale, in the
Manor of East Malham in Craven, Yorkshire, the property
of Lord Ribblesdale)*. Painted in about 1813 by James
Ward (1769-1859).

Contents

Acknowledgements

David Burnett generously invited me to write a geological account of an English county of which I am very fond, and I am grateful to him for that. He has shown boundless enthusiasm and given support throughout this project. Thanks also to David's colleague Elizabeth Dean for her advice and good humour. I have been taken on a fascinating voyage over both known and uncharted 'waters'. My two sons, Tom and Jamie have been wonderfully patient while I have been on this journey, accepting both my occasional absences, and the sea of maps, papers and books which have ebbed and flowed across our kitchen table! On this last note, I wish to record a very real tribute to the generations of geologists, professional and amateur, who have observed, mapped and written on the geology of Yorkshire and the surrounding areas, and who continue to do so, enriching the multitude of strands which weave the county's varied geological history – a tapestry in rock. I have drawn on their collective knowledge. Textual references are not usually given, but lists of published works under 'Further Reading' give some idea of the wealth of literature which has been published.

Special thanks go to my father Donald Ensom, to Monica Price, and Richard Tayler who have read and provided thoughtful and constructive comment on the text during the writing process, and as importantly, encouraged and supported me in that task. Dr Mike Romano very kindly agreed to act as 'the publisher's reader' of the complete text, and we are very grateful to him for his comments. I alone accept responsibility for the information provided. In the dedication I have acknowledged the part played by my parents.

The Yorkshire Museum which employed me from 1989 to 1997 continued that educative process, providing me with the opportunity to further expand my horizons, to steep myself in the fabulous geological collections, and of course to meet those geologically active in the County, many through the Yorkshire Geological Society, for which I am most grateful.

My colleague on the staff, Stuart Ogilvy, must be acknowledged for the part he played in this phase of my career, as should Meriel Ensom for her considerable support during our sojourn in Yorkshire.

Many individuals and organisations have been generous in the help and advice they have given, in providing illustrations, and allowing details to be quoted. Staff at the British Geological Survey including Rob Armstrong, Paul Lappage and Alex Rotten (illustration production), Alan Clayton (publications) and Dr Mike Howe and Jim Rayner (collections) are thanked; special thanks go to Dr Dave Lowe (The BGS Lexicon of Named Rock Units), and to Roger Parnaby (cartography) for his expertise in the production of the maps of bedrock and superficial geology, and his ever cheerful involvement in overseeing the different elements generated for the book by BGS. Christopher Chaplin produced the map showing general physical features, and Dennis Burden the diagram illustrating processes and environments, and an ammonite.

I am grateful to Stuart Widdowson of the Coal Authority, and White Young Green plc, for kindly providing the data concerning water treatment at Woolley referred to in Chapter 13, and to Imogen Holmes-Roe (National Coal Mining Museum for England) for assistance with images in their collections.

The Yorkshire Geological Society's officers have been generous in granting permission for me to use published figures from the *Proceedings of the Yorkshire Geological Society* and in this respect I am especially grateful to Drs John Powell, Martin Whyte and Stewart Molyneux. These are acknowledged in the figure captions. Thanks also to Dr Tony Cooper for kindly providing an image of a Yorkshire Geological Society fieldtrip.

At the York Museums Trust, Mary Kershaw, Stuart Ogilvy, Richard Stansfield and Jackie Logan have been most helpful in providing images of specimens and pictures from collections in their care.

Craig Arditto (Northern Geological Manager for Tarmac Ltd) and Tony Lobban (Chief Operating

Officer, Viking UK Gas Ltd) have kindly provided images and information concerning their industries. I thank Dr Robin Cocks for generously offering us the use of the *Geodynamic* palaeogeographic reconstructions, and Dr Danielle Schreve for her explanation of some of the subtleties within the stratigraphy of the Pleistocene, and commenting on Table 12.1. Piers Browne has very kindly allowed me to use one of his etchings of the Yorkshire Dales. Mick Stanley communicated his now published *Alice in Wonderland* theory concerning the interaction of Charles Dodgson and large holes, and Pam Ross, one time employee of UK Coal and a coal enthusiast, has provided details of the industry's recent history and especially the Selby Coalfield. Mike Mandefield generously made available images of quarrying at Northowram and confirmed the use of Frosterly Marble in York Minster. The photographic collection of Trevor Croucher has been the source of many of the wonderful images used in this book; I am very grateful to him for the additional information he has freely given.

In addition, my thanks to the following who have provided advice on the sourcing of, or have most kindly provided images for the book: Dr Phil Allen (PGL), Chris Ambler (The Gritstone Club), Katie Anderson (NHM), Wendy Cawthorne (The Geological Society of London), Jamie Ensom, Dr Trevor Ford, Professor Jane Francis, Eliza Howlett (Oxford University Museum), Thomas Jorstad (Smithsonian Institution), Trevor Jowitt (r.ps.), Sharon McCutcheon (William Anelay Ltd), Dr Gerard McGowan (Cliffe Castle Museum), Dr Paul Kenrick, Angela Martin (for the Wild Cat Archive, held by the Women's Library London), Dr Angela Newton, Camilla Nichol, David Reid (Bluesky), Dr Mike Romano, Dave Ryall (Bradford Pothole Club), Adrian Sayers (Mother Shipton's Cave Ltd), Tom Sharpe (NMW), Mick Stanley, Shirlie Stone and Will Watts (Scarborough Museums Trust), Professor Barry Thomas, Dr Tony Waltham, Dr Ian West, Dr Martin Whyte, Matt Williams, and Martyn Wright (C W Sellors). Finally, my thanks go to Professor Joe Cann, Andy Currant, Ruth Maxwell-Hudson (Farrar Natural Stone), Dr Phil Manning, Dr Phil Murphy, Dr Roger Pabian, Dr Jon Radley, Sue Rawson, and Dr Andrew Ross, who kindly provided answers to specific questions. I would also like to thank Ildi Clarke for the superb index.

Source and copyright details of the illustrations in this book are as follows (Chapters in **bold**): Phil Allen (PGL) and Simon Stewart (BP): 14.3; British Geological Survey: 1.2, 3.2a-b, 4b, 6, 7b, 9, **5**.2, 6, 6.3-4, 7.4, 8.2, 7, 16, 19, 22-23, 26, **9**.6, 13, 18, 20, 12.10-11; Piers Browne: 7.2; Dennis Burden: 2.3, 9.21; C.W.Sellors: 10.13; Chris Chaplin: 1.3; Alan Clayton: 3.8; Robin Cocks and Trond Torsvik: 2.4a-d, 2.5a-d, 7.5a-b; Tony Cooper: 10.38; Trevor Croucher: Front cover, Frontispiece, Introduction, 1.1, 2.1, 3.1, 4.1, **3**, 5, **5**.1, **7**.1, 11, **8**.1, 3, **9**.1, 15-16, 10.1, 22, 11.1, 12.1, 13.1, 15.1, Donald Ensom: 10.9a; Jamie Ensom: 4.2, 5.5, 7.9, 9.10, 12.15, 13.5; Paul Ensom: 3.3, **5**, 7a, **4**.4, **5**.3-4, 8-9, **6**.1-2, 7.3, 6-7, 10, 13, 16-22, 8.5a-b, 6, 10-12, 15, 18, 21a-c, **9**.2, 3a, 7a, 8, 11a, 12c, 14, 10.2-3, 6-7, 8a-b, 9b, 11, 15a-b, 16-17, 23-27, 28a, 29, 31, 32a-c, 36, 39-41, 43-45, 48-50; 11.03-4; 12.3a-b, 4-5; 8-9; 12-14, 16, 18-21, 23a-b, 13.2-4, 6-8, **14**.2; Paul Kenrick: 7.15; Mike Mandefield: 8.20a-b; Sharon McCutcheon: 1.7; Mother Shipton's Cave Ltd: 13.10; National Coal Mining Museum for England: 8.13-14, 17; Natural History Museum, London: 6.5, 10.19, 37, 47; Oxford University Museum of Natural History: 12.6; David Ryall: 7.8, 12.17; Smithsonian Institution, National Museum of Natural History: 8.29; Tarmac Ltd, a member of the Anglo American Group: 7.12; Tate, London 2007: Contents pages; Barry Thomas: 8.27; Viking UK Gas Ltd: 9.3b, 17; Tony Waltham: 9.5; Martin Whyte: 10.28b, 30, 33; York Museums Trust (Yorkshire Museum): 1.5 (YORYM: 2004.357), 8, 2.2 (YORYM: 2004.358), 7.14, 8.4 (YORYM: YM139), 8 (YORYM: 2007.6520), 24, 25 (YORYM: 2006.2692.3), 28, 9.7b, 9, 11b (YORYM: 2008.884), 12a (YORYM: 2008.883), 12b (YORYM: 2008.886), 12d (YORYM: 2008.885), 19 (YORYM: 1981.55F), 10.4a (YORYM: 1997.142), 4b (YORYM: 1994.3181), 4c (YORYM: 1997.145), 4d (YORYM: 1997.141), 4e (YORYM: YM741), 4f (YORYM: YM430), 12 (YORYM: 1993.315), 14a (YORYM: 1994.1802.35), 14b (YORYM: 1995.6.9), 14c (YORYM: 1995.6.89), 14d (YORYM: 1994.1802.56), 14e (YORYM: 1995.6.68), 18 (YORYM: 1996.384), 20a (YORYM: YM502), 21 (YORYM: YM503), 35a (YORYM: G1012), 35b (YORYM: 2008.888), 35c (YORYM: G1015), 35d (YORYM: 2006.4603), 35e (YORYM: 2008.887), 42 (YORYM: 1986.2F), 11.2, 12.2a-b, 7a (YORYM: 2006.794), 7b (YORYM: G1201), 14.1 (YORYM: 2004.22), 5.

Efforts have been made to contact the owner of Figure 14.4. To them, and anyone else who we may have inadvertently omitted to obtain permission from, or not acknowledged their help, we offer our sincere apologies for having failed to do so.

Y ORKSHIRE has spectacular geology. The rocks and the exhilarating landscapes they create contain information and stories of events spanning millions of years, events that have fashioned and given character to this extraordinary county. Asteroids, colliding continents, volcanoes, huge rivers and catastrophic floods have all played their part in the dramatic geological history of the Earth. The landscapes of Yorkshire are the surface expression of this long and complex history. The stories are not always complete or easy to understand, but with patient detective work, the story becomes clearer and gaps may be filled. The rocks from which these landscapes are made are there to be read like the pages of a book; the stories they tell are quite fantastic!

In writing this book, an attempt has been made to distil the key elements of Yorkshire's long geological history from the great wealth of information generated, reworked and refocused by generations of geologists, all eager to disentangle and understand our geological past. My hope is that for all those who use this account, windows on the world of geology and Yorkshire – sometimes with unusual views – will be opened and appetites whetted, and that they will find themselves better equipped to appreciate the landscapes, urban, rural and industrial, they occupy as resident or visitor.

Introducing the text

Chapter 1 provides an historical and cultural background to geology in Yorkshire. Chapters 2 and 3 contain important scene-setting information, and chapter 4 gives a whirlwind tour through chapters 5 to 12. These latter chapters deal with successive episodes of this great story. Each begins with a synopsis giving certain key information: **Time**

Malham Cove from the south. This imposing rock-face is likely to be the back-wall of an 'extinct' waterfall. The fall was probably initiated along the line of the Middle Craven Fault which crosses from left to right approximately 700 yards south of the cliff (Chapter 12).

gives the geological period and date range covered. (Here and throughout the book, Ma is used in this account to indicate millions of years/millions of years ago and ka, thousands of years/thousands of years ago. The dates provided are mostly based on the latest published timescale of the International Commission on Stratigraphy, 2004). The **Latitude, Climate,** and **Environment** of Yorkshire at that time are given next, and **rocks** lists very basic information on deposits typically present. The synopsis ends with **Stratigraphy**.

Stratigraphy is the science which seeks to understand the relationships between layers of rock of different ages. Over the long history of the study of geology, many names have been allocated to 'label' and identify specific layers, or groups of layers of rock. In simple terms, the smallest unit sometimes used is a bed, which may be named after a commonly occurring fossil, e.g. 'The Sponge Bed' in the Chalk Group at Flamborough, or characteristic, e.g. a coal seam named the 'Better Bed'.

Layers of sediment which are sufficiently distinctive to be recognised and mapped across a geographical area are called members. Their names are often derived from places where good exposures of these rocks have been described, e.g. the Cove Limestone Member is named after Malham Cove. A number of members make up a formation, e.g. Malham Formation, and two or more formations comprise a group, e.g. The Malham and Kilnsey formations form the Great Scar Limestone Group. Beds and members are rarely referred to in this book, but formations and groups are. New research leads to reclassification and not infrequent changes of name. The stratigraphic terminology used here is, as far as possible, that of the British Geological Survey which publishes a wide range of maps and descriptive texts (*see* Further Reading).

Occasionally, a synopsis has two or more sets of stratigraphic detail given for rocks of the same age, such as in Chapter 7, where they are given for three areas: Stainmore and northern Askrigg Block; southern Askrigg Block and Craven Basin margin; and Craven Basin. This is because in a county the size of Yorkshire there are significant variations in the sub-surface structures in different areas and this is very evident in the rock deposited. A particular problem arises in *Drowning* (Chapter 7) and *Life on the Edge* (Chapter 10) where the British Geological Survey has not allocated a parent group to several formations.

At the end of the main text is a glossary of the more technical words used in the text. Words in the *Glossary* are printed in **bold** when they first appear in the text. *Museums – Portals to the past* provides a brief introduction to and list of museums with geological collections and or displays, with contact information. *Geological Societies* lists societies and groups both in and around Yorkshire and at a national level. *Further Reading* provides references to key literature and other suggestions for further reading. Finally there is an *Index*.

In line with, and to celebrate, the schizophrenic approach to units of measurement adopted in the UK, miles are used in preference to kilometres, but for geological measurements (depth of boreholes, size of specimens etc.) the metric system is employed.

Reference to localities in this book does not indicate the existence of a right of access. Permission should be obtained before entering private property. Local bye-laws including those of National Parks and the National Trust, and the Countryside Code should be observed at all times. Please read the *Geological Fieldwork Code* before carrying out fieldwork. The code may be viewed and downloaded at: http://www.geoconservation.com/GCCdocs/fieldworkcode.pdf Copies are available from the Geologists' Association, Burlington House, Piccadilly, London w1v 0ju. Please enclose a stamped and addressed envelope with your request.

Fieldwork is a hazardous occupation. Appropriate clothing, stout footwear and a hard hat are the minimum requirements; if hammering, eye protection is essential. Mountainous areas present an additional variety of potentially severe, and often weather related, hazards. The exploration of caves should not be undertaken by anyone who is not properly trained and equipped. All appropriate codes of conduct should be followed. Before going onto the coast, consult tide timetables and take advice on access etc. Large parts of the Yorkshire coast become inaccessible at high water, cliff bases are washed by the sea, and many of the cliffs are precipitous and very unstable.

Collecting of specimens, where permitted, bestows a certain responsibility on the collector. You may collect a specimen of great importance. Recording where the sample came from and other details is a sensible policy, ensuring that the full scientific value of a specimen may be realised. If possible, take photographs of the site and specimen in the position found.

ONE
Rooted in Rock

1.1 Kilnsey in Wharfedale, nestling below Low Ox Pasture
on the southern edge of a spur of limestone of the Great Scar
Limestone Group (Kilnsey Formation overlain by Malham
Formation). The spur is dramatically terminated by Kilnsey Crag
(Chapter 12), just visible to the right.

A grand design

Yorkshire boasts a combination of dramatic moorland landscapes in the Pennines and North York Moors, karst limestone scenery in the Yorkshire Dales, the rolling Chalk uplands of the Wolds, and a frequently wild and remote coastline. Subterranean landscapes were and are present in the labyrinthine passages, both natural and hewn by man and machine, under great tracts of Yorkshire. Artists and writers have found inspiration within this county's boundaries, drawing knowingly or subconsciously on the geological history bound up in the scenery surrounding them.

How we live is to a great extent tied to the landscape – even in the 21st century. Height above sea level, climate and weather, flora and fauna, agriculture, building materials, architectural styles and field walls are a direct result of geology. Oral traditions, literature, drawing, painting, sculpture, photography and music have been, and will continue to be influenced to a greater or lesser extent by the rocks beneath our feet, their past history, and the landscapes and societies derived from them. Understand our geological history and a greater appreciation of the landscapes of Yorkshire will follow, and from that, how this landscape has shaped both the people and history of Yorkshire – and beyond. This knowledge should be used by planners in National and Local Government, allowing them to make informed decisions regarding such issues as energy and water resources, waste disposal and where to build homes, and all this at a time when many believe the Earth faces a period of unprecedented change from human-induced climate change.

A quest for an understanding of Yorkshire's geological history, a microcosm of much beyond its borders, has fired minds and imaginations for over 175 years, and continues to do so. There is still much to learn about the geology of Yorkshire; discoveries will be made, new ideas and insights will be developed and the debates fuelled by these will challenge and inspire the minds of all willing to listen and read.

Yorkshire is taken here to include the East Riding of Yorkshire, North Yorkshire, and the metropolitan areas of South and West Yorkshire, and Hull. (*Fig* 1.2). This arbitrary unification makes the resultant 'county' of Yorkshire the largest in the United Kingdom with an area of 6,000 square miles. The sheer size of Yorkshire is further emphasised by the fact that there

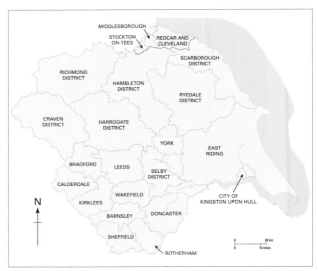

1.2 'Greater Yorkshire'. The map shows the administrative areas which make up this huge 'county'. For the sake of geological tidiness, those parts of Stockton-on-Tees, Middlesborough, and Redcar and Cleveland which lie south of the Tees, and which share the North York Moors National Park with Yorkshire, have been included on this and on Figures 3.2a-b.

are a total of 40 geological survey maps that cover the 'county', compared to 23 comparable sheets for Devon! Yorkshire is part bounded in the north by the River Tees and part by the Cleveland Hills, to the east by the North Sea, to the south in part by the Humber Estuary, and in the west by the Pennine spine, the western flanks of which face what traditionally has been the United Kingdom's prevailing westerly airflow. From the north to the south, an increasingly broad vale divides the county lengthwise, separating the high ground of the Pennines in the west from the 'Yorkshire Moors', Howardian Hills and Yorkshire Wolds in the east. Starting in the north near the Tees, the northern area is known as the Vale of Mowbray. York and surrounding areas, and particularly the area northwards which is bordered to the east by the Howardian Hills, lie in the Vale of York. To the south of York are the Humberhead Levels, the northern boundary of which is about 3 miles south of where the River Ouse becomes tidal at Naburn (*Fig. 1.3*).

Yorkshire inevitably contains a remarkable spectrum of environments and habitats, of different styles of farming and human settlement. The physical relief which has developed reflects the varied geology and ancient **tectonic structures** which lie beneath the surface. Given these stunning landscapes, there should

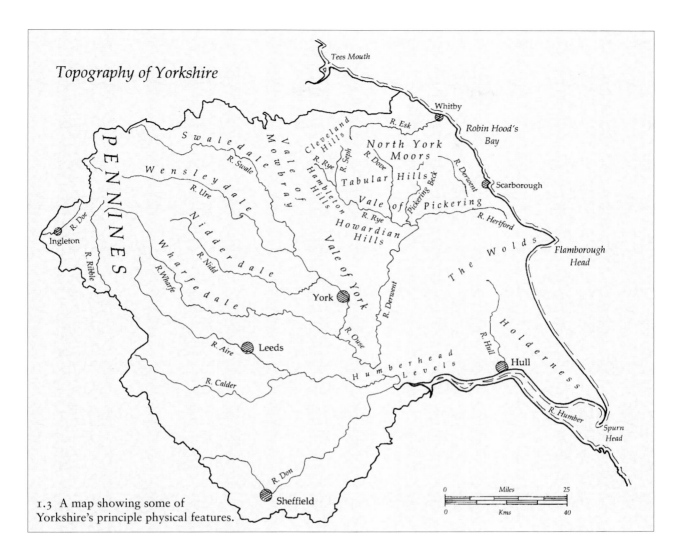

Topography of Yorkshire

1.3 A map showing some of Yorkshire's principle physical features.

be no surprise that most of the Yorkshire Dales and North York Moors National Parks, and part of the Peak District National Park, all lie within its borders. The landscapes which have inspired so many, and which we are privileged to enjoy, are like the images taken on a camera at the instant the 'shutter button' is pressed. In fact, the configuration of the county is part of a far greater and constantly evolving continuum; 'echoes of the past' are all around us, in the rocks and landscapes, and the life they support.

The cultural dimension

A good example of how the geology imparts character within the landscape is the use of local building stones in the buildings and walls across the region; each geologically distinct part of the county develops a vernacular architecture, combining suitability for purpose with the available materials. With the development of the railway network came a change. Exotic stones from outside Yorkshire were readily imported and we see them used increasingly in the 'sophisticated' architecture of the towns and cities, and the sepulchral monuments of the great urban cemeteries. Conversely, Yorkshire's raw products could be sold further and further afield and the quality of these materials ensured a demand which continues to this day from fewer, larger concerns where mechanisation plays an ever increasing role. 'York Stone' paving, in reality an industry based on the Elland Flags around Huddersfield, has been an hugely important industry with stone used on city streets around the United Kingdom.

Yorkshire's inspiring landscapes have been captured

on paper and canvas by residents and visitors for hundreds of years. James Ward (*see pages 4/5*), William Turner, Thomas Girtin and John Sell Cotman were visitors. William Rothenstein was born in Bradford, and Mary Lord at Birstall. The small fishing village of Staithes gave its name to the group of artists amongst whose number was Dame Laura Knight. Piers Browne took up residence in Wensleydale in 1975, since when he has captured the Dales in all their moods (*Fig. 7.2*), and recently David Hockney has returned to the county of his birth, and like so many others, drawn inspiration from the scenery created by the underlying geology. Henry Moore, born in Castleford, said of his Yorkshire roots 'Perhaps what influenced me most over wanting to do sculpture in the open air and to relate my sculpture to landscape comes from my youth in Yorkshire.' Barbara Hepworth, born in Wakefield, also paid tribute to the surroundings of her early years. Writers have also found an equal measure of inspiration. Works by the Brontë sisters inevitably drew on the atmosphere of the brooding and wild moorland landscapes against which their home in the village of Haworth nestles. Charles Dodgson may have been inspired by a large hole at Ripon (Chapter 9), and Alf Wight, aka James Herriot, practiced as a vet in Darrowby (i.e. Thirsk) and the Yorkshire landscapes within which he worked form the backdrop to his accounts of a rural practice. Barry Hines in *A Kestrel for a Knave*, a story set in a 20th century mining community, drew on his childhood near Barnsley. The landscape is the key component in Wainwright's *Coast to Coast Walk*, the 190 mile trek through three National Parks from the Irish Sea en route to the North Sea. Walking guides have been published to the Yorkshire Wolds, the Pennines and North York Moors, and our fascination with these powerful landscapes, with their industries, historic buildings and settlements, has been the *raison d'être* for a wealth of other guides and accounts.

Industries based on the geology have indirectly given rise to many hundreds of brass bands in Yorkshire, amongst which are some of the world's finest. In Queensbury in 1816, the precursor of the Black Dyke Band (formerly The Black Dyke Mills Band) was formed, with members drawn from the local woollen mill, itself a product of both local wool production and abundant water to power the manufacturing processes. The numerous collieries also had their own brass bands; the Grimethorpe Colliery Band is a particularly well known example. They competed with one-another and played on high days and holidays at the head of workers' processions.

Rhubarb, one of our national culinary delights, provides a wonderful example of how a variety of geological influences come together to underpin an important localised industry. The Rhubarb Triangle lies on the eastern flanks of the Pennines between Leeds, Bradford and Wakefield. Here, the Pennines provide a frost pocket delivering the cold conditions preferred at certain times in the growing cycle. A good supply of water is present and in the past the crop benefited from abundant cheap coal for heating the forcing sheds as required. By happy chance, nitrogen-rich waste from the local woollen industry has provided a slow release fertiliser.

In pursuit of knowledge

Yorkshire's mineral wealth was a crucial factor in the Industrial Revolution, which began towards the end of the 18th century and was in full swing by the 1830s. The exploitation of Yorkshire's mineral deposits created both wealth, and a thirst for knowledge. The 'outbreak of peace' across Europe with the defeat of Napoleon in 1815, the growth of industries reliant on natural resources, and the rise of a more leisured class with time to enquire after the sciences and arts, led to a burgeoning of learned societies across the country and Yorkshire was no exception. Philosophical and literary societies were founded in Bradford (1808), Leeds (1818), Hull, Sheffield and York (1822), Whitby (1823), Wakefield (1826), Scarborough (1827), Halifax (1830) and Barnsley (1833). These societies aimed to educate and inform through lectures and field trips, encouraging debate and experiment. Documentary evidence indicates that the events were often 'sold' as social occasions, a necessary palliative to the pursuit of science! Some did not stand the test of time, but others have, and they continue with annual programmes of events. In addition to these survivors, the Yorkshire (of which more anon) and Hull geological societies continue to contribute to our understanding of the geology of the region.

In the case of the formation of the Yorkshire Philosophical Society in 1822, a chance discovery of a hyaena den, *c*.120 ka, in a roadstone quarry on the edge of the Vale of Pickering (Chapter 12), was the catalyst triggering the Society's formation. A

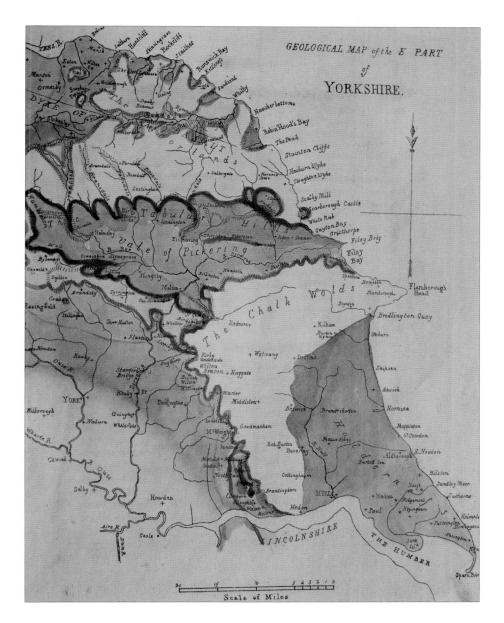

GEOLOGICAL MAP of the E. PART of YORKSHIRE.

Scale of Miles

museum was often a key element in the endeavour of these societies, and the Yorkshire Philosophical Society does not disappoint! Their museum housed the substantial collection of fossils which they amassed, ordered, classified, and exhibited to a public eager to view and learn from the abundance of newly discovered and often sensational remains of prehistoric life. These collections demanded careful attention and soon came under the care of John Phillips (*Fig. 1.5*) (1800 – 1874), the first Keeper of the Yorkshire Museum. He was appointed in 1825, and 1829 saw the publication of the first edition of his remarkable book *Illustrations of the Geology of*

1.4 A geological map of eastern Yorkshire, published by John Phillips, 1829, in *Illustrations of the Geology of Yorkshire; or, a description of the strata and organic remains of the Yorkshire Coast accompanied by a geological map, sections, and plates of the fossil plants and animals.* York. Compare this map with the bedrock geology of 2008 shown on page 30 in Figure 3.2a.

Yorkshire (*Fig. 1.4*). This was followed in 1836 by the companion volume dealing with the geology of the Pennine region. They ran to several revised and enlarged editions and remained the standard work of reference until the first part of the 20th century.

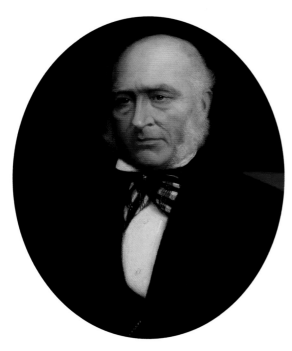

1.5 John Phillips (1800-1874), one of the pioneers of Yorkshire geology.

1.6 William Smith (1769-1839), seen here aged 69, is regarded as the Father of British geology. He was the influential uncle of John Phillips, and spent his latter years in Yorkshire, where amongst the geological legacy he left was the Rotunda Museum in Scarborough.

Phillips' first paragraph in the Introduction of his first volume acknowledges the work of others:

'In laying before the Public the fruits of my own researches into the Geology of the Eastern part of Yorkshire, I think myself called upon to notice the light which has been already thrown upon the subject, by the labours of those who have preceded me in this investigation.'

He goes on to acknowledge the importance of his uncle, none other than William Smith (1769-1839), often alluded to as the 'father of British geology' (*Fig.* 1.6). Phillips was later appointed Professor of Geology at the University of Oxford. After his death, his body was brought to York and afforded an almost state funeral with shops along the route closing as a mark of respect as he was taken from the Yorkshire Museum, his body had rested there overnight, through the city to York Cemetery.

William Smith, who had predeceased his nephew by 35 years, had 'retired' to Yorkshire towards the end of a pioneering and extraordinarily chequered career, which had culminated in the publication in 1815 of a quite remarkable map titled 'A delineation of the strata of England and Wales and part of Scotland' etc. The map, the first of this type to be produced, was based on his deep insight and appreciation that the different strata could be recognised and ordered by the distinctive suites of fossils they contained. Yorkshire is for the first time shown within the geological context of southern Britain. Before finally settling in Scarborough he was land agent to Sir John Johnstone of Hackness Hall, near Scarborough. While there, he suggested the design for the innovative Rotunda Museum (*Fig.* 1.7), built in Scarborough from stone quarried on the Hackness estate. In this museum, the succession of strata and the organic remains they contained, which previously he had both elucidated and described, were charted in what was almost certainly the first contrived 'climb through time'. This museum reopened in 2008 after being imaginatively restored and the historic collections redisplayed, a daunting project in which Johnstone's descendant, Lord Derwent, has performed a pivotal role. The Rotunda Museum both espouses the vision of 'Strata Smith' some 170 years on, and also tells of some of the discoveries and advances in geology made since the Rotunda first opened its doors to the public in 1829.

North of Scarborough, the North York Moors climb steadily, as do the cliffs which topple dramatically into

1.7 The Rotunda Museum, Scarborough re-opened after restoration in 2008. The innovative design of the Rotunda with 'a climb through geological time' was suggested by William Smith. The wings were added in 1860.

the North Sea. Few small towns and villages nestle between the precipitous cliffs along this wild and inhospitable coast, but one with an august part in the development of geology is the port of Whitby. At the mouth of the River Esk, Whitby has long maritime connections, once an important fishing port, and a centre for the jet industry which burgeoned during Victorian times. In 1823 The Whitby Literary and Philosophical Society was founded. Their museum garnered treasures from the local cliffs, famed for their great variety of fossilised remains from both marine Lower Jurassic rocks, and from the inter-fingering sequences of marine and terrestrial **sediments** that here compose the Middle Jurassic. The fossils ranged from the dactylioceratid ammonites, which with the addition of a head were transformed into mystical snakestones, the serpents petrified by St Hilda, and great marine reptiles. One of these became the centre of an ownership dispute, between a local collector, the Earl of Zetland, and indirectly the Yorkshire Museum which had unwittingly been in receipt of 'stolen

goods'! In contrast, the Middle Jurassic sediments yielded fabulous plant fossils; the sediments and their contents have been a focus of research ever since. In the early 20th century these same strata provided the first record of dinosaur tracks from Yorkshire. Their discovery and interpretation is a story which is still being unravelled. Many of the fossils collected along the local coast came to the Whitby Museum, the treasure house of the Whitby Literary and Philosophical Society. Here is a 'museum-piece' of a museum with wonderful displays of many of the specimens collected by the likes of the curator Martin Simpson (1800-1892), and George Young (1777-1848) who was secretary of the Society. The latter also supplied specimens to the Yorkshire Museum whose collections benefited, directly or indirectly, from

the fossil collecting activities of numerous amateur geologists in the region. Of particular importance was William Reed, a member of the medical profession, who developed an extensive collection purchased through dealers, who themselves were purchasing the collections of collectors. Amongst this material was much of scientific importance, and Reed is estimated to have given over 60,000 specimens to the Yorkshire Museum, substantial numbers of which were from Yorkshire (*Fig.* 1.8). These and other similar collections housed in both provincial and national museums throughout Britain, continue to fuel aspects of the research carried out by academics all over the world.

The links, revealed above, between the various players in Yorkshire's geological scene in the 18th and 19th centuries illustrates how Yorkshire's learned societies provide so rich a 'stockwork' for those that delve into the history of geology.

The science of geology, in all its guises, has advanced especially fast since the late 1960s, though our attempts to understand aspects of our world go back a lot further. Miners of metals from pre-Roman

1.8 The Fossil Room at the Yorkshire Museum, York, in the late 19th century.

times have used their powers of observation to predict where to dig for mineral wealth. In Yorkshire they dug increasingly deep tunnels and shafts to extract the immensely valuable ores of lead and iron, and of lesser importance, zinc and copper. Their skills, passed down from generation to generation, were a key to unlocking the mineral wealth of Yorkshire.

The same is true of coal mining. As demand grew, so was there a growing need to understand the geology of the county. This was a significant factor in the formation in 1837 of the West Riding Geological and Polytechnic Society. Their meetings brought together those interested in geology from the coal companies, academics, and amateurs, and provided them with an opportunity to deliver, and listen to lectures, and to debate the burning issues of the day. This organisation evolved via the Yorkshire Geological and Polytechnic Society into the Yorkshire Geological Society. These societies have a long history of publishing accounts of the geology of Yorkshire and beyond, and amongst their officers and membership there have always been numbers of the United Kingdom's leading geologists, both professional and amateur. In 1974 the Society published *The Geology and Mineral Resources of Yorkshire*, a substantial volume which drew on the expertise of academic and industrial geologists working within the county. This publication came exactly 50 years after the privately published, much used and admired, *Geology of Yorkshire. An illustration of the evolution of Northern England* by Percy Fry Kendall and Herbert E. Wroot.

In the 1820s, following the publication of the ground-breaking William Smith map, there were the first stirrings in the formation of a British Geological Survey. Initially the non-geologist field surveyors of the Ordnance Survey, which had responsibility for the accurate survey of the British Isles, were required by their Director to annotate the topographic maps with geological information and collect samples. Experienced geologists also became involved and amongst their number was John Phillips who contributed from 1840. During these early years there was a turf-war between those that wanted the geological survey work to remain as part of the Ordnance Survey, and those who saw the future in an independent organisation.

Finally in 1845, 10 years after the Geological Survey had been recognised and provided with one paid member of staff, The Geological Survey of Great Britain and Ireland was given formal recognition under an Act of Parliament. Twice during the Survey's history, there has been an outstation in Yorkshire, based in York between 1929 and 1938, and at Kippax near Leeds between 1959 and 1984. The first geological survey of Yorkshire was completed progressively during the second half of the 19th and first part of the 20th centuries with a series of 1:63,360 coloured maps with sections which used the small sheet format as published in the First Series Ordnance Survey maps. This format continues to this day though at the scale of 1:50,000 and with appropriate revision. Each geological map was accompanied by a comprehensive explanatory sheet memoir which could be purchased separately. Special memoirs have been published, such as *The Geology of the Yorkshire Coalfield* (1878) and the *Geology of the Northern Pennine Orefield Volume II* (1985) which covers the area from Stainmore to the Askrigg Block. The maps and memoirs, many of which are still available, have provided generations of professional and amateur geologist alike with a quite astonishing level of detail on the geology of Yorkshire (*see* Further Reading).

While the research output of the British Geological Survey is best described as the work of a team using ever more sophisticated techniques, there have been many individuals from Yorkshire, and beyond, who have contributed to the science of geology. Adam Sedgwick (1785-1873), born at Dent in what was then Yorkshire, became an influential figure in the world of geology as the Woodwardian Professor of Geology at the University of Cambridge, an appointment made in 1818. Today, the University's earth science museum is named in his honour.

Another geological son of Yorkshire, and one who deserves special mention, is Henry Clifton Sorby (1826-1908), who was born and died in Sheffield. Sorby was a self-taught scientist with interests spanning geology, metallurgy and the other natural sciences and also archaeology, architecture and art; the epithet of *polymath* does not seem out of place. He helped found Firth College which become the foundation of the University of Sheffield, where he endowed a Chair in the Department of Geology. His development of the study of rocks in thin section elevated an unappreciated aspect of geological science to new heights and this was acknowledged by the Geological Society when in 1907 they described him as the 'father of microscopical petrology'.

Through the activities of these early pioneers and their successors, armed with the wonders of late 20th and early 21st century technology, we inherit a rich literature describing the geology of Yorkshire, both seen and unseen. The rocks we live on are all named, a process which was initiated and systematically pursued by William Smith as he produced the first geological map of England and Wales. Successive generations of geologists have built on his foundations, using the names of places or landscape features to label and subsequently link different rock units across the county and beyond. Examples include the Austwick Formation after the village of Austwick nestling against the western flank of the Dales, and the Long Nab Member after Long Nab on the coast north of Scarborough. The Yoredales, was a term coined by John Phillips from the River Ure of the Dales, where he recognised the distinctive cyclicity of these beds (Chapters 7 & 8), and now named the Yoredale Group. Some of these **lithostratigraphic** terms have been superseded by others as our understanding of

TIMESCALE

Eon*	Era*	Period*	Epoch*	Rocks of this age in Yorkshire	Age	Chapter
PHANEROZOIC	CENOZOIC	NEOGENE	Holocene	√	10 ka - present	Chapter 12
			Pleistocene	√	2.65 Ma - 10 ka	
			Pliocene	x	5.33 - 2.65 Ma	Chapter 11
			Miocene	x	23 - 5.33 Ma	
		PALEOGENE	Oligocene	x	34 - 23 Ma	
			Eocene	x	56 - 34 Ma	
			Paleocene	√	65 - 56 Ma	
	MESOZOIC	CRETACEOUS		√	145 - 65 Ma	Chapter 10
		JURASSIC		√	199 - 145 Ma	
		TRIASSIC		√	251 - 199 Ma	Chapter 9
	PALAEOZOIC	PERMIAN		√	299 - 251 Ma	
		CARBONIFEROUS	Upper Carboniferous	√	325 - 299 Ma	Chapter 8
			Lower Carboniferous	√	359 - 325 Ma	Chapter 7
		DEVONIAN		√	416 - 359 Ma	Chapter 6
		SILURIAN		√	443 - 416 Ma	Chapter 5
		ORDOVICIAN		√	488 - 443 Ma	
		CAMBRIAN		?	542 - 488 Ma	
PRECAMBRIAN				?	Older than 542 Ma	

Yorkshire's stratigraphy has been refined.

From a map of Yorkshire's geology (*Fig.* 3.2a), we are able to note that present within Yorkshire are representatives of ten, possibly eleven, of the sixteen geological periods which make up the 542 million year span of time that geologists call the **Phanerozoic Eon** (*Table* 1.1) During this time, the world has seen the evolution of increasingly prolific and diverse life forms. The following chapters endeavour to bring this geology alive, and illuminate a landscape full of wonderful surprises. And oh yes – you'll never look at a geological map in the same way again!

Table 1.1 The divisions of geological time and date ranges, mostly based on the International Commission on Stratigraphy: http://www.stratigraphy.org/. Ma = millions of years, ka = thousands of years. N.B. The nature of the geological record and the coverage of each chapter are such that the dates given in the synopsis at the begining of a chapter may not always match those given in this table exactly. * Different divisions of geological time.

TWO
Born of Fire

2.1 Roseberry Topping. One might be forgiven for thinking this prominent and isolated feature was the result of a volcanic outpouring. In fact the strata are sediments of Jurassic age (Chapter 10), but hidden by trees in the left middle-distance are the excavations made to extract the sought-after hard igneous rock of the Cleveland Dyke (Chapter 11). The irregular ground in the foreground is the site of the Ayton Banks ironstone mine.

Over the sea and faraway

Mount Pinatubo on Luzon in the Philippines may seem very remote from Yorkshire, but for many months after the violent and spectacular eruption of this volcano in 1991, there were a series of especially memorable sunsets seen around the world. I remember admiring several from the windows of my office in Manor Cottage in the gardens of the Yorkshire Museum. This was a particularly fitting venue for such observations, as here was housed the fabulous collection of photographs of volcanoes, their eruptions and aftermaths, taken by the not inappropriately named Tempest Anderson (*Fig. 2.2*) (1846 – 1913), affectionately known as TA by those who work at the museum. Ophthalmic surgeon, J.P., Sheriff of York, a Director of the York Waterworks Company, President of the Yorkshire Philosophical Society and benefactor, TA had diverse interests, but above all his great passion was volcanoes. He is recorded as having had separate bags packed and at the ready for departure to an erupting volcano in either hot or cold climates. Had TA been alive, doubtless he would have set off to view and document Mount Pinatubo's eruption as he had so many others. Sadly the only visit he made to view Philippine and other Far Eastern volcanoes was in 1913, an expedition which ended with his death, aged 67, while homeward bound sailing through the Red Sea; he was buried in Suez.

2.2 *Tempest Anderson* (1846-1913). Oil on canvas, painted 1911-12 by Sir William Orpen, (1878-1931).

Volcanoes on our doorstep

This eruption on the other side of the world was yet another manifestation of the volcanic activity which has punctuated this planet's history, and while sunsets caused by an individual eruption do not survive for long, the record preserved in the resultant rocks often does. One such record exists for a series of breathtakingly violent eruptions which took place around 455 Ma, on what is now Yorkshire's doorstep, the Lake District.

Meticulous field work by members of the British Geological Survey and others over many years has unravelled the story of this complex series of eruptions and associated **intrusions**. The amazing preservation and the quality of the exposure in the Lake District's deep glacial valleys has made this a classic site for the understanding of this type of eruption in many locations around the world; the volcanic rocks and sediments seen around Mount Pinatubo bear close comparison with parts of the Lake District sequence. While Yorkshire lacks evidence of these cataclysmic events, the **igneous** activity which fuelled the Lake District's eruptions seems likely to have links to the intrusion of the Wensleydale **Granite** (Chapter 3) which lies unseen, some 500 m below Raydale, south-west of Bainbridge. Elsewhere in Yorkshire there is evidence of occasional minor ash-falls, there are a few small intrusions in some of the oldest rocks exposed in the county, and there is a small-scale but significant intrusion preserved across the North York Moors. These will be referred to in the appropriate chapters.

Yorkshire's fiery past

From what has been written above you will appreciate that in Yorkshire, igneous rocks are extremely rare at the surface, and yet the county's origins are entirely fiery. The coming together or accretion of the Earth from cosmic dust and debris took place some 4,567 Ma, initially forming a molten planet. The Earth cooled and had gained a watery hydrosphere by 3,800 Ma. After several evolutionary stages, including a probable interplanetary collision which led to the formation of our moon, the surface chemistry of the earth adapted to physical, chemical and biological changes, and an atmosphere evolved that would support the life forms which, through evolutionary processes,

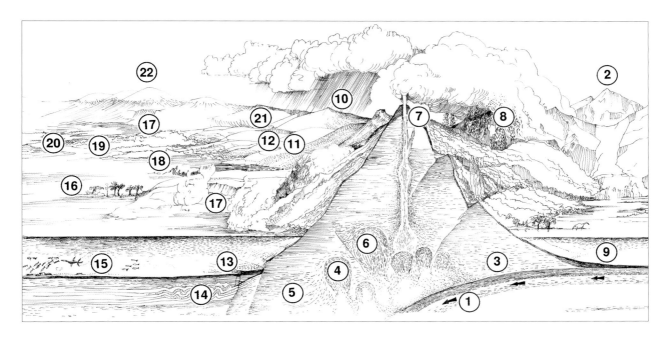

have given rise to the diverse floras and faunas with which we are familiar. The more or less synchronous accumulation and separation of different rock types eventually produced the different layers of the Earth's crust. The core of our planet is still molten and plays a significant role in **plate tectonic** processes. To help understand the geology of Yorkshire, an introduction to these fundamental processes is needed.

Yorkshire adrift through time

The lithosphere or surface of the Earth is composed of numerous plates of rock which float on the elastic and mobile **asthenosphere,** part of the upper mantle which with the underlying mantle surrounds the Earth's core. Some of these plates are denser than others and are generally created from molten rock along mid-ocean ridges; they are destroyed as they sink down under the less dense rocks which make up the continents. When two oceanic plates collide, one will be forced down below the other. As the plunging oceanic crust melts and rises to the surface, a string of island arc volcanoes is created. Sometimes oceanic plates push continental plates ahead of them and these may ride up one over the other; the Himalayas are the result of such an event. Collisions between plates trap recently formed rocks which would include marine sediments and in some cases the remains of volcanic island arcs. This new crust becomes part of the continental plate. Uplift occurs and mountain chains are born (*Fig.* 2.3). Processes like this are seen

2.3 Diagram showing the processes and environments which produce different rocks. The spatial arrangement of these processes and enviroments is purely diagrammatic! The numbers in brackets give chapters in which these processes or environments are referred to. 1. Pull of descending oceanic crust stretches plate leading to new crust being formed at mid-oceanic ridges (2); 2. Mountain building (2,6); 3. Friction and melting of rocks along descending plate (2); 4. Igneous intrusions rise towards the surface (2,3,5); 5. Deep burial and metamorphism (2,5,6); 6. Granite, e.g. Wensleydale (3,5); 7. Volcanism with lava flows and 'minor' intrusions e.g. Cleveland Dyke (11); 8. Volcanic ash falls (5,6,10); 9. Deeper oceans with muds, silts and turbidites (5,7); 10. Flash floods (9,13); 11-12. Deserts with dune sands, debris flows, and internal drainage basins (9); 13. Active faults (3); 14. Earthquake triggered slumps (7); 15. Deeper and quieter water with finer grained sediments. Mudrocks which may be organic. Thin limestones (7,9,10); 16. Shallow sea with pebble beds, sands, silts and mudrocks. (7,9,10); 17. Landslides both in-land and on the coast (11,12); 18. Warm shallow seas oolite shoals and other limestones. Isolation and desiccation leads to the formation of evaporites (7,9,10); 19-20. Coastal flats and river systems with deltas, occasionally inundated by the sea. Colonisation of alluvial plains and river banks by plants may lead to coal formation (8,10); 21. Eroding land surfaces (6,8,9,11,12); 22. Glaciation initiated on high ground and occasionally extending to lowland areas (12).

when simmering stock in the kitchen. A thin skin, the equivalent of the earth's continental crust will form on the surface of the hot liquid. Depending on the circulation of the liquid below, this will fragment and drift across the surface, collecting other smaller fragments on the way. Collisions occur and one may observe small linear crinkles which are the saucepan-equivalents of mountain chains. The plates of rock with their newly captured slabs of crust, in this ever-changing global jigsaw, are called terranes. A terrane will consist of a variety of different rock types. Any sediments may contain fossils quite unlike those in the rocks against which they have been juxtaposed during the collision. This should enable the two terranes to be distinguished. The positions of terrane boundaries, which are usually marked by faults, are not always entirely obvious and remain the subject of debate.

As an example of how Yorkshire fits into the dynamic process of plate tectonics we will skip a mere 4,027 Ma from the formation of the planet and, with the advantage of hindsight, look at Yorkshire over the last 540 Ma (*Fig 2.4-5, opposite and following pages*). In the early Cambrian Yorkshire was part of the **supercontinent Gondwana** and occupied a position close to the South Pole around latitude 60°S, between Cape Horn and the Antarctic Peninsula today. At around 465 Ma, the break up of Gondwana was heralded by the separation of Avalonia. This newly formed **microcontinent**, or terrane, began drifting northwards with Yorkshire occupying the northern margin of the eastern end. Over the course of the next 96 Ma, this northward drift continued until Avalonia collided with **Baltica** at around 30°S. This now enlarged plate continued to drift northwards, until during the late Silurian to early Devonian (420 Ma) there was collision with **Laurentia**, of which Scotland was a part, and closure from south to north like a pair of scissors in slow motion. The resultant continental plate is known as **Laurussia** or Euramerica, and Britain now lay at around 20°S, around the same latitude as Fiji and Tonga today. These continental collisions were the cause of a series of igneous events over many millions of years, including the outburst of volcanic activity in what is now the Lake District, and the associated intrusion of the Wensleydale Granite.

As the Carboniferous ended and Permian began, all the continental plates had merged to form one vast supercontinent named Pangaea. This great landmass remained intact for around 120 Ma. (Chapter 9).

During the previous 4,267,000,000 or so years since the earth formed, there had been six occasions when the continental plates had come together to form a supercontinent. Each cycle of coming together and then dispersing appears to have taken between 300 – 500 Ma, and Pangaea is currently the last example of a supercontinent in the geological record.

The British Geological Survey have adopted a broad three-fold division of these tectonic events, all of which have had a huge influence on the formation of the British Isles during the Phanerozoic. These cycles are the Caledonian covering events in the range 600 – 380 Ma, Variscan from 380 – 285 Ma, and Cimmerian-Alpine from 285 Ma to the present day. Such a neat division is already being questioned by some who believe that the Acadian event, considered to have been the final Caledonian paroxysm, is an early Variscan one (Chapter 6).

During the Jurassic, Pangaea started to break up and drift apart forming two continents, Gondwana and Laurasia. Yorkshire was part of the latter. The fractures, which usually start as **rift valleys** like the Great African Rift Valley, may eventually form new oceans similar to the Red Sea, which is a recent example, and the Atlantic, which is much older. As this 'drifting' takes place, the continents are constantly being eroded and the sediments transported either to the oceans or subsiding areas within the continents. The margins and interiors of continents may sag and be inundated with water. Not only do continents rise and fall, but sea levels do as well, something with which we are becoming increasingly familiar in the 21st century. The present rise in sea-level is in part due to ice sheets and glaciers decaying at the poles and on mountain ranges. These same processes around 311 Ma played a hugely important role in the nature of the sediments which accumulated in Yorkshire and elsewhere, and consequently on the subsequent economic history of Britain (Chapters 7 & 8).

For at least the last 540 Ma, plate tectonic processes have not only controlled where Yorkshire has been on the surface of the Earth, but have played a significant role in how the landscape has evolved. The gargantuan stresses and strains generated as plates slide past each other or collide, have huge implications for the foundations on which Yorkshire rests. Foundations are the focus of the next Chapter.

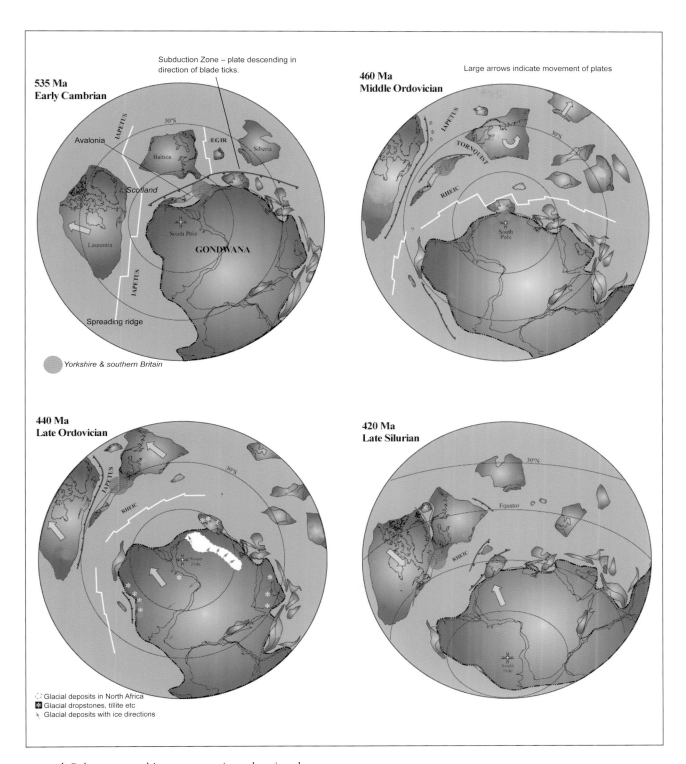

2.4a-d Palaeogeographic reconstructions showing the position of Yorkshire relative to continental plates and oceans during the Cambrian, Ordovician and Silurian. Figure 7.5a-b shows reconstructions for the Devonian to early Carboniferous. (Courtesy Cocks and Torsvik).

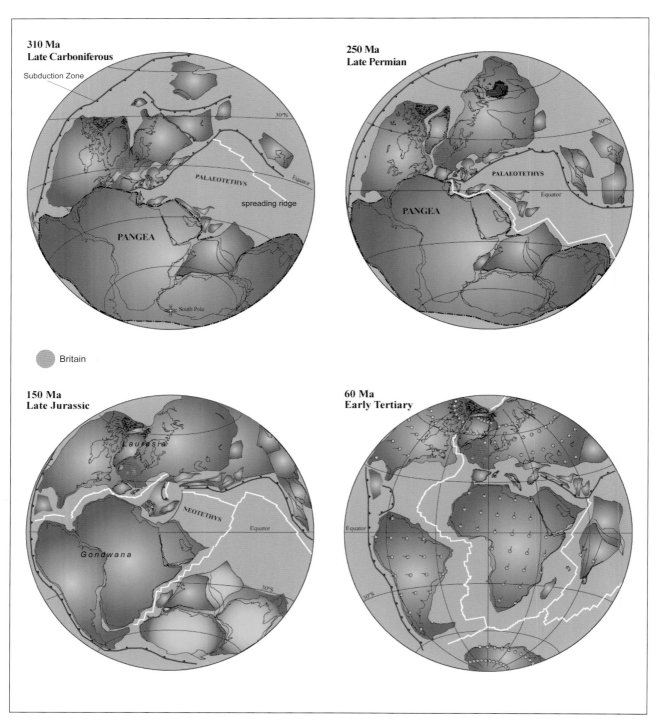

2.5a-d Palaeogeographic reconstructions showing the position of Yorkshire relative to continental plates and oceans during the Carboniferous (see also Figure 7.5b), Permian, Jurassic and Tertiary. (Courtesy Cocks and Torsvik).

THREE
Foundations

3.1 The wooded escarpment of Giggleswick Scar viewed
from just north-west of Settle. The escarpment marks the
line of the South Craven Fault. The Millstone Grit Group in
the foreground has been faulted down against the Great Scar
Limestone Group.

Setting the Stage

The **bedrock geology** (*Fig. 3.2a, see page 30*) of Yorkshire is often visible in crags, scars and sea cliffs. This helps geologists produce detailed maps of the different rocks present. Not infrequently the bedrock lies hidden beneath the often thick layers of **superficial deposits**, most of which have been deposited within the last 470 ka (*Fig. 3.2b, see page 31*). Mapping the bedrock geology of such areas is invariably challenging!

The character and distribution of the different rocks which form the bedrock geology of Yorkshire are closely linked to the structural framework of the **basement** rocks which underlie the county (*Fig. 3.3*). Over the last 400 Ma, different bits of Yorkshire's foundations have jostled with each other, reacting to the stresses and strains produced by plate tectonic processes (Chapter 2). This may be likened to a theatre set where sections of the stage come together, move apart and slide past each other while rising and falling at the same time. A more home-spun analogy may help you visualise this process if you imagine a group of young children lying close together on the floor. Loosely cover their bodies with a single layer of cushions and pillows. Leave them for a few minutes and watch as they become increasingly restless! See how some cushions collide and move upwards, others are pulled apart and collapse downwards while some slide past each other. Now imagine the same scenario

3.3 A diagrammatic representation of the geological structures which have controlled, and will continue to influence the geology of Yorkshire and the surrounding areas.

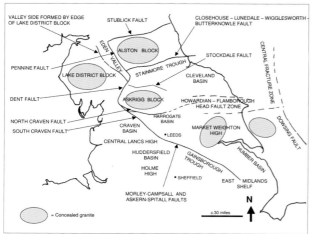

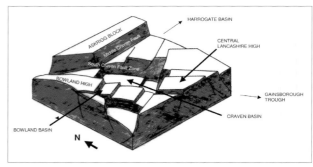

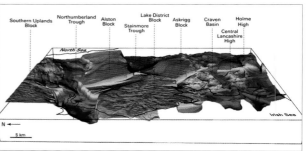

3.4a-b TOP (a) Block diagram (after Lee, 1988) showing the inferred positions of faulted Lower Palaeozoic 'basement' blocks which had a significant control on sedimentation during the Lower Carboniferous (Chapter 7).
BOTTOM (b) A 2005, computer generated, 3-D perspective of the top of the Lower Palaeozoic basement beneath Northern England produced by the BGS, based on seismic, borehole and outcrop data. There is a vertical exaggeration of x2.

but drape the cushions with two or three tablecloths with a damp paper tablecloth on top to represent the sediments deposited over the foundations. Watch how the table cloths between the cushions are warped, forming a variety of folds including **anticlines** and **synclines**. The weak paper layer may tear like some rocks do to form a **fault!** Over geological time, areas which once subsided may suddenly rise up, and *vice versa*, a process called inversion. This nicely demonstrates what the foundations of Yorkshire have been doing, over millions of years, as they are stretched and squeezed by plate tectonic processes (*Figs. 3.4a-b*).

Geologists use special terms to describe the different structural units which are jostled about, and over which the rocks seen at the surface have been deposited. The terms **block** and **high** are used to describe the buoyant or uplifted areas and **trough** and **basin** those areas between them where there has been greater subsidence. They are usually named after the locality where they occur; the Askrigg Block after the

village in Wensleydale, the Holme High after Holme to the south of Huddersfield, the Harrogate Basin after the famous spa town, and the Stainmore Trough (*Fig. 3.5*) after the Pennine pass between Barnard Castle in Durham and Brough in Cumberland are a few examples. Major faults are also named, as in the Dent Fault, or Howardian-Flamborough Head Fault Zone, so named because there are numerous faults and interrelated structures (Chapter 11).

Yorkshire's Foundations

The foundations of Yorkshire consist of rocks of at least Lower Palaeozoic age which having been deposited, were folded and faulted (Chapter 5). Their characteristics are in large part the result of the earliest phases of the Caledonian **orogenic** cycle, though even these structures doubtless echo events in that great expanse of time that predates the Phanerozoic. Though rarely seen, they underlie Yorkshire. These are the rocks into which the highly significant Wensleydale Granite was intruded. The presence of this medium-grained pink granite (*Fig. 3.6*), was initially deduced from **geophysical surveys** or 'geophys' in *Time Team* parlance. The granite was proved at a depth of 498.83 m. in a **borehole** in Raydale (*Fig 3.7a-b, see page 32*), south-west of Bainbridge, completed in June 1973. Impressively, interpretation of the 'geophys' had led the geologists to predict contact at a minimum of 500 m! The properties of this granite were recognised in the first description in 1974 as being very different from those of the Weardale Granite underlying the Alston Block. Controversially, subsequent studies have led scientists to suggest an **Ordovician** age of around

3.5 The desolate western end of the Stainmore Trough viewed from the northern margin of the Askrigg Block, looking north. The high ground in the distance is the Alston Block.

3.6 Two longitudinally cut sections through pieces of 6.3 cm diameter core from the Wensleydale Granite. They were taken from between *c.*506.5 - 507.5 m. below ground level near Raydale House, Raydale, in 1973. Until recently the granite was thought to be Devonian, but an Ordovician age is now considered likely.

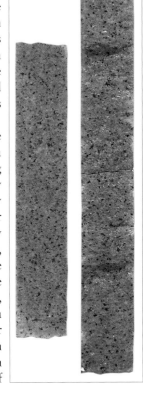

450 Ma rather than the younger 410 Ma **Devonian** tag previously worn by this intrusion, a date based on **radioactive isotopes**. The Askrigg Block is where and what it is because of this intrusion.

To the north, the Stainmore Trough and a concealed east-west trending fault form the boundary and are in turn bounded by the Alston Block, another uplifted block underlain by an intrusion of a younger, Devonian, granite. The Cleveland Basin lies to the east of the Askrigg Block, and the Carboniferous strata disappear beneath younger and unconformable Permian sediments. The southern and western boundaries of

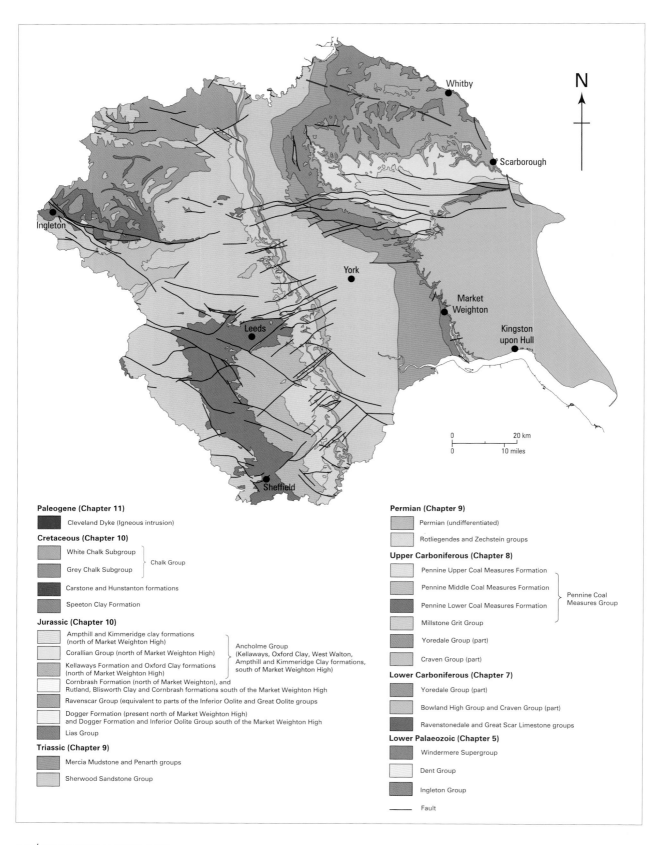

Paleogene (Chapter 11)

■ Cleveland Dyke (Igneous intrusion)

Cretaceous (Chapter 10)

■ White Chalk Subgroup
■ Grey Chalk Subgroup } Chalk Group

■ Carstone and Hunstanton formations

■ Speeton Clay Formation

Jurassic (Chapter 10)

■ Ampthill and Kimmeridge clay formations (north of Market Weighton High)
■ Corallian Group (north of Market Weighton High)
■ Kellaways Formation and Oxford Clay formations (north of Market Weighton High)
} Ancholme Group (Kellaways, Oxford Clay, West Walton, Ampthill and Kimmeridge Clay formations, south of Market Weighton High)

■ Cornbrash Formation (north of Market Weighton), and Rutland, Blisworth Clay and Cornbrash formations south of the Market Weighton High
■ Ravenscar Group (equivalent to parts of the Inferior Oolite and Great Oolite groups
■ Dogger Formation (present north of Market Weighton High) and Dogger Formation and Inferior Oolite Group south of the Market Weighton High
■ Lias Group

Triassic (Chapter 9)

■ Mercia Mudstone and Penarth groups
■ Sherwood Sandstone Group

Permian (Chapter 9)

■ Permian (undifferentiated)
■ Rotliegendes and Zechstein groups

Upper Carboniferous (Chapter 8)

■ Pennine Upper Coal Measures Formation
■ Pennine Middle Coal Measures Formation
■ Pennine Lower Coal Measures Formation
} Pennine Coal Measures Group

■ Millstone Grit Group
■ Yoredale Group (part)
■ Craven Group (part)

Lower Carboniferous (Chapter 7)

■ Yoredale Group (part)
■ Bowland High Group and Craven Group (part)
■ Ravenstonedale and Great Scar Limestone groups

Lower Palaeozoic (Chapter 5)

■ Windermere Supergroup
■ Dent Group
■ Ingleton Group

— Fault

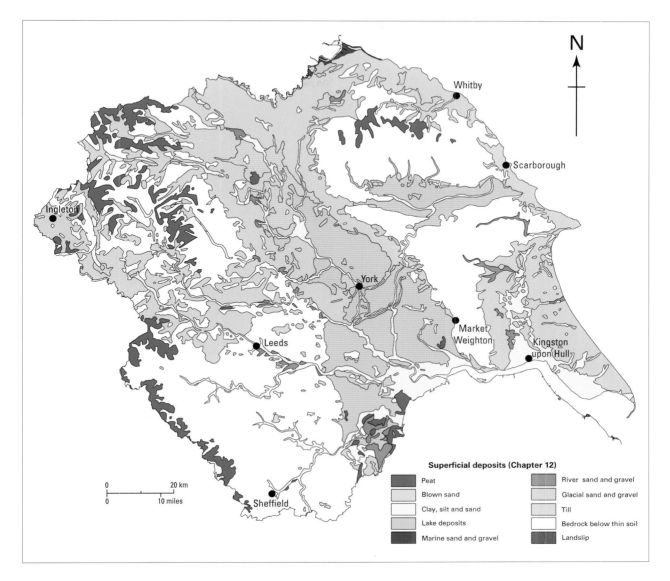

3.2a-b (a) OPPOSITE PAGE The bedrock geology and (b) ABOVE superficial deposits of Yorkshire. Those parts of Stockton-on-Tees, Middlesborough, and Redcar and Cleveland which lie south of the Tees and which share the North York Moors National Park with Yorkshire have been included on these maps.

the Askrigg Block are well defined. In the west, the Askrigg Block is bounded by the Dent Fault, with the **Craven Fault System** bounding the south-western and southern margins. Travel around the edge of the Yorkshire Dales, from Kirby Lonsdale, south and west of Giggleswick Scar and then skirting Settle, and you will be running alongside the Craven Fault Belt. Giggleswick Scar (*Fig. 3.1, see page* 27) is the

exposed fault-scarp of the South Craven Fault. This major fault zone passes eastwards, north of Skipton where the Middle Craven Fault is taken as the southern edge of the Askrigg Block, north of Bolton Abbey through Burnsall, and Pateley Bridge and then disappears beneath the Vale of York. Further east-west faulting is observed in the **Jurassic** strata in the Coxwold – Gilling area. Then slightly north of east from here at Flamborough Head there is a complex fault zone which is on a similar alignment; coincidence? Some suggest a connection of these two fault systems at depth. Some of these faults have long histories; faults within the Craven Fault Belt were active during the Carboniferous and on the down-faulted side sediments are seen to thicken into the

3.7a-b (a) Raydale from the road between Countersett and Marsett. The site of the borehole drilled by the Institute of Geological Sciences (now the BGS) was on the valley floor below the forested area on the right.
(b) The drilling rig on site between Raydale Grange and Raydale House, May-June 1973.

Craven Basin (Chapter 7). Faults such as this which continue to move through geological time, sometimes intermittently, are called growth faults.

The Market Weighton High or Block is a highly significant geological feature which separates the Cleveland Basin to the north from the Humber Basin to the south. The explanation for this high was identified in 1978, on the basis of geophysical evidence, as another influential granite intrusion. The top of this granite is about 2,500 m below the surface compared to Wensleydale's 500 m, and extends down for up to 13 km. The age of this granite is not known for certain, though the British Geological Survey tentatively suggests a Lower Devonian age. Geophysical evidence suggests that like the Wensleydale granite, the Market Weighton granite caused thinning of Carboniferous strata over its surface, and the rocks exposed in the area demonstrate that there was uplift during the Jurassic and Lower **Cretaceous** (Chapter 10).
How do granite intrusions control sedimentation,

mineralisation, and ultimately landscape? While we think of nearly all rocks including granites as heavy, the densities of different rock types vary considerably, and large volumes of different rocks will behave in different ways. Granites and other similar rocks are less dense than those which underlie the earth's crust of which the 'granites' are a part. This means that the granite and the overlying rocks have a tendency to 'float' upwards. Whatever its age, the Wensleydale Granite has helped keep the Lower **Palaeozoic** rocks, into which the magma was intruded, at or close to the surface, and has influenced sedimentation over the succeeding millennia. Without these granites buoying them up, overlying sediments would have been more akin to those in the surrounding troughs and basins and been buried to a greater depth. The Askrigg Block is seen to have influenced sedimentation, or the lack of it, during the Devonian and **Carboniferous**.

Cross from the Askrigg Block to the surrounding basins, and exposures will make you very aware of a dramatic contrast between the two environments.

In the former, the strata are almost horizontal with often massive limestones dominating much of the Lower Carboniferous sequence (*Fig.* 3.8), whereas in the latter, one encounters limestones and mudstones which are not infrequently contorted into great folds (*Fig.* 3.9). As for the mineralisation, heat generated by radioactive elements in the Wensleydale Granite has almost certainly driven the formation of the southern part of the Northern Pennine Ore field, centred on the Yorkshire Dales; the process is believed to be much the same as that which created the ore field of the Alston Block overlying the Weardale Granite (Chapter 9). Recent tests carried out in a borehole drilled into this 410 Ma granite have shown that there is still a valuable source of **geothermal energy** generated

3.8 'The horizontality' of the Askrigg Block landscapes is emphasized by Pen-y-ghent (right) and Plover Hill (left) with limestone pavements in the foreground. The Settle-Carlisle railway line runs across the centre of the photograph, which was taken from north of Selside in Ribblesdale, Easter 2008.

3.9 Anticlinal fold in Draughton Limestone (Craven Group), Wheelam Rock, Draughton, near Skipton. The alternating limestones and shales were deposited in the Craven Basin south of and adjacent to the Askrigg Block

by radioactive elements; the Wensleydale Granite is known to be less radioactive and its geothermal potential is commensurately reduced. Given their past impacts on the evolution of Yorkshire, there should be no surprise that many of the landscapes familiar to us are the product of these intrusions which continue to influence erosion and sedimentation. The Askrigg Block is still an area of significant relief today, with major rivers such as the Swale and Ure draining from west to east, following the dip of the strata; the River Tees occupies the Stainmore Trough between the Askrigg and Alston Blocks.

One school of thought has suggested that during the **Cenozoic, magmatism** in the northern North Atlantic connected to the development of Iceland, and possibly beneath the Irish Sea, imparted an easterly to south-easterly tilt across the British Isles; uplift of the Scottish Highlands has been in the order of 1-2 km with inevitably massive erosion. Unsurprisingly, the oldest bedrock formations exposed in Yorkshire are found in

the north-west and the youngest in coastal south-east Yorkshire. Often such simplification is misleading, and this is no exception. While the statement is true when describing the bedrock geology, a pedant would point out that much of Yorkshire is covered by the veneer of superficial deposits previously noted (*Fig. 3.2b*). These youngest sediments include deposits of sand and gravel which are of great economic importance, and are the product of the glaciers and rivers responsible for the most recent episodes of the sculpting of Yorkshire's landscape. Most of these sediments result from the **Devensian**, the last of the great glaciations to have affected the British Isles and which was followed by the **Holocene**, a period of climatic amelioration which continues to the present day. Strip away these superficial deposits and the map of the bedrock geology of Yorkshire (*Fig. 3.2a*) illustrates the way in which the strata become younger from the north-west to the south-east, and also shows that there is a central belt where there the strata have a slightly sinusoidal, but nevertheless dominant north to south trend. The pattern of outcrops, even when simplified, is nothing like as straightforward as the above description might suggest, a result of the long and complex geological history of Yorkshire.

FOUR

The Geology of Yorkshire in a Nutshell

4.1 The valley of the Little Don, or Porter, viewed from near Ewden, west of Sheffield. The lowest strata in the escarpment running from right to left and receding into the distance is the Rough Rock, at the top of the Millstone Grit Group. The top of the escarpment (Pennine Lower Coal Measures Formation) is capped by the equivalent of the Elland Flags (Chapter 8).

The essence of Yorkshire's long and complex geological history is distilled in the next eight chapters. The content of each is summarised here in a series of brief synopses providing a 'route planner' for what follows.

Glimpses of the Past (Chapter 5) opens the account as we catch sight of our foundations in the inliers of Lower Palaeozoic rocks. The rocks exposed are the worn down remains of mountains, with ages greater than 416 Ma, and possibly older than 542 Ma. These Ordovician and **Silurian** sediments, with possibly some of **Cambrian** or late **Precambrian** age, stretch from Ingleton to Malham. Folded, uplifted and then eroded on more than one occasion, they contain rare fossils, and occasional minor intrusions. They have been the subject of rigorous debate for over a century

4.2 The River Doe flowing through Baxenghyll Gorge. The strata are of the Ingleton Group.

and new ideas are still emerging regarding how old they might be! These rocks give rise to distinct landscapes and building stones, which contrast with those of the overlying limestones. They are in large part the rocks of the Waterfall Walk at Ingleton, known locally as 'The Scenery' (*Fig 4.2*), and provide important sources of roadstone. Lower Palaeozoic rocks form the foundations on which the deposits of the last 400 million years or so have accumulated.

Associated with the episodes of folding which these sediments were subjected to as Avalonia drifted northwards and collided first with Baltica and then with Laurentia (Chapter 2), there was at least one period of mountain building and granite intrusion. By early Devonian times, upland and mountainous areas had formed over large parts of northern Britain. There was now a period of intense erosion with the deposition of **continental deposits**. These are referred to as the **Old Red Sandstone** and are especially well exposed in south Wales and parts of Scotland but are absent from Yorkshire. Marine sediments were being deposited at this time over southern England on the northern fringes of the gradually closing Rheic Ocean which lay to the south of the microcontinent of Avalonia (Chapter 2) and north of the super-continent of **Gondwana**.

As described in *White mica and the missing millions* (Chapter 6) there is no evidence of rocks dating between 418 and *c.* 348 Ma in Yorkshire; in adjacent areas in the north-west thin **conglomerates** are present, but these are thought to be of early Carboniferous age, *c.* 359 Ma.

The uplift with consequent erosion of the Lower Palaeozoic rocks had been caused by the compressive forces produced by continental collision. Plates in motion now caused these ancient basement rocks, with their granite intrusions, beneath Yorkshire to be stretched. The result was the formation of blocks and basins (Chapter 3, *Fig. 3.4a-b*), some faulted against each other, some gently tilted. The blocks became islands as *The Drowning* (Chapter 7) of this eroded landscape started during the early Carboniferous. The sea gradually lapped onto a landscape which lay just south of the equator, eventually hiding all traces of this ancient sculpted surface. **Limestones** and mudrocks predominate in the lower parts of the sequence, the former giving rise to the distinctive limestone scenery of the Dales (*Fig. 6.1*), and provide the medium in which the fantastic cave systems were to form millions of years later.

Above the predominantly limestone, and limestone/shale sequences of block and basin comes a distinct change (*Fig. 4.3*). Sediments appear from a northerly source, representing a terrestrial influence in what had been a marine world. These sediments provide the first hints of the *Great Rivers, Deltas and Swamps* (Chapter 8) which will dominate northern England and eventually smother the irregular 'block and basin landscape' which existed at the start of this period. This 'smothering' more or less culminated in the formation of the coal deposits which were to fuel the Industrial Revolution, and have continued to provide a major source of power, including the potential for **coal bed methane.** The sandstones and gritstones have been extensively quarried and are used in many Yorkshire towns and villages, and for the small barns which so frequently dot the hillsides in the Dales. Carboniferous rocks are present across almost the whole county, though only exposed in the west where they rise from beneath overlying strata to form the Pennine spine with the band of bordering foothills on the eastern flank (*Fig. 4.1*). These foothills rise gradually from under the thick cover of the Permian to **Holocene** sediments. In the northern portion of Yorkshire, they form a broken, yet gentle and farmed,

4.3 Part of Wensleydale's southern skyline viewed from Appersett Pasture on the slopes of Widdale Fell. The peaks from left to right are Addlebrough, Green Scar, and Yorburgh. The rocks forming the valley side belong to the Alston Formation of the Yoredale Group.

landscape of scarps and dip slopes, dissected by valleys and scattered with towns, villages and farms. South of a line from a little north of Keighley and Leeds, coal bearing strata are present and suddenly we see a landscape with juxtaposed industry and agriculture (*Fig 4.4*), and appreciate the significance of the term Carboniferous, derived from the Latin, meaning 'carbon bearing'. Here the much enlarged towns frequently merge to become the great conurbations of Yorkshire. Though much change has been wrought through the late 20th century decline of coal mining, the monolithic coal fired power stations sometime described as 'temples of power', each with their hour-glass cooling towers, still dot the landscape, especially close to rivers east of the exposed coalfield.

The continental plate of which Britain was a part had by now drifted north of the equator. The northward movement of Gondwana, from which Avalonia had split millions of years before, saw the

4.4 Maltby Colliery, Maltby, near Rotherham, South Yorkshire. The Parkgate Seam of the Pennine Middle Coal Measures Formation is worked for coking coal (Chapter 8).

final closure of the Rheic Ocean and continental collision. The coming together of Gondwana and Laurussia, of which Avalonia had become a part, resulted in the formation of a new supercontinent called Pangaea (*Fig. 2.5*). Collision caused mountain building in the south of Britain, and in the area now occupied by Yorkshire, Carboniferous sediments were subject to uplift and erosion so that the overlying Permian sediments rest unconformably on them. Continental collision is certain to have contributed to an increasingly arid climate towards the end of the Carboniferous and set the scene for the Permian and Triassic.

The Heat is On (Chapter 9) during the **Permian** and **Triassic**. The scene opens with Yorkshire, a part of Pangaea, in an arid landscape with stony desert and scattered sand dunes; the desert's size has led to comparison with the present-day Sahara. Later the basin was flooded and an inland sea formed, stretching out across what is now the North Sea and over northern Europe. On the western margin this sea lapped onto a north to south trending line of low hills along the line of the Pennines of today. The inland sea was a vast evaporating basin where deposits of limestone, **gypsum**, salt and other evaporites accumulated. Yorkshire was on the fringes of this, with the maximum developments of these beds to the east and north-east of the county towards the

basin's **depocentre**. The sand dunes, limestones and evaporites of this period have played a significant role in the UK's gas and oil industry, and specifically in Yorkshire. The evaporites have an ongoing and significant impact on the stability of ground in parts of the vales of Mowbray and York. Deposition of the overlying Triassic sediments continued without apparent break, though low in the succession increasingly coarse sands and gravels do spread from south to north. These are the product of river systems flowing northwards from upland areas to the south of Britain, and may have been generated by monsoon rains. The water bearing qualities of these deposits have presented significant problems during the sinking of mine shafts. Higher in the sequence, the sediments are generally fine grained mudstones with a characteristic reddish orange colour. Evaporite minerals such as gypsum and salt are present, in part, probably the residues left after the incursion of the southern ocean known as Tethys had dried up. The main evaporating basin lay out in the central North Sea. Gypsum from these beds has been exploited within Yorkshire. Mineralising solutions invaded Carboniferous sediments across parts of the Askrigg Block. The Permo-Triassic strata are frequently draped by superficial deposits and poorly exposed across the band of relatively low lying land which runs from Middlesborough down to and through the vales of Mowbray and York, then southwards to south and east of Doncaster.

As the Triassic closed, the sea, which had made only a rare appearance during the last 100 Ma began to encroach on this arid region of the old supercontinent

of Pangaea. So began Yorkshire's *Life on the Edge* (Chapter 10). For the next 135 Ma, throughout the Jurassic and Cretaceous, the land now forming Yorkshire was sometimes submerged beneath a sea centred on the North Sea, sometimes above, and not infrequently somewhere twixt the two! This was a time of successive **transgression** and **regression** which led to the deposition of a wide variety of rock types, providing a splendid challenge to those trying to interpret the environment they represent. Jurassic rocks are superbly exposed along the east coast, and in the deep valleys, and along the escarpments of the North York Moors (*Fig. 4.5*) providing opportunities for further detailed study.

Despite this, a complete understanding of how extensive were the marine transgressions during this phase of Yorkshire's history remains somewhat speculative. The reason for the uncertainty is the limited extent of rocks of this age; little exposure exists west of the escarpment below the Hambleton

4.5 The Hambleton Hills escarpment with prominent landmark, 'The White Horse of Kilburn'. The escarpment is composed of the Ravenscar, Great Oolite and Corallian groups.

Hills on the western margin of the moors. To the south of the moors the uppermost Jurassic strata dip below the superficial deposits of the Vale of Pickering to only make rare appearances, and then disappear beneath Cretaceous deposits of the Wolds on the vale's southern edge. Though seldom exposed south of this line, the lowest beds are present as a narrow belt fringing the western margin of the Chalk where they form the western edge of a south-east plunging syncline. Most of our knowledge of these strata comes from **seismic surveys** and boreholes which have been drilled down in the search for oil and gas. What is now the North Sea remained a significant depocentre, sometimes connecting southern and northern oceans, sometimes becoming a more isolated feature into which rivers drained from the north and west.

Assisting in our interpretations are the great variety of fossilised remains found in the preserved rocks. Amongst these are the tracks of dinosaurs, and fossil plants. The former are at times abundant with such colossal numbers of tracks present at different **horizons** in *c.*240 m of sediment, that they collectively mark out Yorkshire as a **megatracksite!** These same strata are often rich in the remains of the plants which clothed the landscapes occupied by the dinosaurs. Over 600 plant bearing horizons have been identified and their contents have been a source of fascination to geologists and palaeobotanists since the early nineteenth century.

Though the Cretaceous saw the persistence of the pre-existing marine basin to the east, Yorkshire has a gap in the sedimentary record across the Jurassic – Cretaceous boundary indicating a period of stability at least, and possibly uplift. At around this time, the influence of the Market Weighton Block was growing, and the thinning of strata in the vicinity of this important feature is often apparent. To the north of this stable block, in the Cleveland Basin, Lower Cretaceous marine sediments of the Speeton Clay Formation are preserved along the coast, and for a little way inland along the northern edge of the Yorkshire Wolds. The east coast of England is particularly well known for the red chalk which lies between the Speeton Clay and the more typical white chalks. Yorkshire provides one of the two classic coastal localities where this rock can be viewed. The overlying white chalk forms the mass of the Wolds, now dissected by the great dry valleys which furrow their surface, and the lofty sea cliffs from Bempton around Flamborough Head to Sewerby.

The impact of a large **asteroid** closed the Cretaceous with a commensurately big bang, though there is speculation over the exact timing, and consequences, of this event. This mighty impact produced the Chicxulub Crater on what is now the Yucatan Peninsula in Mexico. The rocks of the British Isles record nothing of this event as they have been eroded away. However, a structure 80 miles east of the Humber Estuary, beneath the floor of the North Sea, is thought by some to be an impact site produced by one of many *Visitors from Outer Space* (Chapter 14) that have struck our planet. After 35 Ma, during which time the whole of Yorkshire along with most of Britain had been submerged progressively beneath the chalk sea, we loose sight of exactly what happened across Yorkshire. Uplift in the west is likely, though deposition may have continued to the east of the Pennines. The most recent phases of our landscape's evolution had commenced.

From the increasingly exposed landmass, the Britain we know would eventually emerge. *Landscape Evolution* (Chapter 11) considers what may have happened over those 63.7 Ma, when apart from a **dyke**, a fascinating igneous intrusion related to volcanicity in north-western Britain, no rock within Yorkshire represents this period of time which includes the **Paleocene, Eocene, Oligocene, Miocene** and **Pliocene**.

The final drama in Yorkshire's geological history began as the Pliocene came to a close, and Britain was plunged into the succession of often rapidly alternating warm and cold periods of the **Pleistocene**. Frequently the latter have been accompanied by more or less widespread glaciations creating *Ice Worlds and the Yorkshire Underground* (Chapter 12). Detailing exactly what happened is extremely difficult because each new advance of the ice sheets did much to obliterate evidence of the last! Existing valleys in the Pennines and their foothills, themselves possibly relicts of valleys formed during the Permian or Triassic, were deepened by the gouging action of the ice, much of which originated from beyond Yorkshire's boundaries, merging with local sources and creating larger ice sheet flowing south through the vales of Mowbray and York. Ice sheets encroached from the North Sea. Ice dams and **moraines** across some coastal valleys forced melt-water to find alternative routes such as the River Derwent's Kirkham Gorge.

Pleistocene climatic swings have been impacting on Yorkshire for around 2.65 Ma. Present generations are living through the Holocene, which apart from minor cold fluctuations has been a period of sustained warmth. The Holocene is regarded as the latest instalment in the Pleistocene saga. We now confront an uncertain future where we believe humans are having a significant impact on the world's climate with unpredictable consequences for Yorkshire's current inhabitants wherever they might live.

FIVE

Glimpses of the Past

5.1   Thornton Force, near Ingleton. The River Twiss flows over strata of
the Great Scar Limestone Group onto rocks of the Ingleton Group. The
unconformable contact is marked by the overhang seen clearly between the
main fall and overflow fall.

Time: Late Precambrian? – Silurian: c.542 – 418 Ma
Latitude: 60°S – 20°S
Environment: Marine – generally ocean floor
Rocks: Sediments include turbidites, conglomerates, sandstones, mudstones, limestones and calcareous nodules. Sedimentary rocks of volcanic origin include tuffs and bentonites. Igneous rocks are represented by an altered basalt dyke, and possibly the Wensleydale Granite which was proved in a borehole.
Stratigraphy:
INGLETON GROUP (Late Precambrian and or Cambrian and or Ordovician)
DENT GROUP (Ordovician): Norber and Sowerthwaite formations;
WINDERMERE SUPERGROUP (Silurian): Crummack, Austwick, Arcow, Horton and Neals Ing formations.

Setting the Scene

The oldest rocks present at the surface in Yorkshire are Lower Palaeozoic sediments. Occasionally they are cut by small dykes related to a later period of igneous activity. The sediments, grits, sands, silts and variable amounts of mud, were deposited in deep waters. They are generally hard and dark coloured in stark contrast to the pale grey of the overlying limestones. They are collectively described as turbidites, a term which relates to the mechanism of deposition. Sediments washed from the surrounding landmasses, accumulated on the continental shelves surrounding the shrinking ocean. Inherent instability and occasional earthquakes would trigger slumping, sending the precariously perched sediment cascading down to the deeper ocean floor as turbidity flows, a dense mixture of water and sediment. A super-dense flow of watery sediment does not mix with the surrounding water, but will hug the bottom, flowing over previously deposited sediments, often carving out distinctive sculpted flutes. Examples of such **sedimentary structures** may sometimes be seen in the outcrops of these ancient rocks, preserved as casts on the base of a bed of rock (*Fig. 5.2*). The most deeply incised end is at the upstream or proximal end. The groove then becomes shallower at the downstream or distal end. Flute casts belong to the group of

sedimentary structures called sole marks, providing a valuable indicator of the direction of the turbidity currents. A stack of beds each with their own sole marks preserved may provide evidence of turbidity currents changing direction over time.

Great thicknesses of turbidites accumulated over what is now Yorkshire but are only seen in the Craven **Inliers** on the western and southern fringes of the Askrigg Block, from Ingleton to east-south-east of Malham Tarn (*Fig. 5.3*). The inliers can be likened to a series of 'windows' which provide tantalising glimpses of the surface geology of Yorkshire before the Carboniferous transgression; they are limited in extent but much studied, and provide an invaluable view of a buried landscape. The only other way of sneaking a peek at these strata is by drilling holes down through the overlying rocks.

The oldest of these sediments are thought to form the foundations of much of Yorkshire (Chapter 3). Where exposed, they and the overlying Ordovician and Silurian sediments are responsible for a very different type of scenery compared to that associated with the overlying limestones. The great horizontal escarpments are absent; the landscape is frequently littered with a scatter of dark, algae and lichen covered boulders or angular blocks. In Crummack Dale, a

5.2 Sole marks known as flute casts seen on the base of steeply inclined turbidites of the Austwick Formation, Windermere Supergroup, near Moughton Nab. These sedimentary structures demonstrate that these turbidity currents came from a south-easterly direction.

5.3 Malham Tarn viewed across eroded strata of the Austwick, Arcow and Horton formations of the Windermere Supergroup. The tarn is underlain by rocks of the Horton Formation. These Lower Palaeozoic strata are overlain unconformably by the Great Scar Limestone Group which forms the high ground beyond and to the left.

little north-east of Austwick, one of the anticline's limbs can be seen forming an arched wall across part of the valley (*Fig.* 5.4). Taking a rather blinkered view of these areas, one could be forgiven for thinking this is a southern Lakeland landscape – and of course – the rocks are not dissimilar!

5.4 Lower Palaeozoic Austwick Formation exposed in a northward-dipping limb of an anticline in Crummack Dale, north of Austwick. Scattered blocks in the foreground are relics of glacial ice moving from left to right, plucking blocks from the exposed face (see also Chapter 12).

How old is the oldest?

Dating these ancient sediments and correlating, or linking, them to other sediments of a similar age has proved challenging. The problem faced by geologists is more easily understood if you can visualize what happened to these turbiditic sediments after they were deposited. Imagine layering and, in the food-preparation sense, folding together, but not too much, several different varieties of chocolate. This is the culinary equivalent of achieving a folded sequence of these Lower Palaeozoic rocks. Now slice off a horizontal layer and cover the remaining slab with marzipan representing the overlying Carboniferous rocks! Next take a knife and scoop out some small areas of marzipan in order to expose some of the layers of chocolate below. By doing this, you have in the geological sense created several inliers, or windows, which give you those glimpses of your

5.5 Steeply inclined strata within the isoclinal folds of the Ingleton Group exposed along the 'Waterfalls Walk' near Ingleton.

In view of this, one cannot fail to be impressed by two undergraduates from Leeds University who in the late 1940s carried out field work on the Ingleton inlier. They were able to shed new light on this ancient problem, and challenge the long-held wisdom. By interpreting their detailed observations of different sedimentary structures in the Ingleton Group, they were able to identify which way-up the steeply dipping beds (*Fig. 5.5*) were, and this led them to suggest that the oldest rocks of the Ingleton Group were folded very tightly like a series of compressed Ws, a type of folding described as isoclinal. Significantly this style of folding is very different to that of the sediments which overlie them.

Recently they have been reinterpreted using the sedimentary structures called flute casts, produced by turbidity currents, their value unrecognised when the first study was carried out. This has shown that while in essence their conclusions were correct, a lesser number of folds are present. The unfolded thickness of the Ingleton Group sediments has been recalculated and is now estimated to be in excess of a staggering 3 km. The rocks are turbiditic grits, sands and silts which can be collectively categorized as **greywackes**. The sediments are derived from a source where volcanic and metamorphic rocks were present. Dykes of altered **basic igneous rocks** have been recognised cutting the sediments, and these may be related to the same volcanic activity which was the source of the sediment of volcanic origin.

Poor exposure and faulting meant that the relationship between these oldest and the younger rocks overlying them remained something of a mystery until the discovery, in the 1920s, of fossils in sediments filling a fracture in the Ingleton Group turbidites. The fossils included a **coral, bryozoans, brachiopods, trilobites,** and **ostracods** and permitted the rocks to be identified as late Ordovician age. The deposit, called a neptunean dyke, was considered to be the product of sea-floor sediments being drawn into ancient rocks fractured by a contemporaneous earthquake. This type of dyke differs from neptunean dykes formed by the passive fill of an eroded surface. They are in distinct contrast to a fracture filled by molten rock forming an igneous dyke, which as previously noted, also cut Ingleton Group sediments. The differences between the turbiditic host rock and fossiliferous fill gave some credence to those who proposed an **unconformity** at the contact between these different strata. This view was confirmed in

earlier creation, i.e. the underlying strata. Now try and explain the relationship of the different layers you have exposed to each other! Remember you already have one advantage over the geologist trying to do this with the Craven Inliers, you know the original order of the different layers of chocolate. Enough said!

Because the rocks seen in these inliers have been subjected to more than one phase of **metamorphism**, folding and faulting, and are relatively unfossiliferous, interpretations of their age, their relationship to each other, and to strata exposed in the Midlands, the Welsh Borders, Anglesey, and the Lake District, has been the subject of considerable debate. They were first documented around 200 years ago and have been the subject of much scientific study since then. The methods used have become increasingly sophisticated, especially in the last decade or so, but still we struggle and especially with the oldest rocks preserved.

the 1970s when an exposure in a stream section unambiguously demonstrated the unconformable nature of the contact. While the more gently folded overlying rocks are identifiable as Ordovician and Silurian, there is an active debate about the age of the underlying turbidites and how they fit in with this early episode of our global wanderings. For a great many years researchers suggested a Precambrian age. In the 1980s a tiny fossil **acritarch** was found in one sample of sediment from the Beckermonds Scar borehole on the Askrigg Block. The sediment was considered to be the same age as those of the exposed Ingleton Group, and the acritarch was identified as early Ordovician. In 2005, and not for the first time, a Cambrian or possibly late Precambrian age was suggested as one scenario for these oldest parts of the sequence (See Chapter 2). A more recent study using **isotope geology** has suggested a minimum age of not more than 479 Ma, placing these rocks back within the Ordovician!

While these debates continue, comparisons of these sediments have been made with both those of the Welsh Borders and the Lake District; one school of thought leans towards the late Pre-Cambrian with a Welsh Borders link, and the other with the Ordovician and Lake District. In all this I cannot help but be reminded of US President George W. Bush's ex-Secretary of Defense Donald Rumsfeld's 'immortal lines', *there are known knowns; there are things we know we know. We also know there are known unknowns; that is to say we know there are some things we do not know. But there are also unknown unknowns -- the ones we don't know we don't know.* A final resolution of this conundrum is still awaited, but when forthcoming, will have huge importance for the positioning of a terrane boundary across this part of northern England!

Dating's placed on firmer ground

Conundrums aside, there are aspects of this story, the *known knowns*, which are relatively straightforward. The unequivocal Ordovician sediments which rest on the Ingleton Group were deposited after a significant lapse of time during which the underlying rocks were buried, folded and subjected to low-grade metamorphism. Uplift and significant erosion followed before the sediments of the Norber Formation were deposited around 445 Ma. Bearing in mind the *known unknowns*, this gap in deposition may have

been as long as 100 Ma or as little as 25 Ma! During this time interval, in the Lake District, there were the great volcanic eruptions that formed the Borrowdale Volcanic Group (Chapter 2). The volcanoes were part of an **island arc** which formed where the Iapetus Ocean Plate, and possibly that of the **Tornquist's Sea**, were being subducted beneath the Avalonian microcontinent (*Fig.2.4*). The uplift and erosion of the Ingleton Group sediments is likely to have been as a result of this process. While Yorkshire has no volcanoes dating from this period, the Wensleydale Granite, proved in a borehole at Raydale south of Wensleydale, has characteristics which suggest an equivalent age; perhaps Yorkshire came closer to a volcanic episode than is ever acknowledged – an *unknown unknown*?

The Ordovician Norber Formation, deposited over the eroded surface of the folded Ingleton Group, contains a fauna including trilobites and brachiopods. Fossils are generally scarce in the Lower Palaeozoic rocks of these inliers, so these are a welcome occurrence. Fossils are a bit like a torch, providing palaeontologists with one of the tools they need to illuminate and explore past environments, what are called palaeoenvironments. The careful description and study of fossils from the Phanerozoic has allowed the recognition of faunal provinces which are characterised by distinct groups of organisms, especially those that live in or attached to the sediment in shallow water and are confined to certain latitudes, much the same as we see in modern oceans today. Recognition of parts of the same faunal province, split up as continents have been torn apart and drifted away from each other, or different faunal provinces have been juxtaposed, has provided one form of evidence when attempting plate reconstructions through geological time. A detailed knowledge of the number of different types of organism which have existed through geological time permits the identification of a series of global extinction events. These occur over periods of short duration when varying numbers of **species** become extinct. The Norber Formation's fauna is a small picture of life before a major extinction event, the second largest in our planet's history, when 85% of all marine species died out.

There is much discussion about the causes of mass extinctions, but significantly, this event is coincident with a period of major glaciation, a time of falling sea levels and of global cooling as ice sheets developed.

5.6 The Austwick Formation, Windermere Supergroup, exposed in Arcow Quarry, Ribblesdale.

The overlying, fossiliferous Sowerthwaite Formation coincides with this episode and interestingly has a conglomeratic horizon. Conglomerates are normally indicative of shallow waters and a high energy environment, and this would be compatible with the changes in sea-level known to have occurred at this time; an initial regression with sea level falling by as much as 100 m was followed by a rapid transgression as the ice sheets waned and sea levels returned to where they had been and even higher still. Another interesting feature of this formation is the occurrence of layers of volcanic ash called **tuffs**. These may well be the calling cards of eruptions in the Lake District igneous province, though the length of time separating these from the earlier eruptions leads experts to state that they represent a distinct phase of igneous activity and were not the reawakening of a dormant volcano.

The Crummack Formation is of earliest Silurian age. The sediments consist of black mudrocks, siltstones and occasional limestones. The nature of these sediments, and the **graptolites** they contain, indicate deeper water conditions which is in keeping with the rapid rise in sea level following the end of the Ordovician glaciation. The overlying sediments include turbiditic and **arkosic** sandstones, bioturbated siltstones, micaceous siltstones and muddy silts of the Austwick (*Fig.* 5.6), Arcow, Horton and Neals Ing formations with a total thickness in the order of 1600 m. These sediments are all that remains, at least visibly, of the final filling of the narrow oceanic trench which was all that was left of the once mighty Iapetus Ocean. This was in sharp contrast to environments elsewhere in Britain; while the Arcow Formation was accumulating, the clear warm waters of the Welsh Borders and Midlands saw the deposition of the Wenlock Limestone with the development of coral reefs and spectacularly rich faunas. There at least is evidence of the rapidly evolving life forms which had found so many niches to occupy after the great extinction at the end of the Ordovician. Here life was much less flamboyant. The deep water environments filling with **clastic sediments** washing down from the continental margin were not ideal habitats for corals, brachiopods, trilobites, and **crinoids** and their ilk. The rapidly evolving planktonic graptolites and rare **cephalopods**, which could drift or propel themselves through the water, are occasionally found. The former are especially important as sometimes their distribution provides a means of linking different layers of rock in widely separated parts of the world today. This process is called correlation and the fossils which make this possible are zone fossils; throughout this book, other types of fossil will be referred to in this context. Because oceans were connected, the colonial, tuning-fork like graptolites were able to disperse over great distances. Where remains of the same species of graptolite are found, we know we have rocks of the same age!

The Horton Formation, exposed in quarries in the area, provides an example of how a well known and much studied rock unit can still come up with the unexpected. Towards the close of the 20th century, researchers examining several beds of more readily weathered sediment in the Horton Formation, found evidence of what are likely to have been the closing paroxysms of the igneous province which had fuelled the super-charged 'Lake District eruptions' 35 Ma before. They found several layers of volcanic ash,

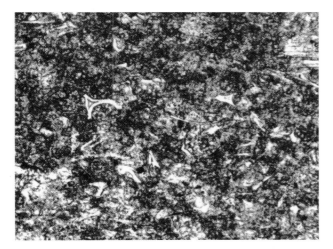

5.7 Photomicrograph (image x 10) of a thin section of a bentonite (volcanic ash) from the Horton Formation, Combs Quarry, Foredale. The cuspate glassy shards are stark white. From Romano and Spears, 1991, *Proceedings of the Yorkshire Geological Society*, Vol. 48, 277-285, by permission of the Council of the Yorkshire Geological Society.

known as bentonites, which had been carried by the wind from a more distant source, before settling on the ocean surface and sinking to the sea floor. Analysis of the sediments indicate a water depth of between 500 – 1000 m where nothing lived. Fortuitously the ashes' chemical composition had triggered the formation of **nodules** soon after the ash settled on the sea floor. This rapid lithification, associated with the nodule formation, preserved the outlines of the shards of volcanic glass which were a component of the ash fall (*Fig.* 5.7). Shards not preserved in the nodules were subject to rapid breakdown and are not preserved in

the bentonite. The bentonites have gone on to play an extraordinary role in the research being carried out to explain what happened to this region after the Silurian (Chapter 6).

A valuable resource

These rocks, the finest grained of which may have developed a **slatey cleavage** during one or two phases of metamorphism, are rather jagged in appearance, in marked contrast to those above the **angular unconformity**. As already noted, where exposed, they contribute a very different landscape to the western edge of the Dales. They have been a source of building materials and roadstone for centuries, and the industry continues today; approximately 1 million tonnes of 'gritstone', which is especially valued for its anti-skid qualities, is produced annually from the two operating quarries, one near Ingleton and one at Helwith Bridge in Ribblesdale (*Fig.* 5.8). This volume may decline as existing planning consents expire, and tougher controls on quarrying within the National Park take effect. There is of course a complex web of issues which have to be weighed in such debates; examples are the demand for local employment

5.8 Helwith Bridge Quarry (foreground) and Dry Rigg Quarry (left distance) extracting Horton Formation gritstones. The silhouette of Moughton Nab is seen above Dry Rigg Quarry. To the right is Arcow Quarry working Austwick, Arcow and Horton formations. Barely visible above Arcow Quarry is Foredale Quarry, exposing the Great Scar Limestone Group. Between Arcow and Dry Rigg quarries is Combs Quarry, Foredale (*Fig.* 6.3), exposing Horton Formation flagstones.

5.9 Drystone walling near Austwick. Lower Palaeozoic rocks predominate but some Carboniferous limestone (pale grey) has also been incorporated.

James Sowerby (1757-1822), naturalist, illustrator, publisher and founder of the 'Sowerby dynasty' of natural history illustrators and publishers. Sowerby already had both an earthly, he had been publishing illustrations of Yorkshire fossils since 1812, and an heavenly connection to Yorkshire, through the **meteorite** which had struck close to Wold Cottage in 1795 (Chapter 14). He illustrated and described two samples of the Moughton Whetstone on Tab. CCCCXVI of volume V of his *British Mineralogy* in 1817 (*Fig.* 5.10). The distinctive banding is thought to be the result of weathering of the iron minerals in the original sediment, a process which some think took place after these rocks were forced closer to the surface during the later phases of the **Caledonian Orogeny**, or what is now being mooted as the first 'ripples' of the **Variscan Orogeny**. They were subjected to weathering taking place in relatively arid conditions during the following 59 Ma. An alternative view has been voiced, which invokes the 'freezing' of stress fields in the rock.

5.10 Liesgang rings in Moughton Whetstone, Austwick Formation, Windermere Supergroup. Two samples (top right and top left) illustrated by James Sowerby, 1817, *British Mineralogy*, Tab. CCCCXVI.

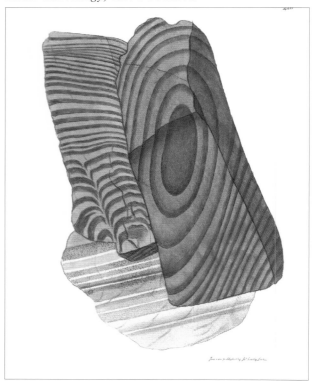

opportunities even within a highly mechanised industry, and spin-off work in the local community, *versus* the visual impact on a National Park and the large number of lorry movements each day. Some of these 'gritstone' quarries were colloquially known as 'granite' quarries. Perhaps the name was a marketing ploy, or perhaps the coarse rock with a passing resemblance to granite, and a toughness to match, which was quarried at Old Ingleton Quarry, was responsible for initiating this geological travesty! Whatever, the name Old Ingleton 'Granite' Quarry has stuck and is to be found in published accounts of the geology of the area.

Field walls are built entirely or partially from irregular pieces of these local rocks (*Fig.* 5.9), and gate posts have in the past been fashioned from the larger slabs. Houses and farm buildings have also drawn on the supply of this durable local stone. A more unusual product, and particularly delightful, were the whetstones produced from a siltstone of the Austwick Formation. Whereas most whetstones have a uniform colour, the Moughton Whetstones have distinctive, alternating and sharply demarcated, deep red and pale green bands that rejoice in the name of Liesegang rings. A specimen of this unusual rock had been supplied 'by favour of the friendly Mr Danby' to

SIX

White Mica and the Missing Millions

6.1 Studrigg and Studrigg Scar viewed from Norber. The valley floor and lower slopes are composed of folded and eroded Lower Palaeozoic strata, further significantly modified during the Pleistocene. The overlying and unconformable Great Scar Limestone Group forms the prominent limestone cliffs along the west side of the tongue of limestone which lies between Ribblesdale and Crummack Dale, and which is terminated at Moughton Nab. The grassy slope to the left of Studrigg on the extreme left of the image is Hunterstye where the east-west trending Crummack Anticline is present.

Viewing the towering bastion of Pen-y-ghent from
Horton-in-Ribblesdale, or the valley sides below
Moughton and Studrigg scars from Crummack
Dale, you will be aware of a change in character
between the valley floors and lower slopes, and the
higher, often steep and sometimes precipitous valley
sides of Carboniferous limestones (*Fig. 6.1*). Here,
in the valley bottoms, are exposed the foundations
of Yorkshire as described in the previous chapter.
The change from the folded and faulted, gritstones,
sandstones and mudstones of the Lower Palaeozoic

6.2 The distinctive notch at Moughton Nab west of
Helwith Bridge, Ribblesdale, marking the angular
unconformity between the folded Horton Formation and
the overlying and horizontal Lower Carboniferous Great
Scar Limestone Group.

6.3 The angular unconformity between the Lower
(folded) and Upper Palaeozoic (horizontal) is superbly
demonstrated at Combs Quarry, Foredale, near Helwith
Bridge. The time that elapsed between the deposition of
these two very different strata with their different faunas
and floras is around 60 Ma.

strata to the overlying and almost horizontal Upper
Palaeozoic, Carboniferous rocks (Chapters 7 & 8) is
sometimes marked by a thin dark line, occasionally
developing into a notch representing a pause, a
hiccup in the continuum of deposition. The notch-like
development is particularly well seen in the silhouette
of Moughton Nab (*Fig. 6.2*).

The junction between these very different rocks is
specifically called an angular unconformity (*Fig. 6.3*)
because the beds above do not lie in the same plane as
those upon which they rest. This can leave no doubt
that sufficient time elapsed for all the sediments, bar
the very last deposited, to be buried, to become rock, to
be folded and faulted, and finally to become an eroded
land surface. The eroded surface was progressively
inundated by a slowly rising Carboniferous sea, a sea
in which the sediments deposited were very different
from those upon which they rested. We know from
the age of the overlying Carboniferous rocks on the
Askrigg Block (Chapter 3), the time interval between
the last Silurian sediments and the first Carboniferous
sediments to cover them was approximately 70 Ma.
This is around 5 million years more than has elapsed
since the dinosaurs became extinct, and during which
time our modern flora and fauna has evolved to what
we see today! Thornton Force above Ingleton provides
an excellent view of the unconformity (*Fig. 5.1*).
Here, the even older, possibly Precambrian, Ingleton
Group is overlain by Carboniferous sediments. Off

the Askrigg Block, the pause in sedimentation was not quite so long.

In the last chapter mention was made of the discovery of bentonites in the Horton Formation. Serendipity was on the side of geologists when these ashes were deposited and lay undisturbed on the sea floor. Buried and gently heated, these rocks were metamorphosed. While undergoing this process, the minerals in one particular bentonite layer were transformed into a remarkably pure deposit of clay-like white **mica** called **illite**. The bed of poorly preserved volcanic ash has turned out to be a bit like a digital camera. Years of study and experiment, often driven by the oil industry, has led to the development of some remarkable techniques which permit geologists to read the rocks burial history using minerals like these. In this case the isotopes of potassium and argon, present in the illite, were isolated and provided dates for the final phase of metamorphism, the time when these rocks were buried to the greatest depth. The illite was re-crystallised, and the weak cleavage in these rocks was developed, somewhere between around 418 – 397 Ma at a temperature of around 250°C. But this is by no means all that was revealed. Study of the physical properties of the illite crystals allow the pressure at which the metamorphism took place to be calculated, and by drawing parallels with other well studied metamorphic areas, an estimate of the minimum depth of burial was calculated. This turns out to be in excess of 3,500 m, and according to some of the calculations could be greater than 10,000 m.

If the latter calculations were correct, we are confronted with the astonishing thought of the bentonite buried under a pile of sediment thicker than Everest is high, before erosion started! The immediate questions that spring to mind are: Could this really be? What sediments were deposited? Where have they all gone? The presence of the Mell Fell Conglomerate at the northern end of Ullswater, and another similar deposit called the Polygenetic (= rock types from many sources) Conglomerate which crops out a few miles north-east near Melmerby (*Fig.6.4*) and Cross Fell, are of interest as they are considered to be rare relics of a more extensive Old Red Sandstone (ORS) cover in this region, lending some credence to the findings based on the study of the white mica. What remains of the Mell Fell Conglomerate is thought to be greater than 1,500 m thick. Based on the burial history of the bentonite, the assumption is that further Silurian marine sediments were deposited above the

6.4 The Polygenetic Conglomerate, thought to be of Lower Devonian age, exposed near Melmerby, on the northern margin of the Vale of Eden in Cumbria. Though approximately 22 miles north-west of Yorkshire, this outcrop provides a rare clue as to what happened during the Devonian across this region.

Neals Ing Formation, perhaps continuing into the Devonian, but how thick this sequence was can only be guessed at.

In order to achieve the correct burial depth, researchers have made the assumption that thick piles of the ORS **facies** including conglomerates and sandstones, accumulated over Yorkshire during the Acadian Orogeny, previously thought of as the last paroxysm of the sequence of mountain building events known as the Caledonian Orogeny. At this time, northern Britain, Scandinavia and the Appalachian Mountains in the United States of America which were part of the same landmass (*Fig. 7.5a*), had been forced up to form a significant mountain chain (*Fig. 6.5, see page 52*). In an interesting and exciting departure, recent research has led to the conclusion that the Acadian deformation event during the Devonian was being driven by tectonic activity to the south and represents the start of the next mountain building phase known as the Variscan Orogeny (Chapters 2, 7 and 8). Whatever the event that formed these mountains, their erosion generated colossal volumes of coarse sediment including boulders, cobbles and pebbles, as well as sand. These sediments were washed southwards and deposited over north-west England, including Yorkshire.

After many millions of years, a change in the **tectonic regime** led to uplift and erosion across north-west England and these very same sediments were stripped off and recycled along with the now newly exposed uppermost Silurian sediments. All this rock debris, recycled and freshly eroded, ended

6.5 An artist's impression of a Devonian (Old Red Sandstone) landscape. Initially Yorkshire and the surrounding region were buried beneath great thicknesses of sediments eroded from mountain chains like these which lay to the north. Later these sediments and parts of the folded Lower Palaeozoic rocks were eroded. The resulting landscape was progressively submerged by the Lower Carboniferous sea.

up being transported still further south towards Wales and the Midlands. Here tectonic stretching was causing subsidence, making accommodation for the great volume of sediment. This erosive cycle explains the absence of any obvious trace of ORS sediments across Yorkshire. No evidence of the very earliest Carboniferous has been recorded across Yorkshire either, and we must conclude that the pause in sedimentation which began during the Devonian lasted for around the first 10 Ma of the Carboniferous.

To matters igneous. To say there are no Devonian rocks in Yorkshire would be disingenuous. While we know of no buried sedimentary relicts of the ORS, the Devonian may be represented by a minor intrusion of **lamprophyre** which cuts the Ingleton Group, and there is the disputed age of the Wensleydale Granite (Chapter 2). What, if any, are the implications of an Ordovician or Devonian age for the intrusion of the Wensleysdale Granite? The intrusion would have increased the geothermal gradient, and contributed to the uplift of the basement rocks which are now missing. Evidence from the Raydale borehole shows that the Lower Palaeozoic rocks into which the granite was intruded had been removed, and that Carboniferous sediments rest directly on almost 4 m of weathered granite. Another minor intrusion of **quartz microdiorite** was intersected by the Beckermonds Scar Borehole, drilled midway between Pen-y-ghent and Raydale in 1976. While of uncertain age, the intrusion is considered to postdate the Wensleydale Granite, and pre-date the mineralisation of the Askrigg Block (Chapter 9). Last but no means least, an early Devonian granite is believed to lie, at considerable depth, below the Market Weighton High (Chapter 3), exerting considerable influence on the east of Yorkshire during the Carboniferous, and Mesozoic (Chapter 10).

Finally, what of life? With no sediments of this age across Yorkshire, the county contributes nothing to the fossil record. Elsewhere in the UK and around the world there is evidence of life aplenty, and amongst that life, fishes with bony fins abound. Then something extraordinary happens which will have a profound affect on our planet. Somewhere, a water-based vertebrate, with rudimentary limbs adapted from the bony fin structure, emerges on to the land. In so doing, a more than 360 Ma odyssey of tetrapod evolution is triggered, towards the end of which our own species will emerge.

SEVEN

The Drowning

7.1 Limestone pavements in Great Scar Limestone Group at Long Scar.
Pen-y-ghent and Plover Hill in the distance capped by strata of the Yoredale
and Millstone Grit groups.

Time: Lower Carboniferous: 348 – 325 Ma.

Latitude: 5°S – 0°

Climate: Semi-arid tropical – humid tropical.

Environment:

ASKRIGG BLOCK: Emergent, shoreline, shallow marine, and later, deltaic.

CRAVEN BASIN: Emergent, then shallow becoming a moderately deep water basin

Rocks: Boulder beds, conglomerates, sandstones, quartzites, siltstones, shales, clays, seatearths, marls, limestones including dolomites, minor evaporites, chert and coal.

Stratigraphy:

STAINMORE TROUGH & NORTHERN ASKRIGG BLOCK:

Ravenstonedale Group: Raydale, Marsett and Penny Farm Gill formations.

Great Scar Limestone Group: Tom Croft Limestone, Ashfell Sandstone, Fawes Wood Limestone, Garsdale Limestone and Danny Bridge Limestone formations;

Yoredale Group (part): Alston Formation (part only – to the base of the Great Limestone Member).

SOUTHERN ASKRIGG BLOCK & CRAVEN BASIN MARGIN:

Stockdale Farm Formation (No parent group*).

Great Scar Limestone Group: Chapel House Limestone, Kilnsey and Malham formations.

(* No higher ranking stratigraphic unit has been allocated for this formation)

CRAVEN BASIN:

Bowland High Group: Chatburn Limestone and Clitheroe Limestone formations.

Craven Group: Hodder Mudstone, Hodderense, Pendleside Limestone and Bowland Shale (part) formations.

7.2 'Winter: buzzards and Addlebrough'. Etching by Piers Browne. The artist combines acute observation with fascinating distortion in a landscape subtly enhanced by winter snow fall.

Setting the Scene

Lower Carboniferous strata, capped by outliers of Upper Carboniferous rocks, are well exposed within the Yorkshire Dales National Park in the north-west of Yorkshire, and underlie much of the county at varying depth. The limestones within these strata have been sculpted to form the unforgettable landscapes and challenging cave systems of the Dales, hugely attractive to fell-walkers and cavers. Travel across the central belt of the Dales, from Ingleton in the west to Leyburn in the east, and you cannot help but be impressed not just by the grandeur, but by the extraordinary horizontality of the landscapes you pass through; Littondale, Wharfedale, Bishopdale and Wensleydale are all fine examples. The eye is teased by endless perspectives, and left marvelling at the startling contrast of the great sweeps of pale grey limestone pavement (*Fig.* 7.1), of the occasionally tree-clad escarpments, of the grit-stone edges, and the vegetated drapes of peaty moss. Frequently these vast features are delicately bisected by miles of dry-stone wall running parallel to the array of stepped escarpments, and then tumbling precipitously down to the valleys below. First dustings of a winter's wind-blown snow, and the lingering drifts at thaws-end, enhance these features with dramatic effect (*Fig.*7.2). Beneath these timeless hills, horizontal beds of limestone are intricately perforated by the water courses which have formed as the host rock has been dissolved and worn away; cavers heaven! (Chapter 12). The great flat-topped fells of Whernside (736 m), Ingleborough (724 m) and Pen-y-ghent (694 m), stand sentinel on the western edge of the Dales (*Fig.* 7.3), their profiles a further dramatic testament to this horizontality.

While faults, vertically dislocating beds of rock by tens of metres, and folding of the strata become

increasingly common towards the Stainmore Trough, and original **sedimentary structures** are revealed in the beds of sandstone and grit, we see little that interferes with what is an overwhelmingly horizontal grand-design within the central part of the Dales. The 1:50000 Geological Survey maps of this region are like the subtlest of marbled papers, predominantly of swirling blues for the limestones with flashes of orange picking out the impersistent sandstones (*Fig.* 7.4). Why should these rocks maintain virtually the same attitude as when they were deposited?

Blocks and basins take control

The Lower Carboniferous strata of the troughs and basins south of the Askrigg Block are very different. Information from boreholes and exposures show us that significantly more Lower Carboniferous sediment accumulated in the basin (more than 2,200 m) than on the Askrigg Block (around 800 m). Despite the absence of any exposures of the most deeply buried Carboniferous strata, we do know that those sediments mantling the eroded basement rocks, predate the sediments which eventually overwhelmed the similarly eroded basement rocks of the Askrigg Block. In the Craven and Harrogate basins and Bowland Trough, **mudrocks** are more abundant in the succession. In contrast to the Askrigg Block, folding and faulting of strata in the basins and troughs is common (*Fig.* 3.9). Why have these rocks been much more disturbed than those across the central and southern parts of the Askrigg Block?

The answers to the questions posed in each of the

7.3 High peaks to the east of Ingleborough poke above the clouds on the south-western edge of the Yorkshire Dales; Ingleborough (right foreground) and Simon Fell (left foreground). The distant peaks from left to right are Buckden Pike, Plover Hill, Great Whernside, Pen-y-ghent, and Fountains Fell.

7.4 'Natural marbling'. A portion of the 1:63,360 Hawes geological map (E050), published by the British Geological Survey, illustrating the intricacies and great beauty of mapped geology.

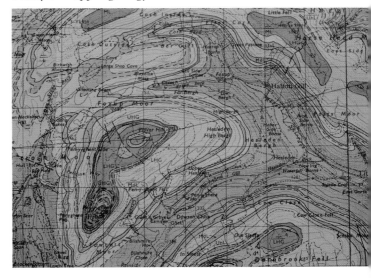

last two paragraphs are down to plate tectonics and granite. During the Lower Carboniferous, block, basin and trough were united in the shared eroded landscape upon which these strata were to be deposited, but there the similarity ends. The behaviour of this old landscape during the Lower Carboniferous

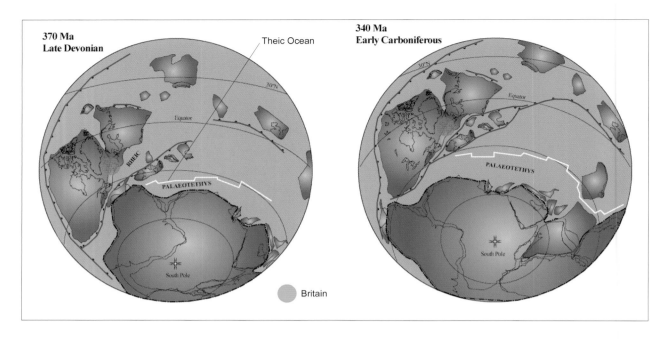

7.5a-b Palaeogeographic reconstructions showing the position of Yorkshire relative to other continental plates. (a) Late Devonian; (b) Early Carboniferous. (See also Figures 2.4 and 2.5). (Courtesy Cocks and Torsvik).

reflected the change in tectonic regime which was being experienced across southern Britain. Following the compression in the aftermath of the closure of the Iapetus Ocean and associated continental collision which had forced up the now eroded mountain chains, there was tension across northern England. This was brought about by the start of the next, Variscan, tectonic cycle (Chapter 2) now evolving in southern Britain and beyond. Here a narrow gulf separated the Avalonian part of Laurussia, of which Yorkshire was a part, from the united microcontinents of Armorica and Iberia. Moving northwards towards them was the ancient continent of Gondwana, gradually closing the Theic Ocean which lay between them (*Fig. 7.5a-b*). The oceanic crust was being subducted northwards beneath Armorica and Iberia. This process saw the continental crust to the north of the subduction zone being pulled downwards, stretching the crust across northern England. The eroded and already fractured landscape began to react to these new stresses and strains. The lithosphere beneath northern England, like a piece of blue-tack when stretched, became thinner in places, and encouraged an increase in heat flow from deeper in the mantle. This in turn caused localized melting of the asthenosphere with important

consequences for the Upper Carboniferous when charmingly named 'sag basins' formed (Chapter 8).

Though no volcanic deposits of Lower Carboniferous age are known from Yorkshire, rocks of the same age in the Peak District have two volcanic centres where **vent agglomerates**, lavas, and tuffs are preserved. The closest of these is a mere 12 miles south-west of Sheffield. Towards the end of the Carboniferous and into the succeeding Permian, compressive forces, generated in the final phase of the Variscan Orogeny, triggered faulting and folding (Chapter 9); the Wensleydale Granite was like a great structural bastion, protecting the overlying sediments from these effects. Using a similar analogy to the children, cushions and tablecloths (Chapter 3), this time place a large saucepan (granite) upside down on a protected surface and surround with cushions. Now drape tablecloths (sediments) over the top. Now push the cushions and draped fabric towards the static saucepan; crumples will occur in front of but not over the rigid pan. *Voilá* – a kitchen table Askrigg Block and Craven Basin!

The briny comes to Yorkshire

Across Yorkshire, the plate tectonic, tension-triggered rift faulting, and the resultant higgledy-piggledy assortment of faulted and tilted blocks, and **half-grabens,** came into being (*Fig. 3.4a-b*) as described

in Chapter 3. The scene was set for the return of the sea after an interval of some 60 Ma. The marine inundation was a slow process, and for a while the old landscape continued to shed sediments of varying degrees of coarseness into the low lying parts of the basins and troughs. A borehole just over the county boundary, near Nelson in Lancashire, penetrated Old Red Sandstone-like sediments which may be a record of some of the earliest Carboniferous deposits. In Yorkshire, the earliest unequivocal Carboniferous deposit is the Stockdale Farm Formation where the Craven Basin abuts the Askrigg Block. As in the Stainmore Trough, sediments accumulated on coastal tidal flats in arid conditions. A type of limestone called a **dolomite** is frequently found in these lowest beds, and deposits of **anhydrite** are also known, precipitated out where sea water evaporated away. Similar deposits extend from the Stainmore Trough onto the Askrigg Block, and were revealed when the c. 342 Ma Raydale Dolomite was found resting on the weathered surface of the Wensleydale Granite in the Raydale Borehole (Chapter 3).

As Yorkshire was progressively overwhelmed by the encroaching Carboniferous sea, so a coastal landscape developed and near-shore deposits were laid down. Around 14 miles south-west of the Raydale borehole, near Austwick, there is a fossil cliff face where Ordovician rocks have been entombed by Carboniferous sediments. The section shows boulder and cobble sized pieces of rock from both Ordovician and Silurian rocks. These and the cliff were covered by pebbly Carboniferous Limestone (*Fig. 7.6*). Today this cliff is re-exposed on a hillside; this may not be coincidental. The exhumed cliff is facing down the valley and the glacier which is known to have filled and flowed down Crummack Dale, may have plucked away the more weakly bedded Carboniferous strata resting awkwardly against the Lower Palaeozoic that formed the fossil cliff-line. In one of the sections at this site, a number of vertical structures are visible, defined by parallel rows of rotated and aligned rock-fragments (*Fig. 7.7*). These puzzling features may be of an organic or inorganic origin, formed in this marginal environment composed of coarse presumably Carboniferous sediments banked against the sea-cliff. If the Carboniferous Limestone is traced up the section, the rocks become progressively finer grained, a characteristic expected in sediments being deposited during a transgression as more and more of the land's surface became covered by water.

7.6 Carboniferous conglomerates banked against the cliff cut in the Ordovician Norber Formation at Nappa Scars. Rounded boulders, cobbles and pebbles of Lower Palaeozoic sediments are visible below increasingly finer grained and horizontal rocks. 10 cm scale bar in middle distance. Could these clasts be reworked from the Devonian cover (Chapter 6)?

7.7 Pebbly conglomerate in the Nappa Scars section with rock fragments rotated and aligned vertically. The origin of these structures is unknown; are they trace fossils or sedimentary structures? Scale bars are 10 cm.

If this is an unfamiliar concept, think what you feel with your feet as you walk down the beach and into the sea. There may be thick deposits of cobbles and pebbles near the top, typical of shallow water with high energy breaking waves. Lower down, the pebbles become more scattered, and there may be more grit sized particles. As the water deepens, and the energy levels decrease still further, the sediments become finer grained, until eventually, some way off shore, if you could touch the bottom, you would find fine silts and mud. Now imagine the sea level rising over a period of time. As this happens, the coarse deposits move shore-wards in step with the high energy wave environment, and the increasingly fine-

7.9 Mealbank Quarry, near Ingleton. Limestones of the Great Scar Limestone Group with shale and coal seam seen in the quarry face. Roots present below the coal seam demonstrate that this is not composed of drifted plant material but developed in situ during an emergent phase.

7.8 A passage in the Gaping Gill cave system beneath Ingleborough.

grained sediments then migrate over the top, covering over what had been deposited before. This is called a 'fining up sequence'. The opposite occurs during a regression when sea-levels fall and the sediments gradually become coarser, giving rise to the term a 'coarsening up sequence'.

The foundations of the Askrigg Block and the earliest Carboniferous deposits which were deposited on its flanks were eventually mantled by the massive grey limestones of the Great Scar Limestone Group, which attain a thickness of around 180 m. While a casual glance at the grey limestones which make up this group may suggest that they are all much the same, in fact they are distinctive, show cyclicity, and were deposited over a period of 8 Ma. This sequence of shallow water limestones is divided into units which may be identified and mapped throughout a particular area, and which carry evocative names such as the Kilnsey (*Figs.* 1.1 & 12.9) and Malham formations. These are then subdivided into yet smaller packages of distinct sediments called members. Once again the locations where they are best exposed are used to provide their names, so for example, the upper unit of the Malham Formation is the Gordale Limestone Member named from Gordale Scar (*Fig.* 12.10).

As already indicated, the drowning of the landscape did not take place at once, in fact evidence suggests that the process may have taken as long as 15 Ma.

During that time there are signs that there were periods of inversion, a reversing of the process of subsidence where part of the sea floor which had been sinking starts to rise. Observations made of these sediments forming the beautifully worn and polished surfaces of caves and potholes (*Fig.* 7.8) in the Great Scar Limestone Group reveal up to 16 beds of shale within the sequence of limestones. Sometimes shales rest on eroded surfaces which are presumed to have been created before the shale was deposited. Around Ingleton, two of the shales have coal seams associated with them (*Fig.* 7.9); one is 20 cm thick. These surprising features provide evidence for periods of emergence and erosion, and in some cases for sufficient plant growth to have taken place to form coals – a first hint of things to come before the end of the Lower Carboniferous. Such deposits were either the result of slight changes in the direction and speed of movement of the tectonic plates, or changes in sea level. Traced northwards, these strata thicken into the Stainmore Trough where the Great Scar Limestone Group is represented by the sediments of the Tom Croft Limestone, Ashfell Sandstone, Fawes Wood Limestone, Garsdale Limestone and Danny Bridge Limestone formations.

The blocks which formed the basement on which the Carboniferous was deposited continued to move up and down in relation to each other for

7.10 Malham Cove, Malham, the locality from which the Cove Limestone Member and the Malham Formation of the Great Scar Limestone Group take their names. (See also Introduction).

the duration of the Lower Carboniferous. Amongst them, the Askrigg Block is remarkable for being the most buoyant and stable. This is evident from the previously mentioned thinning of Lower Carboniferous strata over the block, and for there being little evidence of the contemporaneous and later faulting and folding of the strata which afflicted the surrounding basins (Chapter 3). These attributes have been maintained through geological time, a consequence of the Wensleydale Granite beneath the block. One especially active boundary lay between the southern edge of this stable block and the Craven Basin along the line of what is now the Craven Fault Zone. This provided the scenario and stage-set for more dynamic events, and hazardous environments. These are recorded in the rocks preserved over, and more especially on the subsiding side of that line. Close to and banked against the flank of the Askrigg Block are the deep-water equivalents of the Great Scar Limestone Group, namely the Bowland High and Craven groups. An example of the great variation in thickness across this line is the Cove Limestone Member of the Malham Formation. At Malham Cove (*Fig. 7.10*), from where the name is taken, there are 72 m, but south of the Middle Craven Fault a borehole cut down through 114 m of sediment! While sediments formed in relatively shallow and quiet water on the block, the basin filled with sediments which were frequently dislodged

from the edges of the Askrigg Block by earthquakes along this important structural line. The quakes triggered slumps of sediments on the edges of the basin. These could become debris flows which might in turn evolve into turbidity currents, reaching far out into the basin. Here thin limestones and sandstones within the muddy deeper water sediments have been explained as the products of this type of event.

The mud-middens of Cracoe

For visitors to the southern edge of the Dales with an eye for unusual landscape features, several exhumed 'reef' knolls (*Fig. 7.11*) are exposed in the valley to the north-east of Rylstone – a village between Cracoe and Burnsall, famed, thanks to the film *Calendar*

7.11 Cracoe 'reef' knolls exposed along the flanks of moorland south-west of Grassington; Skelerton Hill with a clump of trees on top, rounded Butter Haw Hill in the middle-distance, and on the left, the lower slope of Embolton. In the far distance is Pendle Hill in Lancashire.

7.12 Swinden Quarry near Cracoe is owned by Tarmac Ltd. Since quarrying first started in the 18th century, a substantial part of the core of a 'reef' knoll has been removed. The quarry is largely screened by the outer slopes of the knoll when viewed from ground level.

Girls, for exposures of a different kind. These are some of the much-studied Cracoe 'reef' knolls, or more accurately lithified mud-mounds, which developed just south of the Middle Craven Fault along the 'hinge' of block and basin. The knolls are the **carbonate** mud-middens of countless millions of bacteria, and green algae which manufactured fine carbonate muds over a period of around 7 Ma. The muds were initially held within a framework of other organisms including sponges which flourished, bryozoans, corals and brachiopods, before turning to rock, preserving as fossils the skeletal remains of these same animals which lived in and on them. The exact reason why these mud-mounds formed where they did is unknown. They may owe their existence to nothing more than the nature and depth of the Lower Carboniferous sea floor and patterns of circulation. May be their formation owes something to the close proximity of the Craven Fault Zone. Could the fractures associated with this fault, which we know was active at the time, have provided conduits for the flow of water enriched with chemical nutrients released from the earliest Carboniferous deposits of the Craven Basin, and warmed by geothermal energy emanating from the Wensleydale Granite?

Whatever their origin, the scale of these deposits is made clear when one considers the 'reef' deposit at Swinden. Here limestones formed from the mud-mounds have been quarried since operations first began sometime between 1775 and 1793. There are proposals to extend the life of this quarry by another 10 years until 2030. When working stops, the quarry floor will be roughly 195 m below the original knoll's surface. During the 200 plus year history of the quarry, more than 100,000,000 tonnes of stone will have been produced. (*Fig. 7.12*).

The mud-mounds had developed at the boundary of the quiet clear waters of the block and the deeper waters of the basin, with their tops keeping up with subsidence. Their death knell and that of the rich fauna they supported came with an increase in the rate of subsidence. As if to confirm this change of status, just briefly their tops were inundated by basinal sediments from the south – but all this was about to radically change.

The first hint of this change, as already noted, had been seen during the deposition of the Great Scar Limestone Group on the Askrigg Block and its northern flank, with occasional emergence and the deposition of shales and rare coal seams. Two forces were coming into play at about the same time, firstly, changes in the tectonic regime of northern

England, and secondly the start of major glaciation. The tensions which had driven fault block and basin movements, and so accommodated the sediment, were in decline. Where there had once been crustal-thinning and heating, cooling at the junction of the asthenosphere and lithosphere would lead to gradual collapse and the onset of a process in which the whole region began gently sagging. There was simultaneous uplift around the margins of this basin, contributing to the generation of the substantial volumes of sediment which were now being carried towards the sag-basin to be.

These regional changes to the crust started to kick-in a little after the first evidence is detected for the onset of the great ice ages which developed during the Carboniferous around 337 Ma and ended in the early Permian. Though the greatest extent of the ice cap's development was over southern Pangaea roughly where the Antarctic is today, many thousands of miles from Yorkshire, the effects would be felt across the world. Where sea levels had been relatively stable, there were now cycles of shallowing and deepening, estimated to have ranged from early fluctuations of as little as 10 m, to as much as 95 m at the close of the Lower Carboniferous. The limestone sea's clear waters were suddenly overwhelmed by mud and sand fed by rivers flowing from uplifted land surfaces around the basin margins to the north, and forming deltas where they met the sea. These are the Yoredales.

The Yoredales make their mark

The Yoredale Group might be thought of as a stratigraphic memorial to John Phillips (Chapter 1). He introduced the term 'Yoredale Series' in 1836 to describe the youngest of the Lower Carboniferous sediments which cap the Great Scar Limestone. The word comes from Uredale, the valley of the River Ure which is a tributary of the River Ouse, and now known as Wensleydale (*Fig. 7.13*).

The term Yoredales has become synonymous with cyclic sedimentation, caused by **eustatic** changes in sea level. The sedimentary structures tell of a northerly source, the sediments spreading down across the Stainmore Trough, and finally capping the limestones of the Askrigg Block. They mostly form a recurring sequence of thin marine limestone followed by marine mudstone, and then the **deltaic** sandstone which actively extends out into the marine

7.13 Hardraw Force on the northern flank of Wensleydale near Hawes. Alston Formation strata of the Yoredale Group are superbly exposed.

environment as the river born sediment is dumped. Exposed surfaces were colonized by plants, and the soils in which they grew might be either clay or sand-rich. They would become increasingly important rock types as these conditions came to dominate during the Upper Carboniferous (Chapter 8).

Occasionally **quartzites** formed from the especially pure **quartz** sand, and these sometimes carry the distinctive pattern left by the root systems of the tree-like plants growing in the swamps. Most familiar amongst these is the distinctive impression of *Stigmaria*, so named as the fossilized mould and cast

7.14 *Stigmaria*, the root system of a lycopsid (a tree-sized club moss). The rhizomorph is preserved as an external mould perforated by numerous holes left by the side roots in quartzite. The roots grew through a sand towards the top of one of the Yoredale cycles. 10 pence piece for scale.

7.15 *Lycopodium clavatum*. This club moss is found growing on Pennine moorlands in Yorkshire today, and by coincidence in close proximity to the fossilized remains of its enormous ancestors. The erect cone-like strobilli, formed from spore-bearing leaves, are not more than 15 cm high.

of the rhizomorph, or main root, has numerous holes or stigmata all over their surfaces (*Fig.* 7.14). On the cast of a rhizomorph the dimples mark where the side roots were attached, and the holes on the mould's surface are the moulds of the side roots. *Stigmaria* is the name used to describe the root systems of a number of different giant arborescent club mosses or lycopsids. Their diminutive present day representative, *Lycopodium* (*Fig.* 7.15) still thrives on some of the Pennine moors of Yorkshire alongside their ancestors' remains, a curiously apposite echo of the past!

Back in the swamp, accumulating plant debris might

be submerged by the next marine transgression, or when a segment of a delta complex became inactive and started to subside caused by compaction of the underlying sediments. Once submerged, sediments accumulated and the peat beds were buried, compressed and altered, eventually forming seams of coal. While these processes were taking place,

7.16 The spoil heaps mark the disused adits of coal mines, on the east side of Sleddale south of Hawes. The workable coal seam lay within the Alston Formation of the Yoredale Group.

distributary channels could change course and cut down through earlier deposits removing parts of the sequence. The succeeding cycle begins when the delta and coast are inundated by the next rise in sea-level. The repeated packages of these rocks are called cyclothems. Though by no means as common as in the Upper Carboniferous Pennine Coal Measures Group (Chapter 8), occasional seams of coal are present in the Yoredale Group across the Askrigg Block. Evidence for this may be a line of spoil tips running horizontally across a hillside (*Fig. 7.16*), a pock-marked area of moorland, or from the names such as 'Tanhill Colliery (dis)' and the nearby 'Mould Gill Coal Level (dis)' on Ordnance Survey maps. The former is documented as providing coal for Richmond Castle in 1384, and only ceased working in 1934!

While the Craven Basin remained a marine environment, the deltaic influence of the 'new boy on the (Askrigg) block', the Yoredale Group, can be seen in the sediments deposited. Muds now dominate and amongst them are beds of sandstone. The infilling of the Craven Basin has begun.

Life on block and in basin

Because of the varied environments produced by the complex patterns of blocks and basins, each with differing water depths and different sedimentary environments, there were a wide range of niches for a variety of plant and animal communities. Once these communities are documented and understood, their recognition provides the geologist with clues about the conditions which existed when the rocks they are in were deposited. The fossilised remains of marine organisms are sometimes abundant, and include corals (*Fig. 7.17*), brachiopods, bryozoans, trilobites, crinoids and graptolites. The latter, more often thought of as typical fossils of Lower Palaeozoic rocks, became extinct during the Carboniferous. Some organisms remained attached to the sea floor, but some drifted or swam, and these are especially important as they provide the best opportunities for geologists to link, or using the technical term – correlate, specific horizons between different places. Spectacular and not uncommonly seen in cross-section in broken limestone, are the curving white lines of the fossilized shells of a variety of brachiopod which are known as productoids (*Fig. 7.18*). Some attained considerable size and are appropriately named *Gigantoproductus*.

7.17 *Lithostrotion*. A colonial coral where each coral-animal (polyp) formed a columnar skeleton, which packed together with others developed a polygonal shape. Great Scar Limestone Group. Old style 50p piece with 30 mm diameter for scale.

7.18 The strongly curved white shells of productoid brachiopods seen in section in the 'Middle Limestone', Alston Formation, Yoredale Group, north of Lofthouse, near Pateley Bridge. 10 cm scale bar.

Researchers have shown that these brachiopods evolved a variety of strategies to both stabilize and protect themselves. Some embedded their largest curved valve into the sediment on which they rested. Spines growing from their shells were buried in the sediment, helping both to hold them in place and to stop them from sinking into the soft sea floor sediments, and above the sediment, providing a degree of protection. The less heavy and flatter valve which rested on top of the big curved one was raised and water filtered over an elaborately looped feeding structure called a lophophore. Because of the shape of the shell, these organisms were liable to be flipped over during storms when strong currents scoured the sea-floor. If turned upside down, they had the dubious distinction of achieving a more stable orientation, because the water currents would flow over their hydrodynamically orientated shells, while suffering from the major draw-back of being unable to open their shells to feed. Inevitably, premature death ensued! Others were attached by their spines to substrates, and some had spines which twined around and clasped other anchored organisms such as crinoids. The crinoid is another easily recognized fossil which may be so abundant as to form a decorative stone (Chapter 8).

Goniatites, a variety of cephalopod, are one of the fossils which are especially useful for correlating different parts of the sequence over wide areas and have been much sought after and used in resolving the stratigraphy of the Upper Carboniferous (Chapter 8). They moved vertically through the water by regulating their buoyancy, and across wide areas by drifting with the currents and using their own method of self-propulsion. Such mobility had the potential to widely distribute this type of **zone fossil**, an especially valuable attribute in situations where the environments on the sea-floor dictated what animals lived where. Similarly widely distributed organisms are the **foraminifera** and the tiny individual elements of the jaw apparatus of the **conodont animal**. Microscopic plant remains have also been used for correlating strata. The remains of vertebrate animals are less common, though shark's teeth have occasionally been found.

7.19 Carboniferous limestone used for dry stone walling near Starbottom, Wharfedale.

'There's "gold" in them thar hills'

The economic importance of the Lower Carboniferous is considerable. Tourism is a major industry which is underpinned by the geology and the landscapes that result. The different rocks have been quarried for countless generations. The buildings of the area are made of materials gathered from the surface or hewn from intractable outcrops. As ever, the character of the walls which thread the landscape reflects the availability of local raw materials. The tumbled walls made of the awkwardly shaped lumps of stone from the Great Scar Limestone Group, or garnered from the river beds are the most unruly, frequently collapsing to cascade scree-like onto field and road (*Fig. 7.19*). In stark contrast, the regularly ordered bedding so often associated with the sandstones and grits of the Yoredales make for a more manageable medium with which to attempt to tame this landscape. These same beds are the source of the skilfully cut and size-graded roofing flags seen on houses and the ubiquitous small barns and byres dotted across the valley sides (*Fig. 7.20*). The working of these flags and other stone to meet a local demand has all but ceased.

A singular feature of the Dales is the disused, solitary stone-built, lime kiln strategically placed against a hillside and adjacent to a source of limestone. With the minimum of effort the limestone was quarried and fed into the top of the kiln (*Figs 7.21*). The product was in demand for the improvement of agricultural land, for building and the maintenance of property. As the industrialisation of the north progressed, the demand for lime grew to meet the needs of new and rapidly expanding industries, and of the farmers who were under pressure to supply the rapidly growing market for food in the great conurbations. Production became increasingly large-scale and centralized. Quarries around Horton-in-Ribblesdale and at Swinden are examples where lime was once produced and exported by rail. These and other limestone quarries such as Coldstones, Redmire, and Threshfield have flourished, and at present are supplying a national market for limestone products, while simultaneously providing an important source of local employment. Until 1992 limestone from Redmire Quarry went by rail to the steelworks at Redcar. Swinden (*Fig. 7.12*) maintains an important railway connection to Skipton and beyond, and at Horton-in-Ribblesdale, where ironically the railway sidings serving a quarry were

7.20 Hay barn built of local sandstone, near Gunnerside, Swaledale. Building like this are especially characteristic of the Yorkshire Dales.

7.21 Lime kiln built on the side of a hill adjacent to a source of limestone. The main walls are of limestone, the arch and heat resistant structures within the arch are of flaggy sandstone or quartzite. Near Yockenthwaite, Langstrothdale.

7.22 Fremington Edge Chert Quarries above Reeth. The Underset Chert (Alston Formation, Yoredale Group) has been worked for the manufacture of buhrstones used for grinding and milling.

taken up many years ago, there is talk of reinstating the link! Perhaps railways will become increasingly important arteries for an industry which sits a little uneasily within the National Park.

At certain horizons in the Yoredale Group and more especially in the Upper Carboniferous part (Chapter 8), a hard black to pale grey siliceous rock called **chert** is developed. The origin of the chert has been, and remains, a matter of debate. Some have suggested that sponges were able to utilise the minute traces of silica in the sea-water to form the spicules which provide an interlocking mesh that forms their skeletons. After death, the skeletons dissolved, the silica becoming available to form the beds of chert; spicules have been observed in **thin-section** in these rocks lending support to this idea. Later research has cast doubt on the sponges being of the siliceous kind, principally because the quantities of silica dissolved in normal sea water would not have provided sufficient silica to form the volumes of chert present. Instead it has been suggested that submarine springs were pumping silica-rich waters onto the sea-floor. The siliceous sponges would have capitalised on this chemical bonanza, proliferating and then, after death, releasing their silica into the sediments that entombed

them. This would have provided ample silica from which the cherts would form. This hypothesis has an additional attraction, perhaps being a precursor to the event or events when hot hydrothermal solutions, ascending from fractured Wensleydale Granite and basement rocks, formed the Askrigg Block's mineral wealth (Chapter 9). While chert was undesirable when producing lime, the demand for powdered chert to be used as an additive in the manufacture of fine china, led to the development of yet another important, though relatively short-lived, extractive industry within what is now the National Park. The industry developed from around 1896 and survived into the 20th century. Chert was worked between Reeth (*Fig.* 7.22) and Richmond, and around Leyburn.

The southern section of the Northern Pennine Orefield is present across parts of the Askrigg Block and its margins, and has produced significant volumes of lead and other minerals in the past. Mining has made a dramatic impact on some parts of the Dales landscape (Chapter 9).

The Lower Carboniferous draws to a close; initially great thicknesses of sediment had collected in the deeper parts of the old basins, but as these filled, so gradually the region became much flatter. The Upper Carboniferous which followed saw the full development of the gently subsiding sag-basin, a nice description for an elderly, if not ancient 'landscape'! This phase in Yorkshire's history, the Upper Carboniferous is the subject of the next chapter.

EIGHT

Great Rivers, Deltas and Swamps

8.1 Damflask Reservoir west of Sheffield, looking south-south-east from near High Bradfield towards Dungworth. In the foreground are the uppermost strata of the Millstone Grit Group, including the Rough Rock which is present along the north side of Loxley Road seen in the bottom left of the picture. Along this outcrop and just out of view, the ground shows evidence of quarrying. The hills in the distance are composed of the Pennine Lower Coal Measures Formation.

Time: Upper Carboniferous: 325 – 299 Ma **Latitude:** 0° – 10°N **Climate:** Hot humid equatorial with occasional wetter and drier phases triggered by polar glaciations; becomes increasingly dry towards the end of the Carboniferous. **Environment:** Extensive rivers and deltas progressively infill the marine basins and cover the highs of the Lower Carboniferous. Flood plains and delta tops are colonised by plants. The frequency and scale of colonisation increases and creates coal-forming swamps. Widespread marine incursions are triggered by periodic global climate warming. The death knell for the 'coal swamps' comes towards the close of the Carboniferous as increasing aridity is caused by uplift and the rain-shadow affect of mountains forming across southern Britain. **Rocks:** Grits, sandstones, siltstones, shales, clays, seatearths, limestones, cherts, ironstones and coal.	**Stratigraphy:** STAINMORE TROUGH: *Yoredale Group* (continued): Alston (continued to the top of the Great Limestone Member) and Stainmore formations. ASKRIGG BLOCK: *Yoredale Group* (continued): Alston (continued to the top of the Great Limestone Member) and Stainmore formations. *Millstone Grit Group*: Pendleton, Silsden, Samlesbury, Hebden, Marsden, and Rossendale formations. PENNINE BASIN: *Craven Group* (continued): Bowland Shale Formation (continued). *Millstone Grit Group*: Formations as for the Askrigg Block. *Pennine Coal Measures Group* [PCMG]: Pennine Lower [PLCMF], Middle [PMCMF] and Upper Coal Measures [PUCMF] formations. *Warwickshire Group*

Setting the Scene

Whernside, Ingleborough, Pen-y-ghent and Plover Hill summits, and Dodd, Firth, Fountains, and Widdale fells have something in common, they are crowned with **outliers** of the lowest Upper Carboniferous strata (*Fig.* 7.3). These beds are the continuation of the Yoredale Group and the lowest beds of the overlying Millstone Grit Group. Follow the gently inclined strata north and east and rocks of this age become much more widespread and substantially thicker, forming a great embracing arc around the ice-gouged and dissected landscapes of the south-western Dales. Roles are reversed as Swaledale and Arkengarthdale, with the tenuously attached Gilling valley to their north, form a spidery but contiguous inlier of Lower Carboniferous strata encompassed by Upper Carboniferous sediments.

The Millstone Grit Group of the eastern flank of the Dales runs from Richmond southwards to Pateley Bridge, forming the high moors below which reservoirs such as Scar House and Angram nestle, and then the adjoining Grassington, Hebden and Embsay moors (*Fig.* 8.3). The foothills of the moors are altogether softer, gentler, a pastoral landscape, farmed and cut by small steep-sided river valleys and with an abundance of trees. Once in a while, we are reminded of the true nature of this land as the Millstone Grit pokes through and provides the medium for the extraordinary variety of sculpted edifices collectively

8.2 Plumpton Rocks are weathered tors of cross-bedded Upper Plompton Grit of the Millstone Grit Group. They have been incorporated with superb effect in a wild pleasure garden created in the second half of the eighteenth century. Turner was commissioned to paint this landscape by Lord Harewood in 1798.

known as Brimham Rocks, and the similar but more understated Plumpton (also spelt Plompton) Rocks, which possess a Miltonian quality in their watery and silvan setting (*Fig. 8.2*).

These tough dark weathering rocks with their glowering gritstone edges extend south, forming the high spine of the Pennines; Blubberhouses Moor between Harrogate and Skipton, Rombalds Moor of which Ilkley Moor (of baht'at fame) is but a part, Oxenhope and Haworth moors to the south-west of Keighley, the latter with the Brontë connection, Heptonstall, Midgley and Widdop moors, and many more besides, stride and tumble their way southwards. They reach a geological crescendo in the High Peak with the brooding and inhospitable Kinderscout, which lies just outside Yorkshire. Sheffield sits on their edge with an array of reservoirs, once again sited on rocks of this age, in the lower catchments of the rivers Loxley and Don. (*Fig. 8.1*)

Overlying the Millstone Grit Group is the Pennine Coal Measures Group (PCMG). The eroded Upper Carboniferous strata dip eastwards under the unconformable Permo-Trias sediments (Chapter 9) of the vales of Mowbray and York, the Humberhead Levels and southwards through the valley of the Trent towards Newark. To the north of a line drawn roughly from Bradford passing just to the north of Leeds, exposed PCMG strata are rare. There are several outliers to the west of Ripon and beds of similar age, but uncertain extent, are present beneath the Permo-Trias to the east of this. Similarly, to the north-east of Harrogate, PCMG are present as a faulted outlier with the outcrop extending below the Permo-Trias to the east. The northward extent of the PCMG is still not fully known, though boreholes at Whitwell north-east of York, and in Esk Dale and at Robin Hood's Bay to the south of Whitby did prove these strata. From around Harrogate southwards, the top of the Millstone Grit Group is marked by the 15 m thick Rough Rock, a coarse, pebbly sandstone, which forms an encircling collar, dislocated only by faults, cropping out to the north and west around the PCMG. This deposit marks the end of the major infilling and levelling of the central Pennine Basin, and as a result is a deposit which extends widely across the region. From a little north of Harrogate the Rough Rock is absent. Here the top of the Millstone Grit Group is marked by the Laverton Sandstone.

To the south, of the 'Bradford – Leeds line', folding of the Carboniferous strata prior to the deposition

8.3 Deer Gallow Crags on Embsay Moor. In the distance are the gritstone fells north of Bolton Abbey and east of the River Wharfe which include Carncliff Top and Simon's Seat.

of the Permian conspired to preserve exposed Coal Measures. These strata form one of Britain's great coalfields, present across a vast swathe of country and extending south into Nottinghamshire and north Derbyshire. On a simplified geological map, the outcrop of the PCMG has a quite coincidental, but curious resemblance to a silhouette of the cartoon character Bart Simpson. The traveller who uses trains to move between the great cities and towns on and bordering the Yorkshire Coalfield including Leeds, Bradford, Halifax, Shipley, Wakefield, Huddersfield, Barnsley, Rotherham and Sheffield, will inevitably pass through deep cuttings and tunnels which have been driven through the cyclic sediments of the PCMG. In this context, mention must be made of Kendall and Wroot whose *Geology of Yorkshire* of 1924 provides an excellent, if dated, rail-users guide to the geology of the county. Upper Carboniferous strata are also present along the south-west border of the Dales on the west side of the Pennine spine, on the **downthrow** side of the Craven Fault Belt which has displaced these strata by more than 549 m. At Ingleton there is a small outlier of PCMG which has been mined, and this is overlain by reddened sediments which may belong to the Warwickshire Group.

The previous chapter explained how towards the end of the Lower Carboniferous, tectonic changes

8.4 The crinoid *Rhabdocrinus swaledalensis* was a variety of echinoderm fixed by a holdfast to the sea floor. This specimen is just under 16 cm long and shows the stem and calyx. They sometimes grew together in substantial numbers and their remains may be so abundant as to form rocks (Figure 8.5a-b).

occurred which foreshadowed the end of the basin and block controls on sedimentation. Until then, the basins and troughs had subsided as fast as, or exceeded, the rates at which sediment accumulated in them. Throughout the Upper Carboniferous, rates of subsidence slowed and basins filled with sediment during the deposition of the Millstone Grit Group, leaving the Pennine Basin sagging just fast enough to accommodate the coal-producing swamps of the Pennine Coal Measures Group.

The end of the Yoredales and some decorative stones

Sediments of the Yoredale Group continued to be deposited across the Askrigg Block for no more than the first 2 Ma of the Upper Carboniferous. As before, and unsurprisingly, they are represented by a cyclic sequence of marine limestones and shales, intercalated with the sediments being brought from a northerly source by rivers forming deltas which spilled southwards towards the southern margin of the Askrigg Block. Chert commonly occurs in this part of the sequence (Chapter 7). A prominent and extensive limestone named the Great Limestone Member (previously known as the Main Limestone) lies at the top of the Alston Formation, attaining a maximum

thickness of 40 m, and forms the lowest unit of the Upper Carboniferous. This limestone is remarkable for the distinctive and laterally persistent beds of fossils, also known as 'fossil posts'. In this context, the word *post* which has a vertical connotation is curious. Derivation from the Old English seems likely; there is an account in 1589 which records a browe post or transome. So the term for a flat bed of stone used in a building, finds a use in the description of beds of limestone, sandstone, and even fossils in quarries and mines. Perhaps any bed which yielded transoms or beams would by association end up, no pun intended, labelled as a post?

Crinoids became especially prolific during the deposition of the Great Limestone Member. Also misleadingly known as the sea-lily, these animals sometimes grew in large numbers, fixed to the sea floor. Their long stems, made up of hundreds of polo-mint-like columnals, supported a **calcite** box called a calyx, made up of numerous often ornamented plates. The calyx contained the animal's body and is a far less common fossil than the abundant stem fragments. Arms around the edge of the calyx were used to pass food down to the mouth at the top of the calyx. The area around Richmond is well known for beautifully preserved specimens of a number of species of crinoid (*Fig. 8.4*). Some limestones contain significant numbers of the stems of crinoids and are cut and polished for use as a decorative stone. An example of this is the Barton Limestone, available from a quarry between Richmond and Darlington. Slabs of this attractive and distinctive crinoidal limestone were being traded under the name 'Swaledale Fossil' in the 1990s. Another crinoidal limestone is 'Nidderdale

8.5a-b (a) Crinoidal limestone at outcrop and (b) detail showing abundant stem sections. This bed is the Great Limestone Member which lies at the top of the Alston Formation, Yoredale Group, between Hawes and Langstrothdale.

Marble', which found use as a decorative stone in the buildings of Fountains Abbey.

Near Hawes one such mass of crinoid debris (*Fig. 8.5a-b*) attains a thickness of over 3 m and possibly as much as 8 m, forming an elongate body orientated north-north-east to south-south-west and estimated to have been almost 12 miles long! This spectacular deposit is all that remains of a crinoid reef which built up over a prolonged period. Using crinoids, productoid brachiopods, and corals in the various fossil beds of the Great Limestone Member, research has shown that across the Askrigg Block the seawater currents maintained a constant south to north direction, flowing with a velocity that ranged between 15 and 30 cm/second.

As in the Lower Carboniferous, limestones have been quarried for use as decorative stones in Yorkshire, as in Nidderdale, or Dentdale which was in Yorkshire but is now part of Cumbria. Though quarried in Weardale in County Durham, the magnificent black limestone peppered with startling white corals and known as Frosterly Marble (the marble here is not a metamorphic rock but an unaltered limestone taking a high polish) is also from the Great Limestone Member. Perhaps most famously this stone was used for shafts in the Chapel of the Nine Altars in Durham Cathedral. The excuse for mentioning this 'marble' which is not a native stone of Yorkshire is twofold. Firstly examples are to be found in York Minster and some churches in the county, for example in St John's, New Briggate in Leeds. Secondly, observations of the corals in the Frosterly Marble point to storms of

sufficient severity to undermine the corals attached to the sea floor, causing them to fall over and to be swept along and concentrated by the storm-induced current activity. Using the known growth rate of the type of coral preserved, research has shown that the storms were occurring every 6-7 years, and by inference, the same conditions might be expected to apply across the Askrigg Block.

While the Yoredale Group's cyclic mixture of marine and deltaic sediments were deposited over the northern part of England including the Askrigg Block, to the south, the marine mudstones with occasional sandstones and limestones of the Bowland Shale Formation (*Fig. 8.6*) continued to carpet the basins and troughs (Craven, Huddersfield, Alport, Edale, and Gainsborough) and drape thinly over the highs (Central Lancashire and Holme) of what

8.6 The Bowland Shale Formation (Craven Group), a deeper water deposit of the Craven Basin, exposed in the banks of the River Wharfe at Bolton Abbey, north-west of Ilkley.

may be conveniently called the Yorkshire part of the Pennine Basin, extending down to the county's southern boundary (*Figs. 3.3, 3.4a-b*). The Bowland Shale Formation accumulated over a period of 8 Ma, being progressively overstepped and buried beneath the Millstone Grit Group sediments as, having overwhelmed the Askrigg Block, they extended southwards, completely filling the Lower Carboniferous basins and troughs. Just before the start of this much more rapid phase of sedimentation across the Pennine Basin, movement along the Craven Faults coupled with subsidence along the Stainmore Trough caused the Askrigg Block to develop a slight northerly tilt. This led to erosion of the most recently deposited strata in the south of this area. Where most deeply eroded, all the Yoredale Group sediments were removed, exposing limestone of Lower Carboniferous age. Perhaps significantly, this tectonic adjustment seems to have coincided with an increase in the rates of erosion of an area far to the north, as this eroded surface was soon overstepped and buried, unconformably, by the southward flood of coarse sands and pebbly grits of the Millstone Grit Group.

Filling the basin with the Millstone Grit

The great river system which flowed from a northerly direction fed colossal volumes of sediment into the major deltas, progressively levelling the 'landscape' as they built southwards across the region. These sediments are frequently **cross-bedded**. Around 300 m of Millstone Grit Group sediment was deposited over the Askrigg Block, but the thickness increased dramatically to 1,225 m across what is now Wharfedale, on the northern margin of the Pennine Basin to the north of Bradford. The processes associated with the filling of the Pennine Basin generated a wide range of sedimentary environments which may be briefly summarised as follows. River systems carried sediment from the source area to the marine basin. On the lower reaches, rivers might flow within meandering channels, or form shifting **braided** systems (*Figs. 8.7, 12.23b*). Flood plains, with marshes or swamps, developed. On reaching the sea, the ability of the river to carry sediment was reduced and the coarser sediments were deposited while being sorted by size. The sediments accumulated to form deltas fed by intricate patterns of distributary channels. Blocking of channels and floods would lead to the creation of new channels. The form of the deltas would be dictated by the rate of sediment input, bathymetry, and marine processes; bird's foot deltas, and more simple forms, have been recognised in the Pennine Basin. With time, plants occasionally colonised flood plain and delta surfaces, sometimes giving rise to thin coals. There is every reason to expect these deltas to have been quite as complex as those of major river systems across the world today, where the sea would erode and redistribute sediments from the delta margins, gradually destroying abandoned **lobes**. The delta margins migrating into ever deeper water on a steep marine slope became increasingly unstable, and would from time to time slump, cascading dense turbidity flows (Chapter 5) into the basins.

The succession of sediments deposited in the Pennine

8.7 The Rough Rock exposed below Albert promenade in Halifax, photographed in 1926. This thick, coarse grained and pebbly sandstone with well developed cross-bedding is regarded as the product of a braided river system which developed over much of southern Yorkshire at the close of the period of time when the Millstone Grit Group was deposited. A small-scale example of a braided river can be seen in Figure 12.23b.

Basin reflects these environments and processes. Furthest from the active delta, fine grained basinal marine sediments were being deposited, and from time to time these were buried by the turbidities sweeping down from the delta front. As the basin filled and the water mass became shallower, so the sediments became coarser, until deltaic and **fluviatile** sands and grits were being deposited. From time to time the sea inundated the delta and near-shore environments depositing marine muds. A fall in sea level resulted in delta distributaries and river channels cutting back through previously deposited sediment, sending still greater volumes of grit, sand and mud into the basin. As the infilling proceeded from north to south, the turbiditic sediments were being deposited for longest towards the south of the region. Conditions were shallowest, and dominated by rivers and deltas for longest in the north. At any one time, many of these environments, processes and resultant sediments were present in the Pennine Basin.

In such excruciatingly complicated sequences of rocks, the only hope of making sense of them is by the use of fossils to correlate between different parts of the basin. In this, the keys to our understanding are the sporadic but often extensive marine bands and the precious goniatites (*Fig.* 8.8), a distant ancestor of the ammonite, which occur in them. The most extensive marine bands were, as you will recall (Chapter 7), the product of rises in sea-level caused by melting ice-sheets, and are known to have occurred on a regular basis. Recent research has shown that fluctuations in sea level occurred every 65 ka years at the beginning of the Upper Carboniferous, and at an average of every 120 ka years as the coal swamps started to form. During the Upper Carboniferous, these sea level fluctuations ranged between 45 and 75 m. The repeating pattern of sedimentation which led to the cyclothems was driven by these global processes.

Order out of chaos

The first field geologists of the British Geological Survey to map Yorkshire had initially, and not unreasonably, presumed that the beds of pebbly grit of the Millstone Grit Group could be simply correlated across the region. They had not appreciated just how complicated were these strata, deposited in different places at different times from a constantly shifting series of rivers and deltas which were themselves periodically inundated by the sea. During early 20th century re-surveys of areas where these rocks predominated, their true complexity had become apparent. While not appreciating the driving forces behind the marine bands, they did recognise that their fossil contents provided the means to link disparate sequences over wide areas. The field geologists gave talks to local geological societies, enthusing about the vital role the goniatites were playing in their deciphering of the geology both locally and far beyond, based on a truth first recognised and applied by W. S. Bisat. At one such meeting they sparked a life-long enthusiasm for these globose coiled cephalopods in one Edward William James Moore. In the course of his long career as an amateur collector, he would occasionally cross into Yorkshire from his adopted Lancashire to search for, and collect, goniatites from the marine bands exposed on fell sides and in stream sections. The Holy Grail of his search were the hard nodules known as bullions, for when split open, they could yield beautifully preserved, 3-dimensional goniatites – he was not toasted the 'bullion-breaker' for nothing! His obituary records a wonderfully non-PC habit; marine bands failing to surrender the sought-after bullions would be subjected to one of his rollies, prepared and lit while uttering the maxim 'let's smoke 'em out'! The exceptional collection of goniatites that resulted from such techniques became part of the collections of the British Geological Survey, contributing significantly to the work of the Survey in

8.8 Goniatites are fossils used to correlate Carboniferous strata over wide areas. This example, *Gastrioceras listeri* from the Pennine Lower Coal Measures Formation, is recorded as coming from the Halifax Hard Bed Coal, Shibden Dale, and is a good example of the preservation found in the bullions so sought after by E. W. J. Moore.

helping to elucidate the tangled web of deltaic deposits across the region. Goniatites remain powerful aids to the interpretation of the geology of this region and the search for, and publication on these illuminating fossils continues.

Forensic science and the sediment's source

Having brought a considerable degree of order to the previously chaotic understanding of these strata through the goniatites they contain, geologists have subsequently turned to the sediments which, like the fossils previously described, more often than not have important tales to tell. Through careful detective work in the field, the study of the sediments, measurements of cross-bedded units, and other sedimentary structures, many of which provide directional information, along with a myriad of other details, geologists have been able to develop a picture of the sedimentary environments in which the different beds were laid down. Samples of the different Upper Carboniferous sandstones and grits across the region have been subjected to meticulous and time consuming laboratory studies of their mineralogy, and especially of the **heavy mineral** grains they contain. Taking into account the weathering processes these have been subjected to, before, during and after transport, these minerals provide distinctive signatures. Comparison with the component minerals in the rocks preserved, or thought to have existed, in possible source areas, may provide answers to the question, where did these sediments originate? In all this, one must bear in mind that the continental plates will have moved significantly since the Carboniferous. Research may be further supported and refined by using minute samples of certain minerals for isotope studies, and at the other end of the size-spectrum, fragments of actual rock found in samples are thin-sectioned and studied under the **petrological microscope**. Fossils and especially **micro-fossils** re-worked from older deposits may also be present, providing yet another strand of evidence in the hunt for the sediment's source.

Such forensic work has been carried out by different groups of researchers on both the Upper Carboniferous sediments of the Pennine Basin and on sediments of similar age in Greenland with fascinating results. Initial studies based on the Yorkshire sediments had shown that at different times during the Upper Carboniferous, three distinct types of sediment had arrived in the Pennine Basin from

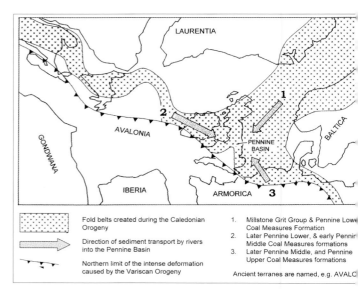

8.9. Sediment transport directions during the Upper Carboniferous. Modified from Hallsworth and Chisholm, 2000, *Proceedings of the Yorkshire Geological Society*, Vol. 53, 43-72, by permission of the Council of the Yorkshire Geological Society.

different sources (*Fig. 8.9*). During the first part of the Upper Carboniferous, sediment was transported into the basin from a northerly direction, leading to the deposition of the Millstone Grit and the earliest Pennine Lower Coal Measures Formation (PLCMF). The famed and long exploited Elland Flags (*Figs. 8.19 & 8.20*) are composed of sediment from this northern source. This flow of sediment from an area identified to be to the north of Scotland, gradually declined during the latter PLCMF during which time a westerly sediment source, from where the North Atlantic is today, came to dominate. Initially the different sedimentary layers interdigitated and even mingled. No northerly sourced sediments occur above the marine band which marks the start of the Pennine Middle Coal Measures Formation (PMCMF). The westerly source is the only one during deposition of the lower part of the PMCMF, but abruptly ends after the next marine incursion. Sandstones (*Fig. 8.10*) composed of sediments from a westerly source include the Silkstone, Parkgate and Barnsley rocks. For the remainder of the PMCMF and during the whole of the Pennine Upper Coal Measures Formation (PUCMF), sediment was carried into the basin from a source to the south or south-east and gave rise to sandstones such as the Glass Houghton, Mexborough and Ackworth rocks (*Fig. 8.11*).

While this research successfully identified directions of flow and likely source areas during deposition of the PCMG, one question remained unanswered, what had triggered the huge increase in sediment shed southwards during Millstone Grit times? One unverifiable suggestion was climate change; higher rainfall in the source area would have enhanced erosion and provided the power required by the rivers to transport the coarse sediments deposited at this time across the Pennine Basin.

Recent studies have now shown that while the early Lower Carboniferous limestones and mudstones were being deposited across Yorkshire, central eastern Greenland was being covered by sediments deposited by a river system flowing in a northerly direction from an area to the north of Scotland. Greenland is now in a new setting much further to the west, courtesy of plate tectonics; at the time Greenland was quite close to Norway. Towards the end of the Lower Carboniferous, tectonic activity between these two countries caused sufficient uplift to reverse the northward flow of that river. Not only did the drainage pattern now run south, but there were the not inconsiderable volumes of sediment being eroded from this newly uplifted region, which were added to the original sediment load being carried.

Voilà! The result was the enormous volumes of coarse to very coarse sediment of the Millstone Grit Group across Yorkshire. In support of this idea, the Greenland sequence is missing sediments from that very same time interval when the Millstone Grit of the Pennine Basin was being deposited. There is also a nice tie-in between the **heavy mineral** signatures of the sediments in Yorkshire and those which were once again deposited in Greenland when renewed rifting of the uplifted area once more reversed the flow of the river. Without this influx of sediment which made such a substantial contribution to the filling of the Pennine Basin over a period of 10 Ma, would Coal Measure swamps have been far less extensive, and what impact would that have had on the industrial, social and cultural history of Britain and the world? Funny to think that so much may have turned on the diversion of a river 326 Ma!

The legacy of the Millstone Grit

The Millstone Grit has left us with a remarkable visual legacy of iconic landscapes across and down the spine of Yorkshire. Mention was previously

8.10 The Haigh Moor Rock (also known as the Kexbrough Rock), a Pennine Middle Coal Measures Formation sandstone, associated with the Swallow Wood coal seam, exposed in a roadside cutting at Kexbrough, north-west of Barnsley. These sediments were transported by river from a source to the west.

8.11 Sandstones used for walling at Ackworth. These are more than likely to have been sourced from the abundant local sandstones belonging to the upper part of the Pennine Middle and Upper Coal Measures formations, all derived from a southerly source. The weathering processes that the wall has been subjected to reveals the varied sedimentary structures preserved in these sediments.

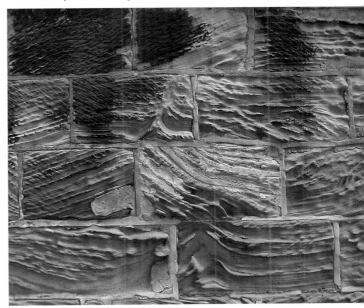

8.12 Brimham Rocks, east of Pateley Bridge. The coarse grits of which these tors (Chapter 12) are composed are the Lower Brimham Grit of the Millstone Grit Group. The sediment was carried by river from a source far to the north.

made of Brimham Rocks (*Fig.* 8.12), not so far from Pateley Bridge. Here the strangely weathered shapes formed from the Lower Brimham Grit have been an attraction since at least the eighteenth century. A relatively modern account from Ward Lock & Co's *Illustrated Guide Book* (1939-40) for Harrogate provides the following colourful explanation within a longer description of the location: 'They [*Brimham Rocks*] were in all probability, produced by a violent disruption of Nature, during which heavy masses of millstone grit were upheaved to the ridges of the great Vale of Nidd and piled around in confusion,' adding for good measure a quotation from *Paradise Lost*, 'Nature here Wantoned, as in her prime, and played at with her virgin fancies, Wild above rule or art.' Sadly this has been omitted from later editions.

Some have suggested that art may indeed have had a hand in some of the appropriately named fantastical shapes, which include heads of Serpent, Baboon, and Parson; there are Lamb, Elephant and Rhinoceros, Tortoise Rocks and Dancing Bears. Druids have a fair share of the action, both in life and death, with a Writing Desk, Coffin and Cave. There is the spectacular bulk of Idol Rock precariously balanced on a slender pedestal, and for the 'romantically inclined' the Lover's Leap, Kissing Chair and Bedroom Cave! The list of named rocks and other features is not endless but certainly long, and W. A. Poucher, perfumer, photographer of mountains, walker and climber, recommends a day to view them all.

These free-standing, intricately weathered gritstone masses are tors, the relics of more extensive beds of grit which has been subjected to deep weathering (Chapters 11 & 12) and subsequent erosion along their exposed outcrop. 'Jenny Twigg and her daughter Tib', also Lower Brimham Grit, east of Lofthouse in Nidderdale, and Plumpton Rocks (Upper Plompton Grit) (*Fig.* 8.2) near Knaresborough are further examples of this weathered gritstone landscape. They are likely to represent the 'tip' of a more extensive series of unexposed tors, their presence hinted at by the not infrequent gritstone blocks and edges seen poking through field and moorland surfaces. Elsewhere, the beds of grit and sandstone concealed beneath peats and thin soils sometimes have been selectively accentuated along the steep valley sides, below the sweeps of Pennine moorland, forming buttresses overlooking valleys and towns. Examples are the Bramhope Grit above Ilkley and the Rough Rock capping the Millstone Grit Group. This forms the Druid's Altar above Bingley and the tilted slab upon which, and of which in part, Halifax is built (*Fig.* 8.7).

The name Millstone Grit is still very much a term of popular culture, clearly associated with a bygone, but once important, Pennine industry. Millstones were used not just for the production of flour from wheat, but were used in other industrial processes, and later were valued for grinding maize and in the production of paper-pulp. Estimates indicate that there were 11,000 working mills in 1400, providing a starting point for the calculation of how many new stones may have been required each year. The domestic or foreign market is estimated to have supplied between two and three thousand individual stones per annum to maintain the supply of stone-ground flour to a population of between five and seven million. There is documentary evidence that Yorkshire was producing some millstones at that time.

Many of the sandstones and gritstones have been used for bridges and other buildings. A volume on building materials published in 1905 provides an illuminating record of some of the stones then being quarried in Yorkshire, and from where they were being exported. Examples include Scotgate Ash Quarry at Pateley Bridge, working the Libishaw Sandstone, known commercially as 'Delph Stone', and chiefly 'used for landings, steps, headstones, heads, copings, sinks etc.'. The North Eastern Railway would transport the stone, delivered as quarried block to the sidings via a steep incline. Shipley Quarry produced 'Blocks,

landings etc.' and used the Great Northern, Midland and North Eastern railways for distribution.

The different beds of grit and coarse sandstone within the Millstone Grit Group are known by a bewildering number of names adopted from the areas where they are exposed. A good example of this are the named grits and sandstones which fall within the Lower Kinderscout Grit; in ascending order they are, the Addingham Edge, Addlethorpe, Caley Crags, Lower Brimham and Eldroth grits, Lons Ridge Sandstone, Lower Plompton Grit, Doubler Stones Sandstone, and Bramhope Grit.

Foundations for a revolution

The Pennine Coal Measures Group (PCMG), which overlies the Millstone Grit Group's Rough Rock, is composed of a cyclic sequence of mudstones, sandstones, siltstones, seatearths and significant coal seams. These strata represent the culmination of the change from fault controlled block and basin, to sag-basin previously described. Despite the relatively slower rates of subsidence, the centre of the Pennine Basin did subside more rapidly than the edges, accommodating 1,900 m of sediments near Manchester; the thickness at Wakefield in Yorkshire is 1,400 m. These sediments to the east of the Pennines form the Yorkshire Coalfield, where the greatest concentration of workable coal seams occur

8.13 Orgreave Colliery east of Sheffield and south of Rotherham. Coal mining commenced here in 1851. Pennine Lower and Middle Coal Measures formations were worked including the Silkstone seam, producing coal for the production of coke used in steel making; now closed.

in the PMCMF (*Fig.* 8.13). The PCMG might have been considerably more widespread but for extensive erosion of these strata over the Pennine Anticline; some of this erosion had occurred prior to the deposition of the Permian sediments (Chapter 9). This major feature which separates the coalfields on the east and west sides of the north – south Pennine axis, resulted from folding associated with the Variscan Orogeny at the close of the Carboniferous and in the early Permian. While the event which triggered the formation of the anticline was the above mentioned orogeny, the structures at depth that caused the anticline to form remain the subject of debate. Clues as to the original extent of the coalfield are provided by the small outlier of PCMG strata at Ingleton. Situated against the flank of the Pennines, the presence of workable coal with 'seams of nine and ten feet' is clear evidence that the coal bearing strata were widespread – this is no marginal deposit but the relic of a much more extensive coalfield.

The delta plain which developed across the Pennine Basin was colonised by plants occupying many different environments. Most important of these were the huge expanses of peat mire which were destined to become the coal seams from which the Carboniferous is named. Flooding by the sea of the swamps, which would eventually turn into coal, was either the result of increasingly rare but widespread marine inundations triggered by the continuing fluctuation of the south polar ice cap, or localised marine episodes caused by subsidence on the margins of the delta plain.

There are 13 marine incursions caused by a global rise in sea level in the PCMG in Yorkshire, and they are recognised by the marine fauna preserved in the sediments. As in the Millstone Grit Group, the fossils preserved have been an invaluable means of correlating these deposits, both within Yorkshire, across the UK and beyond. The decreasing frequency of marine incursions during deposition of the PCMG may be connected to changes in the nature of the glacial cycles, or the degree to which the Pennine Basin was becoming isolated from the normal marine environment. In the absence of marine bands, non-marine bivalves, pollen, spores, and larger plant fossils have been used for correlation within these strata.

The migration of rivers triggered by a falling sea level caused considerable modifications to the delta plain, cutting through the sediments amongst which were accumulations of coal-swamp peat. The rivers were usually hemmed in by naturally formed embankments, called levees, as they crossed the delta plain. Overtopping of these during flooding, or bank erosion leading to failure of the levees, would see water carrying sands, silts and mud spreading out across the plain, filling lakes and covering the swamps and low lying ground alike. Crevasse splays are the delta-like fans of sediment which stretch out from the river channel, forming during a breaching of the levee. The flora would regenerate, or re-colonise flooded areas as soon as the water depths permitted.

Flooding, however triggered, was of critical importance to the quality of the coals which formed from the burial of the accumulating plant debris beds or peats. Calculations have been made which suggest the peat required to form a one metre thick seam of coal would have taken around 7 ka years to accumulate. If frequent floods interrupted the formation of the peats, thinner seams of coal resulted. The sediments swept in by a flood inevitably became mixed with the organic-rich swamp deposits. The degree of disruption would vary, so the quality of what appeared to be one coal seam could change from bottom to top. Areas of

higher relief which remained above the floods and the accompanying clays and silts produced coals which were thicker and cleaner than those formed at lower levels. These subtle but important variations represent the depositional history and have a profound impact on the quality and value of the coal, as when burnt, sediment-rich coals produce more ash than a clean coal.

This dilution of the coal which affects the ash content of the different seams has not been the only problem facing the industry. Faults criss-crossing the coalfield sometimes displace coal seams by many metres. As geological surveys of the coalfields proceeded, the frequent faults were mapped and predictions made concerning their impact. In the days before nationalisation of the industry, colliery boundaries were often set out on the basis of these jumps in the strata and special arrangements made between adjacent collieries to minimise the impact. Apart from the loss of the workable coal seam, they bring real danger. Shattered rock associated with the fault may collapse, there is a risk of flooding, and the ever present threat of methane or fire-damp is heightened.

Less easy to predict are the so called washouts. These take two forms, either relatively discrete troughs where a low-sinuosity river channel has cut down through sediments during a flood event, or a more extensive washout representing widespread erosion of a coal swamp by a meandering river system. Once found, and as mine workings are developed, channels are plotted onto maps of the coalfield and become more predictable features. While for the former, miners holding their nerve and cutting through the channel would find the seam continuing at the same level after a short distance, the latter has the potential for far more serious consequences. In the 1920s the 1.68 m thick Parkgate seam in a colliery near Rotherham was found to have been eroded over an area in excess of 161 hectares with a loss of workable coal estimated at not less that 2.5 million tonnes; the full extent of this washout was still unknown when this was reported.

Coal seams may also split around sediment washed into the plant beds. Carboniferous forests growing on delta tops which flooded were the source of an additional hazard for the miners who worked the coal seams. Lycopsids and other arborescent plants which had been inundated by a flood and subsequently died stood a chance of being at least partially buried *in situ* (*Fig. 8.26*). With their upright trunks gradually rotting, hollow tubes were created which when filled with sandy sediment, formed column-like casts. Once an underlying coal seam is removed, these gently tapering fossil trunks of truly monumental size become accidents waiting to happen, unexpectedly punching through the roof of a mine with potentially fatal consequences.

Fuel for the hearth

The PCMG strata have had a colossal impact on the economic history of the British Isles. Coal in Yorkshire is known to have been worked since at least the 13th century. Initially exploitation is likely to have been serendipitous with coal being gleaned from surfaces where seams cropped out. As these easily won reserves were depleted, the seams were chased back into a quarry-like hole, or reached by shallow excavations known as bell pits on account of their shape.

Not only coal was extracted from the PCMG, for within these strata were nodules and bands of iron carbonate which provided a once sought-after ore of iron. A new technique for extracting iron from the ore using coke was invented by Abraham Darby in 1709. Further advances at the end of the 18th century permitted the use of coal to turn the smelted iron into wrought iron. These discoveries meant that demand for coal increased dramatically to both power the 'hearths' of machine and furnace in the

Industrial Revolution, and to provide the fuel for the domestic hearths of the back-to-back homes of the rapidly expanding workforce drawn to the industrial conurbations; Bradford's population grew from 13,000 in 1801 to 104,400 in 1851 and 280,000 fifty years later!

To feed the insatiable demand for coal for both industry and domestic use, ever deeper shafts were sunk to the coal seams. The mining industry became larger, increasingly dangerous, and increasingly vital, underpinning much of Britain's heavy industry until well into the second half of the 20th century (*Fig* 8.14). Even now coal is the raw material used to generate substantial amounts of power in the UK; in 2004 33% of our power was being generated from coal with only gas providing a greater percentage. New technologies could yet change this balance, a point touched on below. While coking plants, where coal of a particular quality is burnt to produce coke,

8.15 Coke ovens being discharged at a coking plant near Royston. Coal from the Parkgate seam (Pennine Lower Coal Measures Formation) from Maltby Mine (Figure 4.4) is used for the production of coke and chemical derivatives.

8.14 Coal miner and cutter in Frickley Colliery (Wakefield), mid-1900s. Shaft sinking began in 1903. The Barnsley and Dunsil seams of the Pennine Middle Coal Measures Formation have been worked.

8.16 Opencast coal mining became an increasingly significant source of coal during and after World War II. In this 1942 image of Dunstan Hill II opencast site, south-south-west of Temple Newsam, Leeds, two seams in the Pennine Lower Coal Measures Formation were being worked. The Bottom Middleton Little Coal is being recovered from the deepest part of the excavation. The higher, Top Middleton Little Coal has already been removed.

were a common sight, today the numbers have dwindled. Near Royston one such plant remains (*Fig. 8.15*), no longer supplied by coal from a local pit, but brought by lorry from the company's mine at Maltby (*Fig. 4.4*), near Rotherham, where incidentally the Parkgate seam referred to earlier is still worked. In early 2007, 25% of Maltby's output of coking coal was being used by producing smokeless fuel and other chemical derivatives.

In recent years there has been a shift from the deep-mining of coal to opencast production, a process which has made a significant contribution to coal production in the UK since 1942 (*Fig. 8.16*). While the technologies and methods employed have changed with time, they remain simple. Land which has underlying reserves of coal, and may be a brown-field site requiring restoration, is acquired and the overburden above each seam removed. After the seam's surface is cleaned off, the coal is excavated and hauled away for processing. Finally, the site is restored. Extraction is highly mechanised, efficient and cost effective. Ironically opencast pits have been developed on the sites of disused collieries, rubbing salt into the wounds of an industry which had come to see this method of production as an increasingly significant threat to traditional methods.

Since the 1980s, there have been widespread pit closures caused by a combination of cheap imports of coal, a changing and volatile energy market where 'green' sources are encouraged, and the exhaustion of recoverable reserves of coal. The latter may be in part down to the multitude of geological problems that beset coalmines. Amongst these closures were mines that had been worked since the 18th century such as Caphouse, between Huddersfield and Wakefield, where mining records go back to at least the 1780s. Caphouse is now the National Coal Mining Museum for England and is believed to have the oldest coal mine shaft in daily use in Britain. Just how fearsome has been this contraction of the mining industry is brought home by looking at the 1982 edition of the 1:50,000 Ordnance Survey map of the Sheffield and Doncaster area. Spoil heaps litter the map like mole hills on a garden lawn.

Today only a handful of collieries remain. The largest are Maltby working the Parkgate seam (PLCMF) and Kellingley, near Knottingley, which currently works the Silkstone seam, approximately 660 m below the surface. Here they plan to develop the lower Beeston seam; both are in the PLCMF. Hay Royds Colliery between Huddersfield and Barnsley is the most unusual. Avoiding nationalisation in 1947 because of its small size, this **drift mine** exploits the Whynn Moor (or Whinmoor) seam (PLCMF). Finally, there is Hatfield Colliery east of Doncaster. The colliery was opened in 1908 to exploit the Hatfield High Hazel seam as a source of high quality domestic fuel. After nationalisation, the NCB used this mine to supply their Yorkshire workforce with coal for their use. Early this century the High Hazel seam was exhausted and the pit's new owner initially failed in an attempt to raise sufficient capital to reach the greater prize of the 4 m thick Barnsley seam, c.70 m below the High Hazel at just over 700 m depth. Both seams are within, the PMCMF.

Just a few years on, and the changing fortunes of the power industry and the quest for clean energy from coal are putting this 100 year old colliery back on the map. The same Barnsley seam which was key to the development of the Selby complex (see below) in the 1970s and 1980s is now about to be mined for high-tech clean energy production in a new power station right beside the mine, and in a final twist, the financial backing for this is coming from Russia! The damaging by-products which conventional coal-fired generating units have battled to reduce, will be removed, liquefied, and piped into the hydrocarbon reservoirs in the North Sea in order to extend their lives and extract as much oil and or gas as possible.

The northward extension of the Barnsley seam, with thicknesses of up to 3.25 m., attracted the National Coal Board (NCB) to evaluate and then undertake the costly development of the Selby Coalfield. Planning, consents, and development took 11 years and the first coal was mined in 1983. At the time this was the largest deep coal mine project in the world, covering an area of 110 sq. miles, with 5 production mines sending all their coal underground to one processing plant at Gascoigne Wood near Sherburn in Elmet. Exploration for new reserves was maintained, and with the exception of the miner's strike of 1984-85, production continued for 21 years.

A combination of geological problems with difficulty in securing contracts for the supply of coal to conventional coal-fired power stations because of the ash content, forced premature closure. One of the key requisites for efficient and economic electricity production is clean coal. Unwanted sediment costs money to transport from the mine to the power station and when burnt, increases the volumes of fly-ash left

in the furnaces. This adds to the costs of removal and disposal, and has attendant environmental impacts. The closure came despite the efforts of a committed workforce and the opening of new domestic markets for large lump coal. During the life of this coalfield, there was fierce competition between the 5 production mines for the amount of coal that could be produced. Wistow Mine in one week during September 1995 produced 200,743 tonnes which was a European output record! The highest annual output across the whole field was over 12 million tonnes in 1993/94. All that now remains are the mostly restored sites of the deep mines, and apart from the Stillingfleet site and the large spoil heap at Gascoigne Wood, little evidence of this relatively short lived coal field survives.

The Ingleton Coal field cannot be passed by without mention. Ingleton is a small town tucked beneath the Dales and seems the most unlikely of places to have had a coal mine. In fact, coal had been worked in the area since the seventeenth century. Between 1836 and 1837 John Phillips (*see page 16*) advised on the prospects for existing mines in this neighbourhood. In 1913 a speculative venture saw the development of a new colliery. Several workable seams were encountered and production from this faulted, pocket-handkerchief sized, outlier of PCMG continued until the 1930s.

Yorkshire may be standing on the verge of a renaissance in the coal mining industry. World demand for energy, the domination of the market by certain key producers, and the growing demands of new world economies have led to great uncertainty and hikes in prices. There is a desire to restore a degree of energy self-sufficiency and our almost literally 'home grown' coal may yet make a significant contribution to the energy needs of our nation.

Coal the catalyst

The quest for coal and the need for an understanding of the geology of coal were important catalysts in the formation of scientific societies such as the West Riding Geological and Polytechnic Society in 1837, an early precursor of the Yorkshire Geological Society which still flourishes today. In addition to the scientific, the social, cultural and political impact of the Industrial Revolution has been colossal. Non-Conformism found fertile ground in the industrial towns, providing hope for an often hope-less workforce.

8.17 The Gascoigne Wood Branch of the National Union of Mineworkers banner. A traditional surround frames a contemporary image portraying the confrontation at the Orgreave Coking Plant in 1984; 'Our spirits were bruised . . . but never broken'.

One significant improvement in working conditions came when in 1842, women, girls, and boys under 10 were banned from working underground in the mines. Battles for improved pay and conditions continued as mine owners and, after nationalisation in 1947, governments through the offices of the NCB and British Coal, attempted to maintain a firm grip on the salaries of the workforce. The arts have been enriched by the culture and traditions of these industries; music has been mentioned. Marching for the galas and during strikes, individual collieries carried their banners aloft. On the one hand a rallying point, on the other a pictorial record of past events, both aspirational and inspirational, the art of an industry (Fig. 8.17).

The quest for black gold

As already noted, the PCMG is present beneath the more recent rocks to the east, nearly as far north as Whitby. This prompts a mention of the inspired 1921 report of Percy Kendall, Professor of Geology at the University of Leeds, made public for the first time in 1976 in the *Proceedings of the Yorkshire Geological Society*. His report for the Anglo-Persian Oil Company, which would become B.P., was based on astute observation and sound prediction. He first of all predicted that the organic-rich sediments of the Carboniferous could extend at depth as far as Robin Hood's Bay. He went on to suggest that there was a good chance that oil would be found where the organic matter in the Lower and Upper Carboniferous rocks alike had been buried sufficiently deeply to subject them to a natural pressure-cooking treatment; he was already aware of published records of small amounts of oil being found in boreholes further along the coast at Hartlepool, and he had noted traces of oil in Carboniferous sediments near Richmond in N.Yorkshire.

At Robin Hood's Bay he had observed the anticlinal structure seen so beautifully on the foreshore at low tides (*Fig.* 10.3), which he thought was likely to be replicated at depth, and here the porous Permian Magnesian Limestone with an impervious halite or rock salt cap would provide the perfect reservoir! While no exploitable hydrocarbons were found at Robin Hood's Bay, drilling not far from there many years later revealed no commercial oil, but gas was discovered and is still exploited. This and the hydrocarbon industry's experiences in the southern North Sea has been the inspiration for increasingly sophisticated and extensive programme of on-shore exploration in the later 20th and early 21st centuries. Significant reserves have been found where the source rocks are Carboniferous sediments, and Millstone Grit reservoirs are also known, such as Kirby Misperton in the Vale of Pickering. These gas fields are in production (Chapter 9). Kendall died in 1936 before his theory was put to the test.

London's streets are paved with gold

Mention has been made of the use for building of the coarser sandstones and grits of the Millstone Grit Group. The PCMG contains a fabulous array of finer grained sandstones, and these too have been quarried and mined on a considerable scale. Arguably the most famous amongst these are the much sought after and still quarried, Elland Flags, a series of fissile **micaceous** sandstones which have paved many a town and city across England over hundreds of years, under the trade name of York Stone (*Fig.* 8.18). In 1905, South Owram [*sic*] was despatching stone via Elland Railway Station, described as 'Used for steps, landings, etc; much of the stone known as 'York Stone'

8.18 Pennine Coal Measure Group flagstones traded under the name 'York Stone'.

ABOVE 8.19 Hillcliff Sandstone Mine, Allerton, Bradford. Elland Flags (Pennine Lower Coal Measures Formation) were worked underground. Waste from quarries and mines around Egypt, near Bradford, was piled behind great walls of stone known as the Walls of Jericho.

in the London Market comes from this quarry.'

On one level the beautiful textures and fine sedimentary structures revealed in the split surfaces of York Stone, gently worn by thousands of footfalls over the decades, speak of an exotic Carboniferous world. The tooling round the margins of the exactingly sized flags, and the evidence of the skilful chamfering of edges which still stood proud, bring us back to more recent times. They remind us of the miners of the stone from under Elland and surrounding areas (*Fig. 8.19*), working in often treacherous conditions, and of the craftsmen, working in all weathers, dressing the raw stone in their simple shelters on the edges of the quarries. These strata are still worked in the area, as at Northowram 4 miles north of Elland (*Fig. 8.20a-b*). The stone from this quarry is transported to Keighley where computer aided technology has taken over, requiring a different range of skills to those used for much of the last century.

The PCMG sandstones possess characteristics which make them ideal for working into characteristically 'brick-sized' blocks. Numerous buildings across Yorkshire's great industrial conurbations and the surrounding towns and villages are full of examples. Like the Millstone Grit, they are frequently stained black, as theirs is the habit of clinging onto the grime and soot which have been so abundant for so long.

RIGHT 8.20a-b TOP (a) Elland Flags are extracted by Farrar Natural Stone from their Northowram quarry, north-east of Halifax. BOTTOM (b) Some of the quarried stone is dressed using traditional methods in the quarry. Larger blocks are transported to the company's stone yard at Keighley where modern computerized cutting equipment produce stone for a wide range of building projects.

They also find use beyond the cities and towns, with thousands of miles of walling around field and over moor.

'By their walls ye shall know them', though a corruption of a Biblical saying, is usefully applied to those parts of Yorkshire underlain by Carboniferous strata, and does give a good, but not infallible, guide to what part of the succession you are in. The untidy grey walls of the Lower Carboniferous limestones have already been alluded to. The Yoredales with a foot in both the Lower and Upper Carboniferous camps has both limestones and sandstones. The Millstone Grit tends to the unruly with frequently massive and irregular beds, though this time of dark-weathering coarse sands and grits. Also present are sheets and slabs of sandstone, so frequently met with in the PCMG and which make ideal materials for dry-stone walling. Inevitably, there are walls which end up emulating the very strata from which they were created (*Fig. 8.21 a-c*).

These sandstones were also a fine source of the raw material for hones or scythe stones (*Fig. 8.22*). They have been important for as long as our ancestors have sharpened sticks, bones, stones and more typically metals. Archaeologists are fascinated by the distribution of different rocks used as implements, since if the source of the stone is known, they provide the evidence for patterns of trade. Forensic techniques are used in this quest, like those applied to the different sandstones of the PCMG.

8.22 Scythe stones and grindstones of Ackworth Rock (Pennine Upper Coal Measures Formation) at Messrs W. W. Bowman's quarry yard at Ackworth Moor Top, 1936.

8.21a-c TOP (a) Gritstone from the Millstone Grit Group used for walling near Broomehead Hall, south-west of Stocksbridge. CENTRE (b) A dry-stone wall being reconstructed west of Penistone. BOTTOM (c) Pennine Coal Measure Group flaggy sandstones used for walling at Maythorn between Holmfirth and Penistone.

8.23 Storth Brickworks, Elland, between Halifax and Huddersfield, 1926. The seatearth from under the coal was used for the manufacture of firebricks, which were fired in the kilns on the right of the photograph.

The by-products of coal

The PCMG is rich in mudrocks the uses of which vary considerably depending on the properties imparted through their mineralogy and resultant chemistry, and the amounts of coarse material present. They have been used for a great range of products from domestic pottery, through pipes, bricks, tiles and terracotta. Production frequently went hand in hand with coal production (*Fig.* 8.23) where the association of coal and workable clays provided the raw materials for manufacture with minimal transport.

Some of the seatearths underlying coal seams weathered in a particular way, making them especially useful for lining furnaces. They were extracted during coal mining as a valuable by-product, or mined in their own right. An example of this value is seen with one particular fireclay which before World War I was priced at between £1.25 and £1.50 per ton. This equates to between £357 and £428 per tonne in the year 2000.

A particularly famous example of a firm producing both decorative wares and building materials at different times over their long history was the Burmantofts Company in Leeds. Founded to mine coal in the 1840s, the firm went through various mergers and changes of name and eventually closed in the 1950s. The discovery of suitable clays initially led to the production of pipes and bricks. Later the company became particularly famous for the glazed terracotta wares traded as Burmantofts Faience, which enjoyed considerable popularity with architects and builders in Leeds and beyond.

The coal swamp forests grew not only on clays which could become seatearths and fireclays, but on sandy sediments. The conditions in which these sediments were deposited, colonised, and finally buried might produce extraordinarily pure sand rocks cemented by silica and known as quartzites. In industrial parlance they are known as gannisters. Their purity has made these rocks especially important for lining furnaces. The lack of impurities, which could act as fluxes, ensured that they did not melt when exposed to the high temperatures demanded in many of the metal refining processes.

Life on sag-basin Yorkshire

We have established that during the Upper Carboniferous, the nature of Yorkshire changed. River-fed deltas, the delta plains, and coal swamps progressively taking over from the cyclic Yoredales and marine sediments of the Pennine Basin.

The wide range of environments is reflected by the equally varied flora and fauna. Mention has already been made of aspects of the marine creatures of the Yoredale Group limestones, where brachiopods and crinoids were sometimes abundant. The shallower photic zone with more oxygenated waters had the potential to support a wide range of organisms, including bryozoans, bivalves, and even rare trilobites. The sediments of the deeper waters might occasionally pay host to the skeletal remains of the denizens of the shallow waters of the blocks, these spilling down in turbidity currents from the unstable slope.

Also accumulating were the remains of **planktonic** and **nektonic** organisms. One group, the nektonic goniatites, provided the correlative key when, during marine transgressions, their remains ended up in the marine bands covering the delta plain, which punctuate the Yoredale, Millstone Grit, and with decreasing regularity the PCMG. Also present in the marine bands are the shells of the scallop-like *Dunbarella*, a small brachiopod called *Lingula* on account of its tongue-like shape which lived in the sediment, ostracods, and the remains of **conchostracans**.

Marine fish would also move in to the drowned coal forest landscapes and their remains are found in addition to freshwater species. The

8.24 Core with flattened impression of the stem of the horsetail *Calamites*. Compare this with Figure 8.25.

8.25 The sandstone cast of the stem of a Pennine Coal Measure Group horsetail *Calamites cannaeformis* from Barnsley. The growing-tip of the stem is to the right.

development of the delta plain environment led to colonisation by a range of freshwater bivalves. Many of these invertebrates are used for detailed local correlation in the absence of marine bands. Above all, during this time, there was the increasing dominance of plants with the growth of the great tropical forests which would contribute so much to the coal seams.

How do we know what plants occupied the various environments for the *c.*7 Ma over which the PCMG were being deposited? The exploitation of coal has provided ample opportunity for their collection and study. Most plant fossils when observed or collected will be preserved in one of five very different ways, ranging from the 2- to the 3-dimensional. Compression fossils are those where a specimen is completely flattened (*Fig.* 8.24). Three dimensional specimens may be sediment filled casts of roots, trunks or stems, frequently preserving the external patterns but no evidence of the soft tissue (*Fig.* 7.14). Another category is where the plant tissues and cells are impregnated by mineral solutions leading to the most exquisite 3-D details being preserved shortly after burial. Plant-rich calcareous nodules known as *coal balls* are examples of this type of preservation and are known from certain horizons in Yorkshire. Palaeobotanists have spent decades sectioning nodules and quite literally peeling away layers of detail to squeeze as much information as possible out of these extraordinary time-capsules. A fourth method of fossilisation is where plant material is coated by minerals from solution, generating a mineral cast. Finally, another world is revealed under

the microscope, when samples of sediment or coal are dissolved in powerful acids to reveal the tiny pollen grains and spores which occur in their countless millions. These have also been used for the purposes of correlation. Of course, to fully understand the world of Carboniferous plants, all types of preservation are essential, each providing a different insight.

The relationship of different plants and styles of preservation to the associated rock types, combined with studies of comparable environments across the world today, have enabled palaeobotanists to form detailed understandings of the plant communities, their habitats, and the processes which led to their fossilisation. They have even been able to reconstruct individual plants, and in this context one important issue stands out. Plants are invariably complex organisms made up of many parts, e.g. roots, stems, branches, leaves, pollen grains and spores, which at any one time are unlikely to all be found together, and especially after death.

For a case study of this problem, take the ancient equivalent of our modern horsetail. The stems are known as *Calamites. Asterophylites* or *Annularia* are the names for the leaves on the small branches; flattened cones are named *Calamostachys*, *Palaeostachya* or *Paracalamostachys* and *Calamocarpon* is a small cone described from mineralised 3-d specimens. All these are thought to have been parts of the same genus of plant but because they are found in isolation have collected a spectacular array of names. The size of plants may further reduce the opportunities for 'complete fossilisation', though some remarkable examples of partial fossilisation are known! In these circumstances, the reconstruction of an individual plant is a complex process, and one is reminded of the early attempt at the same process with the dinosaur

Iguanodon, when the forelimb's spiky thumb was initially mistakenly placed on the animal's nose!

The coal-forming swamp deposits developed over sandy or muddy sediments washed in during flooding. While the flood waters were present, *Calamites* attained heights of up to 10 m and colonised the lake margins. They also grew on the shifting sediments along the sides of rivers. Their hollow stems are not uncommonly preserved as three dimensional sandstone casts (*Fig. 8.25*). Rafted masses of their stems are also found. They were great survivors like today's *Equisetum*, with the smallest root fragment starting a new plant.

Once the lakes were clogged with sediment, a succession of plants colonised them before giving way to the large tree-sized club mosses, the lycopsids. These were the dominant plants of the swamp and their stumps are occasionally uncovered. A fine example from near Bradford ended up in the Manchester Museum. In 1873 a group of around 10 'tree' stumps were uncovered while excavations were made for an extension to the South Yorkshire County Lunatic Asylum at Wardley to the west of Sheffield (*Fig.*

8.26 The base of one of 10 tree-sized lycopsids (club mosses) discovered during building works at the South Yorkshire County Lunatic Asylum at Wardley, west of Sheffield, in 1873. Bricks in the wall to the right provide a rudimentary scale bar!

8.26). Henry C. Sorby (Chapter 1) became involved in the discovery and encouraged the enclosure and covering of two adjacent specimens. This location is listed as a Site of Special Scientific Interest, and has recently been afforded protective re-burial in the face of a large housing development on the site of the old hospital. Sorby concluded on the evidence of the root system's orientation, which was identical in all those he observed, that the prevailing winds were from the west. He had observed modern trees with identical root orientation, horizontal roots on the windward side and more vertically inclined roots in the lee. Sorby identified the stems of these specimens as examples of the lycopsid *Sigillaria* with a typical root system known as *Stigmaria* (Chapter 7 Fig. 7.14).

Studies of plants like these led to the conclusion that *Sigillaria* was a coloniser of the levees and

8.27 Reconstruction of the lycopsid *Lepidodendron* which attained heights of 40 – 54 m. before developing a crown of branches at the end of their life cycle.

was smaller than the lycopsids of the swamps. The latter could grow to heights of 40-54 m. Lycopsids developed an adorning crown of branches towards the end of their 10 to 15 year life-span (*Fig 8.27*). Research suggests that seasonal leaf-fall as we know the phenomena barely ever happened. Leaves and branches are most likely to have been brought down by strong winds during storms, or when plants died. Such rampant growth goes some way to explaining the rapid accumulation of coal-forming plant debris, along with constant raining down of their spores. Foliage from plants growing on the levees of the river channels would either fall into the water and drift down stream, or be blown out into the swamp areas behind. During floods plant material might be washed through breeches in the levees to be rapidly entombed in the silts and clays of the flood plain. The degree of damage to any part of a plant is a guide to the distance transported. Fossil charcoals are also known, providing evidence for forest fires.

The levees supported a range of plants which preferred 'keeping their feet dry' including ferns, seed ferns (*Fig. 8.28*), and the sphenopsids, a low growing form of *Calamites*. The Cordaites which are related to the conifers have been reconstructed with roots like

8.28 Foliage of a pteridosperm (seed-bearing fern), *Neuropteris*, preserved in a core from a borehole to prove coal reserves in the Selby Coalfield.

8.29 An artist's reconstruction of a coal swamp based on meticulous research and collaboration with palaeobotanists. This picture is based on Upper Carboniferous deposits in Illinois. At the time the UK and USA were very close together (Figure 2.5a).

mangroves, suggesting they occupied similar coast fringing habitats.

Through the succession, changes in the composition of the communities has provided **stratigraphers** with the means to correlate between different successions. Research continues into the flora of the Upper Carboniferous and how the plant species and communities changed with the passing of time. The fruits of all these various strands of research, when shared between scientists and artists, are superb reconstructions of coal swamps (*Fig. 8.29*). We recognise that if we could step back and visit one of these great coal swamps, we might find the experience a little like that of Gulliver in the land of Brobdingnag. While some of the plants might look familiar, their size certainly would not be. Flowering plants had not yet evolved. Miners of the 18th and 19th centuries who lacked any understanding of

these ancient worlds, perceived the large lycopsid's branches and stems as serpents, the diamond-shaped leaf cushions masquerading as the scaly body of a snake – bringing us nicely to the vertebrates.

While fish were relatively common, and their remains are not infrequently found, the evolving tetrapods were still in their infancy. Amphibians had evolved during the Devonian and are presumed to have been major predators on the coal swamp invertebrates. Their remains appear to be rare – though this may be because we are failing to look for them in the right places, and that they are difficult to spot especially in modern mines. The discovery of an amphibian in a coal mine at Toftshaw near Bradford provides us with a fascinating glimpse of attitudes, the lines of communication, and links between those interested in geology and palaeontology in the 19th century.

Louis C. Miall (1842-1921), was an educator and scientist with a keen interest in natural history; he was especially active in Yorkshire. He was a member of the Royal Society, and served in various capacities within the British Association. In a short article published in the *Quarterly Journal of the Geological Society of London* recounting aspects of the amphibian's recovery, Miall gives credit to 'the persevering attention of William Firth, a miner whose zeal was stimulated by some previous knowledge of geology and in particular of coal fossils'. The remains had been spotted in 1868 in the shale above the Black-Bed Coal, the third coal seam above the Elland Flags. The shale was already well known for the remains of fish. The specimen was removed with difficulty – which suggests that there was a willingness of the mine's owners and managers to countenance some disruption while this was carried out.

Miall then brought the specimen to the attention of Thomas Henry Huxley, 'Darwin's Bulldog', a member of the Royal Society and then President of the Geological Society of London. After examination of the preserved remains, which included elements of the upper and lower jaws, and comparison with known species, he declared the fossil to be new to science and named the creature *Pholiderpeton scutigerum*. The estimated two metre long amphibian is one of the treasures of the Cliffe Castle Museum at Keighley. The importance of the preservation of such material in museum collections is highlighted by the subsequent history of the specimen. During the 1980s, the specimen was prepared using air abrasive and dental tools, thereby exposing parts of the fossil, including skull bones, which had not been seen by Huxley, showing the specimen to be the most complete of its kind to have been found in Britain. During the Carboniferous the first reptiles evolved, though none have been found in Yorkshire – yet.

Plant remains show no evidence of having been nibbled by vertebrates, though indirectly plant debris must have played a significant role in the food chains which existed. Evidence for this has come from the rigorous collecting that has been carried out on disused coal tips around Britain. From this work,

scientists know that arthropods were abundant and amongst them, numerous insects have been recorded. Amongst these were dragonflies with wingspans of considerable size, numerous varieties of cockroach in keeping with the incomprehensible volumes of plant material on which they could feed, and one insect like a grass-hopper. Other arthropods included spiders, scorpions, and organisms resembling giant millipedes. Yorkshire doubtless hosted an abundance of creepy crawlies, and the soundscape would have been very different to the one we know today. Birds would not evolve for around 160 Ma, but the coal swamp forests would have been alive with a myriad varieties of arthropod, with the sounds of insect wings beating, of rustling, mastication and may be even stridulation!

Closure on the Carboniferous

The Ingleton outlier provides a fascinating glimpse of what are thought to be the Warwickshire Group, or Barren Coal Measures as they were once known. Though present in the main Yorkshire Coalfield, they are never exposed at surface. The Warwickshire Group strata become progressively younger as they are followed northwards from the coalfields of Warwickshire and Staffordshire. Their character was closely linked to the big changes accompanying the formation of mountain chains rising to the south, a consequence of the Variscan Orogeny which coincided with the sudden change from westerly to southerly sourced sediments during the PMCMF.

At Ingleton these red coloured strata are reported to rest unconformably on the PCMG, evidence of uplift and erosion before their deposition. They are in turn unconformably overlain by Permian sediments (Chapter 9). The red colour may be primary, representing the increasingly arid climate which the region was subjected to as the Upper Carboniferous drew to a close and when these sediments were deposited, or possibly, the reddening was the result of weathering in an arid climate at the start of the Permian – like iron starting to rust. While the uppermost strata of the terminal Carboniferous are not preserved *in situ* at this location, the Permian rocks nearby, like the PCMG sandstones described earlier, have a fascinating tale to tell of the late Carboniferous and early Permian history of this area.

NINE

The Heat is On

9.1 The northern end of the Vale of Mowbray, with Osmotherley in the middle distance, viewed from Thimbleby Moor on the western edge of the North York Moors. The Vale is largely underlain by rocks of Permo-Trias age, in turn overlain by extensive Pleistocene and Holocene superficial deposits.

Time: Permian: 299 – 251 Ma
Latitude: From 10° – to 25°N
Climate: The close of the Carboniferous saw the continuation of major polar glaciation. Yorkshire's isolation from normal marine influences led to the development of an arid climate with extremes of temperature. This continued throughout the Permian.
Environment: Stony and sandy deserts with dune fields. Extensive evaporating basins, especially to the east, with fringing **sabkhas**. Tropical marine marginal carbonate sand-shoals and patch-reefs, sometimes spreading across the basin.
Rocks: Breccias, conglomerates, wind-blown dune sands, sandstones, siltstones, mudstones, limestones including dolomites, halite, gypsum and other evaporites.
Stratigraphy:
WEST OF THE PENNINES:
Appleby Group.
EAST OF THE PENNINES:
Rotliegendes Group: Yellow Sands Formation.
Zechstein Group (represented by seven depositional sequences which are explained in this chapter. They are numbered Z1-7): Marl Slate Formation (Z1), Cadeby Formation (Z1&2), Hayton Anhydrite Formation (Z3), Edlington and Kirkham Abbey formations (Z3), Fordon Evaporites Formation (Z4), Brotherton Formation (Z4), Billingham Anhydrite Formation (Z5), Boulby Halite Formation (Z5), Boulby Potash Formation (Z5), Carnallitic Marl (Z6), Sherburn Anhydrite Formation (Z6), Sneaton Halite Formation (Z7), Sleights Siltstone Formation (Z7), Littlebeck Formation (Z7),

Roxby Formation (Z7) – part.

Time: Triassic 251 – 199 Ma
Latitude: From 25° – to 35°N
Climate: Arid to semi-arid climate continues, strongly influenced by the global monsoonal system. During the Triassic, possibly due to catastrophic volcanic eruptions generating stupendous amounts of the greenhouse gas carbon dioxide, there was significant climate change. Wetter conditions pertained for a time before arid conditions were re-established, these in turn being replaced by a less arid climate toward the close.
Environment: River-dominated environments were replaced by extensive sabkhas in which evaporite minerals were periodically deposited. There is evidence of a period of greatly enhanced monsoonal rainfall linked to the development of 'greenhouse earth' triggered by the volcanicity mentioned above. Towards the close, marine influences become apparent.
Rocks: Pebbly sands, sands, silts, mudstones, limestones including dolomites, halite and gypsum. A bone bed may be present but is not recorded.
Stratigraphy:
Sherwood Sandstone Group: Roxby Formation (continued). Sherwood sandstones.
Mercia Mudstone Group: Sidmouth, and Branscombe mudstone, and Blue Anchor formations.
Penarth Group: Westbury and Lilstock formations.

Setting the Scene

'Fog will be slow to clear and may linger all day in the Vale of York' is not infrequently heard in winter weather forecasts. What a contrast to that time when the Permian and Triassic sediments that floor the Vale were being deposited.

For around 100 Ma, what is now Yorkshire was carried northwards as part of Pangaea, starting from around 10°N to end around 35°N. This journey took Yorkshire across the latitudes which today are straddled by the northern hemisphere's great deserts, including the Sahara and those of the Middle East. During this time, the sun blazed down – even in winter. Summer temperatures were scorching, averaging over 30°C. The annual average temperature is estimated to have been around 25°C, compared to 8.5 – 11°C in the UK today. The nearest thing to fog would have been the dust from sand-storms whipped up by strong winds which swept Yorkshire during the early Permian.

Once the winter fog has cleared, *visibility* of a different sort remains a matter of 'concern', for the bedrock is rarely exposed in the vales of Mowbray and York, and across the Humberhead Levels to the south (*Fig. 9.20*). With the exception of harder limestone beds within the Permian, most of the sediments are relatively soft, and have suffered significant erosion. This culminated in the last glaciation (Chapter 12) and the Permo-Triassic sediments are frequently carpeted with the products of both ice and flood. This has left the vales as an area of generally subdued relief forming a dramatic foil for the Pennines in the west, and more especially the North York Moors and Wolds in the east. The escarpments of the latter two rear-up from the plain, in the case of the North York Moors forming a formidable barrier to east – west routes. North-south routes have had an easier time in the vales, and to some extent benefited from the beds of limestone of the Upper Permian. Their resistance to erosion has provided a slightly elevated and better drained tract along which roads have been built, thus avoiding mire and flood. The A1 has long been a beneficiary, and the latest incarnation of the Great North Road, the A1(M), passes through several revealing cuttings in these strata between Pontefract and the A64 turning to York.

Nowhere in Yorkshire does the Carboniferous-Permian outcrop show a conformable transition. To the west of the Pennines, near Ingleton, there is one small and intriguing outlier of Permian sediments which overlies the Pennine Coal Measures Group. To the east of the Pennines, as the outcrop is followed from south to north, the Permian rocks rest on progressively older Carboniferous strata; the Upper Pennine Coal Measures Group in the south, around Knaresborough the Millstone Grit Group, and in the north the Yoredale Group. Reddening of these older strata, frequently seen at their contact with the Permian, has been explained as both a contemporaneous process and one which occurred later, after burial. Recent pronouncements suggest that both processes played their part.

The Permian sediments lapped progressively onto the Carboniferous of the Pennines. As they did so, these younger Permian sediments overlapped older Permian strata that had already been deposited. Subsequently the Permian and overlying Triassic sediments have, with the exception of those over the Market Weighton High (Chapter 3), been further tilted so they now dip gently down to the east. As a

9.2 Vibroseis trucks parked in the Vale of Pickering in September 2007. They were being used as part of an elaborate seismic survey aiming to refine knowledge of existing gas fields and locate new reserves.

result of this tipping, in eastern Yorkshire, deposits of this age are present at depth, beneath the younger strata of the North York Moors, the Vale of Pickering and the Wolds. In these areas, our knowledge of the strata relies largely on boreholes and seismic surveys carried out in the course of the search for water and economic minerals such as coal, **evaporites**, oil, and gas.

Boreholes provide samples of the rocks penetrated. They may be chippings separated from the drilling muds used to lubricate the drill-bit and flushed from the borehole, or lengths of core cut using annular drill bits studded with industrial diamonds. The knowledge so gained is then combined with the data collected by the use of increasingly sophisticated, down-hole **wireline logging** techniques. Together they provide the framework upon which the interpretation of seismic data is based. Seismic studies use the shock-waves, generated by either explosive charges fired in shallow holes, or specially adapted vehicles which 'stamp' on the ground (*Fig. 9.2*); these are more appropriately used along roads, and especially in built up areas, where setting off a charge of dynamite would be unacceptable! The time taken for the shock waves to travel to and from different rock layers, some of which are better **reflectors** than others, is recorded on an intricate array of geophones – a type of microphone which can detect shock waves travelling through the ground. From the data recorded, distinctive horizons are plotted and a picture of the subsurface geology is built up. Modern seismic studies have advanced in leaps and bounds as computing power has increased. This has allowed geophysicists to produce elaborate

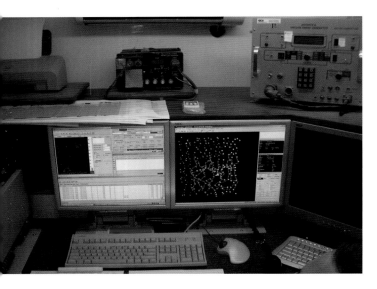

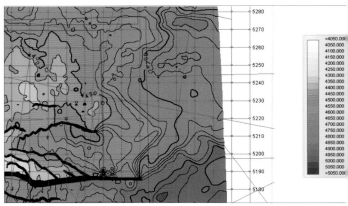

9.3a-b LEFT (a) The nerve-centre of the seismic survey, perched high up on the edge of the Wolds overlooking the Vale of Pickering. A computer screen shows the shot-firing arrays set out across one part of the Vale below in September 2007. The explosives charges are placed in shallow holes and then detonated according to a predetermined plan, controlled from the truck to where all the data is transferred through miles of cable run across fields, through hedges and over roads!

ABOVE (b) The all-important survey results allow the depth in feet of a single layer of rock, probably anhydrite, to be calculated below a fixed datum point. The depth information when plotted on a map shows the structures present, including the presence of faults shown as thick black lines.

BELOW 9.4 An area of the Vale of York which when compared with the bedrock geology map (Figure 3.2a) demonstrates how detailed seismic surveys and information from boreholes has completely redefined our understanding of the distribution and orientation of faults. Modified from Hawkins and Saul, 2003, *Proceedings of the Yorkshire Geological Society*, Vol. 54, 257-267, by permission of the Council of the Yorkshire Geological Society.

three-dimensional models of the features that interest them, enabling them to efficiently exploit oil and, in the case of Yorkshire, small but important gas fields (*Fig.* 9.3a-b).

The narrative provided by the rocks, so readable where exposures are frequent and good, becomes much more difficult to decipher across the floors of the vales. A glance at the 1:50,000 maps that cover the Vale of York highlight the problems faced by geologists. Faults crossing different rock types around the edges suddenly 'disappear' or, more precisely, may no longer be traced. Do they continue? How much may be missed became abundantly clear when studies connected with the **hydrogeology** of the Triassic in an area north-east of York revealed the complexity and scale of faulting across a part of the Vale of York where previous mapping had not picked up any significant faulting (*Fig.* 9.4). There is no evidence to suggest that these faults were active during deposition of these strata, rather that they formed and became active in the late Jurassic and early Cretaceous (Chapter 10). A further complicating factor is that there is a significant thickening and change in the Permian sediments as they are traced from west to east. The upper part of the Permian sequence is rich in evaporites, and the most soluble of these have been dissolved when brought near to the surface.

The 'memory of pebbles'

At the end of the Carboniferous and during the early Permian, compression caused by the Variscan Orogeny led to the old faults moving again, but in the opposite direction, with associated folding of

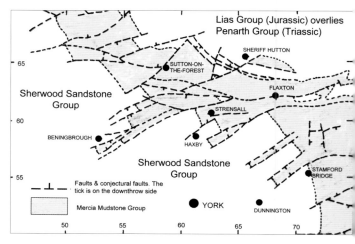

sedimentary rocks, and the progressive uplift of the Pennine Anticline (Chapter 8). This became an important feature dividing western from eastern parts of Northern England. Exposed strata were subject to erosion of the sort witnessed in the uplands within today's desert belts, with extreme fluctuations of temperature shattering exposed rocks, and occasional torrential downpours sweeping the debris towards the basins surrounding the upland areas, perhaps forming valleys comparable to the **wadis** of the Middle East today.

The deposits of the early Permian Appleby Group form an outlier a little north-west of Ingleton on the border with Cumbria. Uplift to the east of the Craven and Dent faults had been a consequence of the Variscan Orogeny. Erosion of the uplifted area brought fragments of the Carboniferous deposits, and infrequent pebbles of the Lower Palaeozoic rocks, into the adjacent basin. The deposit is known to be *c.*100 m thick. The debris is likely to have been washed from wadis, and accumulated along the fault scarps. The deposits are illuminating, for derived rocks are the bearers of 'memories', they are story tellers.

The sediments of this relict of what is believed to have been a more extensive deposit have been variously described as **breccias** and conglomerates (*Fig.* 9.5). The rock fragments, embedded in red sandy sediments which show evidence of being of desert origin, provide a fascinating insight into the **palaeogeography** and bedrock geology of the area. The lower part of the deposit contains fragments of grey and red Carboniferous limestones. The upper part contains pebbles of slate, grey Carboniferous limestone of which some is **dolomitised**, and Millstone Grit. Preserved in the red limestone fragments are the fossilised remains of a tiny coiled calcareous tube which was occupied by a worm called *Spirorbis*. These are identical to those found encrusting seaweeds on modern beaches, and like their modern counterparts are likely to have been attached to plant remains. They are particularly well known from limestones in the latest Carboniferous rocks around Manchester, but have not been recovered from the Pennine Upper Coal Measures Formation at Ingleton, upon which these conglomerates rest. The presence of pieces of *Spirorbis* Limestone, as this rock is called, would suggest that these beds had been present not too far away, probably on the uplifted Pennine block.

The distribution of the different rock types in this

9.5 Breccio-conglomerate of Permian age exposed near Ingleton.

Permian breccio-conglomerate has led to speculation over the sequence of events which would explain the presence of one rock type or absence of another. Suggestions include erosion progressively cutting deeper into the rock sequence, exposing and eroding older rocks through time, and further movement along the fault scarp exposing the Lower Palaeozoic rocks present beneath the Carboniferous sediments. Yet another scenario is that with the passage of time, the rock fragments may have been washed in from along the foot of the fault scarp. Whatever the reason, the lack of any contemporary Permian fossils in these deposits rules out any hope of dating the two phases of deposition which have been recognised.

With water present, albeit infrequently, and by inference the Carboniferous limestones exposed, are we to imagine the beginnings of limestone dissolution taking place? Could, just possibly, the first generation of fissures and caves have formed along joints, other fractures, and bedding planes in the limestones? Examples of Triassic **karst** systems are known from the Lower Carboniferous of Somerset, and in South Wales. These contain remarkable vertebrate fossils dating from that time. If fissures and caves did form, have subsequent Pleistocene glaciations and periods of cave development (Chapter 12) removed any evidence of such features in Yorkshire? Could they have been overlooked so far? Evidence for them might have been expected to occur in the heavily mined orefields of the Askrigg Block, but only cave systems post-dating mineralisation have been recorded. One

9.6 Grimbald Crag beside the River Nidd at Knaresborough. Reddened Upper Plompton Grit (Millstone Grit Group) formed a hill after the erosion of the overlying and adjacent Carboniferous rocks. The hill was in turn inundated during the Permian marine transgression and is unconformably covered by limestones of the Cadeby Formation (Permian, Zechstein Group).

9.7a-b ABOVE (a) Caythorpe near Bridlington, originally a site producing gas from Permian desert sandstones and now a natural gas storage site.
BELOW (b) Cores from gas wells drilled at Caythorpe. A. Gritstone (Millstone Grit Group); B. Red dune sands (Rotliegendes Group); C. Carbonate rock (Zechstein Group). Scale bar 10 cm.

other possibility remains; could the 'small caverns' recorded between beds of limestone, and filled with mineral deposits known variously as flots, flats or floats, be 'fossilised' early precursors of the more extensive systems we see today?

Of rock desert and dune

The intense early Permian erosion was responsible for significant modification of the landscape. After *c.*36 Ma, the margins of the basin over eastern Yorkshire and into the North Sea were in large part an eroded, flat and exposed rock surface or pediment. At the very edge, geologists have mapped a more varied landscape where occasional mounds of Carboniferous rock remained, some reaching heights of around 30 m (*Fig.*9.6). The pediment was at times covered by patches of gravel and sand. Sufficient sand was present in some parts to be blown into dunes such as are exposed in County Durham, and recorded in boreholes at Caythorpe (*Figs* 9.7a-b), near Bridlington, on the Yorkshire Wolds. The sand grains are characterised by their roundness and their frosted surfaces caused by the constant collisions as they are blown about.

The Caythorpe dunes were found to contain gas

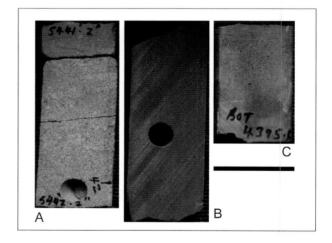

which was for many years exploited. These reserves have now been exhausted, and the reservoir is being used as a gas storage facility. During periods of low demand, gas is pumped down into the porous desert sands and then, when demand is high, drawn off to feed into the UK's gas grid.

By analysis of the cross-bedding found in the sand dunes, a prevailing east-north-easterly wind direction across Yorkshire has been deduced. The winds were the product of intense high and low pressure systems across the northern hemisphere. To the east of the rock desert and dunes, centred on what is now the southern North Sea, was a subsiding basin, as much as 250 m below sea level. Parts of Yorkshire were also below sea level. During the Lower Permian, this basin was occasionally flooded during the sporadic violent storms which affect such regions. Over the next 5 to 10 Ma, this basin was to accumulate sediments which not only had an immediate effect on the world's oceans, but would play a significant role in the 20th century economic history of the UK, as touched on below.

The Saline Giant and 'Gaia's kidney'

Yorkshire sits on the edge of an evaporite deposit known as a 'saline giant', a spectacular accumulation of sulphate and chloride minerals including anhydrite, gypsum, halite, and less common potassium salts, inter-bedded with mudstones and carbonates. The deposit formed in the Zechstein Sea which stretched from eastern England into north-west Europe. This is one of many such deposits which have formed across the world at regular intervals through geological time, and which are known as 'saline giants'.

In 2001, Kenneth Hsü questioned why such major evaporite sequences had not been laid down far more frequently than is the case. He recognised that the cyclic nature of these deposits was linked to the levels of dissolved salts in the earth's oceans. He then suggested that the formation of saline giants would only occur when a certain threshold was reached, and was fulfilling a global need, namely to desalinate the worlds oceans. This process coincidentally removed high levels of toxic heavy metals. He saw this as a natural extension of the *Gaia Theory* as proposed by James Lovelock, and coined the term 'Gaia's kidney' for this salt regulating process.

The series of depressions or sub-basins occupied by the Zechstein Sea are thought to have formed in response to thermal relaxation after a period of igneous activity triggered by a hot-spot beneath the basin's centre, at the close of the Carboniferous. This echoes the process which led to the sag-basin of the Upper Carboniferous (Chapter 8). One especially significant outcome of the thermal relaxation was an opportunity for the intrusion of magma into the Lower Carboniferous rocks of Durham and Northumberland, an event which formed what has been described as the Great Whin **Sill**. Taking into account the frequent changes in the stratigraphic level

of this intrusion, the Great Whin Dolerite Complex has been coined as a more appropriate name. Present from a little north of the county boundary, this imposing physical feature is what the River Tees rages over at High Force in Teesdale, and provided the foundation for much of Hadrian's Wall. The heat from this hot-spot was likely to have further heated the Wensleydale Granite, believed by some to be a seminal event in the mineralisation of the Askrigg Block. Fragments of the rock forming the sill are found in early Permian breccias known as Brockrams on the west side of the Pennines, demonstrating that the igneous activity predated their formation, probably just pre-dating the end of the Carboniferous.

A depression which lies below world sea level and is only separated from the oceans by a low barrier is especially vulnerable to flooding. The deserts of the Lower Permian were no exception. Collective wisdom has pointed to the weak link being an impersistent barrier between the 'Rotliegendes depression' and the northern Boreal Ocean to the north-east of Scotland. Estimates have suggested that once the barrier was breached, due either to a rise in sea level caused by either ice sheets melting or tectonic movements, the flooding may have been completed in less than six years, providing a spectacular sight for any occupants of this inhospitable landscape. As already noted the Zechstein Sea consisted of a series of sub-basins. Separating these were topographic highs, one such being the **Cleveland High** which lay between Yorkshire and Durham, influencing sedimentation and sedimentary processes.

For many years, five cycles of evaporite formation, known as Z1 – Z5, were recognised, each linked to a refilling and subsequent drying out of the Zechstein Sea. Each cycle was thought to have been characterised by deposition of the least soluble carbonates first, especially in the shallower waters fringing the basin. Here **oolite** shoals, like those seen today in the more restricted marine basins of the Middle East, were common. As the isolated water-mass evaporated and became increasingly rich in dissolved salts, so the most soluble minerals were deposited towards and in the centre of the basin.

Work published in the 1990s turned this established concept on its head. In simple terms (for rarely is anything simple!), when after flooding of the basin, a link was maintained with the Boreal Ocean, marine shelf and basin limestones were deposited. The sequence only began once the basin became partially

9.8 Jackdaw Crag Quarry near Tadcaster. Limestones are the lower part of the Zechstein Group. While quarried primarily for aggregate, some dimension stone has been extracted. Compare the giant cross-bedding in the quarry face with Figure 9.9.

or completely isolated and water levels fell. Both scenarios lead to the deposition of evaporite minerals within the basin. During partial isolation, as the water level fell, the carbonates and other fringing deposits were subjected to erosion, and those eroded surfaces mark the base of the sequence.

Simultaneously gypsum was being precipitated in basin-fringing **sabkhas**. In these environments, subsequent dewatering of the gypsum produced anhydrite. If the **relative humidity** fell below 76%, halite and other soluble salts were precipitated from the evaporating water. Continuing replenishment of the Zechstein Sea from seepage through the barrier would lead to sedimentation outstripping subsidence and a temporary filling of the basin. Complete isolation would produce insufficient sulphate minerals to fill the basin. Mud and silt, often halite rich, deposited across the basin are interpreted as the fall-out from clouds of evaporite-rich dust whipped up from the surrounding sabkhas and salt flats. Slumping of basin-margin sediments was common.

A sequence ended when global sea level or tectonism triggered a new marine flooding episode and renewed carbonate deposition on the eroded surface at the margins, and across the basin, hence the evaporite – carbonate sequence. The base of the next sequence formed at the erosion surface on the fringing sediments when water levels started to fall again. Subsidence and isolation recreated the semi-isolated/isolated basin environment. During the cycle, water rich in magnesium, percolating through existing limestones composed of calcium carbonate, was responsible for the formation of dolomites or dolomitic limestones.

During the deposition of the Upper Permian carbonates and evaporites, some have speculated that there may have been a temporary connection across the Pennine 'high', between the Zechstein Sea in the east and the Bakevellia Sea in the west. This body of water covered parts of what is the Irish Sea of today and contains sequences similar to those in the east. Deposits in this basin may have mantled the breccio-conglomerate near Ingleton, but if so, no trace of them has been left for us to see. However, the record of dolomitised Carboniferous limestone pebbles hints at the influence of the Bakevellia Sea.

Riches beyond measure

Yet again, Yorkshire has been endowed with strata which have, and continue to have huge economic significance, not only within the county's boundary, but also in other settings. Stone, evaporites, water and gas are all exploited in Yorkshire. For this whistle stop tour, the time-line adopted will be one of when first exploited, rather than when deposited.

From early historical times, the 'Magnesian Limestone' has been quarried (*Fig. 9.8*) for use as a building stone. The Cadeby (Z2) and Brotherton (Z4) formations have been and still are exploited. The Romans were the first to use them in the construction of their fortress and later developments at York. Stone was brought from near Sherburn-in-Elmett for this work. Here and in many other towns across lowland Yorkshire, such as Wetherby and Tadcaster, this pale creamy coloured limestone, with its tremendous range of sedimentary (*Fig. 9.9*) and diagenetic structures, is a hallmark. The city walls of York, incorporating elements of Roman construction, and the famous bars marking the points of entry into the medieval city are built from this stone, as is York Minster (*Fig. 9.10*) – though other stones have been used for restoration work. Ironically a Jurassic limestone, Lepine, from Poitiers in France was used for the replacement of York Minster's great west window, the 'Heart of Yorkshire' in the 1990s. The majority of churches throughout the city, Selby Abbey and Beverley and Ripon minsters are likewise built of Magnesian Limestone.

The Permian provided the only 'local' source of stone supported by a river system capable of being used to transport stone from the quarries to where it was needed. The levels of industrial organisation and quality control required, from quarry face to

9.9 Blocks of 'Magnesian Limestone' (Zechstein Group) with cross-bedding in the ruins of St Mary's Abbey, Museum Gardens, York. The relationships of the water-laid limestone particles permit one to determine whether the block is the correct way up or not; in this example the upper block is upside down.

9.10 The west end of York Minster, York, viewed from Minster Yard. The Minster, built between 1220 and 1472, was constructed of the relatively local 'Magnesian Limestone'. Restoration work has sometimes incorporated other British and foreign limestones with varying degrees of success.

construction site were astonishing.

In the 19th century, an unfortunate series of events and a failure in quality control led to a 'blemish' on Yorkshire's record as a producer of Magnesian Limestone. The saga concerns the building of the new Houses of Parliament after the Palace of Westminster was destroyed by fire in 1834. Magnesian Limestone from a quarry in Derbyshire was originally specified, but supplies could not keep pace with demand. An alternative source was found at Anston in South Yorkshire; demand could be met, but at a hidden cost. Records show that no one was prepared to fund someone to watch over the quality. The result was that just about any stone that could be dressed at the quarry was supplied, irrespective of quality. The high levels of pollution experienced across London until the Clean Air Acts of 1956 and 1968, soon picked out the poorer quality and elaborately carved stones, and this together with blocks that had been incorrectly laid, suffered premature deterioration. Restoration has been necessary over a prolonged period. The Mother of Parliaments has proved to be a less than satisfactory showcase for one of Yorkshire's finest stones, a stone which elsewhere has stood the test of time. Today, the output from extant quarries is mostly crushed stone for use as aggregate, though some produce stone for building work and craftsmen carrying out restoration of Yorkshire's historic buildings.

Metals have been an important product of Yorkshire from at least Roman times, when lead was exploited from the southern end of the Northern Pennine Orefield. Evidence for minor use has been found in archaeological excavations of Iron Age sites. Since then an estimated one million tonnes of galena, the primary ore of lead, was produced over the working-life of this orefield. The mineralisation of the Askrigg Block is generally accepted as a Permian event, during which the ores of lead, with lesser amounts of zinc and copper were deposited (*Figs 9.11a-b*). They are associated with **gangue** minerals, including fluorite, and more especially

9.11a-b LEFT (a) Galena (lead sulphide) the principle ore of lead which was the backbone of the metalliferous mining industry of the Yorkshire Dales. The shiny area shows a freshly fractured surface. RIGHT (b) Sphalerite (zinc sulphide), on white baryte. Scale bar divisions in cm.

9.12a-c Gangue minerals from the Yorkshire sector of the Northern Pennine Orefield; (a) Purple tinged crystals of fluorite from near Pateley Bridge. (b) Crystals of baryte coated with manganese oxide from Aysgarth, Wensleydale. (c) Baryte (Cockscomb variety) from near Grassington. (d) Radiating acicular crystals of strontianite from Swaledale. Scale bars *c.* 5 cm.

baryte, witherite and calcite (*Fig 9.12a-d*).

The primary ores have been subjected to subsequent alteration, producing a fascinating range of secondary minerals, some of which are very unusual. Smithsonite or zinc carbonate is a secondary mineral which has in historic times been known as the mineral calamine. A powdery form of smithsonite, discovered in a cave system between Malham and Settle, was present in sufficiently large quantities for the deposit to be commercially exploited. Estimates suggest that a maximum of 15,000 tonnes may have been present. Over 40 species of mineral have been recorded, which in addition to those mentioned above, include cerussite (lead carbonate), anglesite (lead sulphate), pyromorphite (lead chloro-phosphate), malachite and azurite (the green and blue carbonates of copper), and fraipontite (a rare zinc-rich kaolinite serpentine group mineral).

Traces of cinnabar (mercury sulphide) are known from some locations, and there is an unverifiable record of gold associated with galena (lead sulphide) from a now inaccessible mine near Pateley Bridge.

If correct, this is the only such occurrence in the northern Pennines.

While the Alston and Askrigg blocks are both classified as parts of the Northern Pennine Orefield, the proportions of the different minerals present in these two orefields are not the same; for example fluorite is much more abundant in the Alston Block. Such variation is probably a result of the different compositions and temperatures of the granite and basement rocks from which the hot mineralising fluids emanated. But where did the colossal volumes of liquid required to transport the chemicals that would be precipitated as minerals originate? By extracting tiny droplets of 'fossilised' liquid, that carried the chemicals which created the minerals, trapped in fluorite, baryte, calcite and quartz, and appropriately named fluid inclusions, scientists are able to provide answers to questions such as this.

Alston Block fluid inclusions were subjected to detailed analyses. Published research concludes that brines originating in the Permian Zechstein Sea, and perhaps similar Triassic brines at a slightly later date, are likely to have been essential to the mineralisation process. Tectonic stresses fractured the crust, allowing brines from the Zechstein Sea to reach the Weardale Granite and surrounding basement rocks. The granite's original heat had long been dissipated, but reheating had occurred as a result of the decay of radioactive elements in the granite, and the intrusion of the Great Whin Dolerite Complex may also have contributed additional heat.

Reaction of the brines with the granite, which is calculated to have reached 300°C at depths of around 10 km, and the surrounding hot basement rocks, created mineralising fluids which because they too became hot, rose up through fractured rocks, eventually reaching levels in the Carboniferous strata. Here the fluids cooled and minerals were precipitated, in the process trapping the tiny 'fossil' fluid inclusions. Mixing of fluids from different sources around the granite may have been significant in defining the range of minerals deposited. The circulating brines cooled the granite and the process gradually came to a halt. The Wensleydale Granite, though unlikely to have been as hot as the Weardale Granite (Chapter 3), was sufficiently hot to mobilise mineralising fluids which, like for the Alston Block, may have originated in the Zechstein Sea. The lower temperatures, and different source rocks deep in the basement, are probably the reasons for the variation in mineralisation seen between these two orefields.

The mineral deposits of the Askrigg Block occur in the Carboniferous sediments as *veins* along faults, *scrins* in fractures along which there has been little or no movement, *pipes* which are thought to develop where two fractures cross, and horizontal deposits called *flots*, *flats* or *floats* where beds of rock have been replaced by minerals. Those mineral deposits with potential to provide an economic return are known as oreshoots. The Yorkshire Dales carry the scars of centuries of intense mining and metal production, as on the moors above Grassington and along the north side of Swaledale. Methods of working surface deposits have included shallow surface excavations and the use of diverted water from dammed enclosures. When released, the water scoured the surface, a process called hushing, something of a misnomer when visualing the churning cataract of sediment and rock laden water racing down valley sides in the Dales (*Fig.* 9.13). There are many examples of such activity around Swaledale. Once surface deposits had been removed, oreshoots were followed underground, either by digging shallow shafts (*Fig.* 9.14) or through adits running into the hillsides. The mixture of rock and ore was processed and smelted, the chimneys situated high on the fells (*Fig.* 9.15) launching the waste gasses, carried from the furnaces by long flues,

9.13 Friarfold Hush in the foreground with Yoredale Group strata exposed. Gunnerside Gill is in the middle distance, and North Hush on the other side of the valley. The shallow valleys called Hushes were produced by hydraulic mining. Water was used to wash away sediment and rock in the search for the economic minerals.

9.14 Shallow depressions are all that remain of the shafts which were dug by miners along the line of a vein. These examples are on moorland above Grassington.

9.15 Cononley Lead Mine, south of Skipton. This is an unusual occurrence of mineralization in Yorkshire south of the Northern Pennine Orefield. The engine house and mine dumps are in the foreground and on the hilltop a chimney. This presumably handled the metal-laden gases from the furnaces and was fed by a now demolished flue.

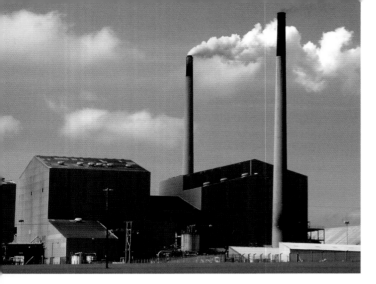

9.16 Boulby Mine between Staithes and Loftus on the edge of the North York Moors. 1,500-1,200 m shafts reach thick beds of evaporites in the Permian Zechstein Group.

skywards. The flues provided an opportunity for the toxic gasses to condense, leaving deposits of metals which were collected periodically.

Water from the Permian strata at Tadcaster has been used for brewing. In 1758, the same year as Sam Smith's Old Brewery was founded, a well was sunk to around 27 m to abstract the mineral-rich, hard water from the 'Magnesian Limestone' for use as one of the essential ingredients for the beers for which the town is famed. The water is especially suitable for brewing pale ales and bitters. Subsequently, a second well has been sunk in order to keep up with the demand. The same aquifer supplies the water for the nearby John Smith's Brewery.

The evaporite minerals have been a particular focus of attention, providing the raw materials for the foundation of the great chemical industries of Teesside, just beyond the county boundary. The search for these deposits led to exploration to the south of the River Tees, across Yorkshire. The result is seen not far along the road to Whitby from Loftus when one happens upon an industrial complex with towering chimneys and silos, and from which emanates the low hum of machinery (*Fig.* 9.16). The industrial complex sits within a valley below the North York Moors, incongruously surrounded by fields and farms and with the sea as a backdrop in the middle distance. Development began in 1969 and production started in 1973 with potash the key product, and Boulby Mine became one of the largest producers in the world. Rock salt is an important by-product, primarily used for de-icing roads during

the winter. A dedicated railway line links the mine to the main rail-network near Saltburn. The Boulby Mine was once in North Yorkshire, but is currently situated in Cleveland. However, the galleries driven out to mine the valuable seams of evaporite minerals of the Zechstein Sea pass beneath Yorkshire, reaching as far as Whitby. Shafts reach down to strata which are followed to depths of between 1,200 and 1,500 m below the surface, making this Europe's second deepest mine. While some of the workings are back-filled with slurry, one disused gallery has become the laboratory for research into the very essence of the creation of the universe around 13.7 billion years ago (Chapter 14). Gypsum has been worked around Sherburn-in-Elmet, and until the late 1980s provided the raw material for the British Gypsum works nearby.

The discovery of hydrocarbons across the eastern part of Yorkshire confirmed the predictions of Professor Kendall (Chapter 8). The exploration for gas in the southern North Sea began during the 1950s and 1960s. This search was driven by the discoveries made in Holland, and once again the Rotliegendes, or literally the Red Sands, with their excellent porosity proved to be a hugely important hydrocarbon **play**. Those reading this book and who remember the days before natural gas came to our homes between 1967 and 1977, will remember the gas works which occupied a site in most towns. Coal was 'cooked' in retorts, producing town-gas along with other by-products. Natural gas is the equivalent of town-gas, but the process has taken millions of years to generate gas from the organic-rich sediments, and especially coal, buried at depth and subjected to heat. The gas migrated upwards until trapped in the Rotliegendes by the overlying cap-rock, the Marl Slate Formation. Bearing in mind the relatively small quantities of coal once used by gas works to provide gas for our homes, there should be no surprise at the enormous scale of the gas fields that formed from the natural 'cooking' of extensive Upper Carboniferous deposits across the southern North Sea.

The expectation that these gas-bearing dune fields would continue beneath much of eastern Yorkshire was not quite matched by reality. Sand dunes became sparse, and Caythorpe on the Wolds, which started producing in 1992, was the most westerly gas field of the Rotliegendes play to be exploited (*Figs* 9.7a -b). The search for similar deposits continued apace for many years. Rotliegendes dunes there were not, but there were Upper Permian carbonates with properties which make them ideal as a reservoir rock for gas. These and the older and more deeply buried Millstone Grit sediments, continue to be the focus for exploration companies in this region. The Permian reservoir rocks are capped by impermeable sabkha deposits in the west, but in the east, the thickening evaporites play an increasingly important role as the hydrocarbon seals.

The earliest significant discovery was at Lockton on the southern edge of the North York Moors in the 1960s. This gas field and one at Wykeham appeared hugely promising and led to the construction of a gas-fired power station at Pickering. Unfortunately, the complex nature of the gas-water interface resulted in poor production rates over sustained periods. The gas fields were mothballed and the recently built Pickering Power Station demolished!

The search continued with wells drilled at various locations across the Vale of Pickering. Significant gas fields were discovered at Malton, Marishes, Pickering, and Kirby Misperton, though this latter field was at greater depth in Upper Carboniferous sediments. On the strength of the discoveries made, a gas-fired power station was built at West Knapton, linked to the gas fields by pipeline (*Fig.* 9.17) and officially opened in 1995.

During the first decade of the 21st century, improved seismic technology, as described earlier (*Fig.* 9.3a-b), is being employed across the Vale of Pickering and surrounding areas to pinpoint both new reserves of gas, and to enable optimum production from existing fields. Amongst those being re-examined are Lockton and Wykeham, which had failed to live up to expectation in the late 1960s and early 1970s.

Alice in Wonderland

In *Alice in Wonderland*, Alice disappears down a rabbit's burrow at the start of her fantastical adventure. A recently published paper speculates that the young Charles Dodgson, better known as Lewis Carroll and whose father was a canon at Ripon Cathedral, may have been a regular viewer of 'The big hole' which appeared beside Ripon Station in 1834 (*Fig.* 9.18). The chasm was caused by solution subsidence, a process which often leads to unexpectedly large holes appearing without any warning.

9.17 Knapton Generating Station near West Knapton, operated by Viking UK Gas Limited. This gas-fired power station tucked out of site in the Vale of Pickering, was opened in May 1995. Natural gas is piped from proven fields nearby and conditioned on-site before being used to power the single gas turbine, capable of generating 4.1 megawatts of electricity. The 2007 seismic survey (Figures 9.3a-b) is part of a programme to prove new fields in order to maintain the supply of gas for this small but important contributor to the UK's energy requirements.

9.18 'The Big Hole' adjacent to Ripon Station was the result of solution subsidence in Zechstein Group deposits. The hole may have been influential in the writings of Charles Dodgson.

While one such hole may have led to the creation of an enduring literary image, on the whole, they are a negative and at times costly side effect of the presence of evaporite deposits close to the surface coming into contact with groundwater. Rapid weathering of the relatively soluble massive gypsum and anhydrite ensues and the ground surface collapses into the void left behind. The holes may be of considerable size, and have been known to swallow a back garden from time to time. There are many records of solution collapse events along a south-south-east to north-north-west belt which follows the line of the outcrop. The complex dissolution structures associated with both the limestones and the evaporites in this zone, along with the hazard of sudden collapse, have to be taken into account when considering waste disposal and construction projects.

Life ....

The severe conditions which resulted from the Variscan Orogeny and the isolation of northern Europe from normal marine influences for most of the Permian, restricted the range of species present, except during the more open marine episodes when the barrier between the Boreal Ocean and the Zechstein Sea was breached or overtopped. The remains of the normal marine faunas, and more impoverished faunas able to survive the increasingly stressed environments in and around the margins of an evaporating basin, were then exposed to selective preservation. Alteration to dolomite (magnesium carbonate) from the original calcium carbonate was a process which altered the fabric of the limestones and in the process destroyed any of the fossils they contained. Despite this, fossils are found, and provide valuable clues as to the diversity of life at this time, and the environments which existed.

Terrestrial faunas are rare, though we may surmise that plants did grow, periodically at least. We base this on the presence of plant fragments, previously ascribed to conifers, in strata preserved towards the southern end of the Vale of Eden, only a brief and scenic journey northwards from Yorkshire on the spectacular Settle – Carlisle Railway. The Hilton Plant Beds are fine grained silts which are thought to have been deposited during floods, around the edge of a lake situated in an inward draining half-graben where evaporite minerals, including halite, accumulated. The Permian rocks of the Vale of Eden are reported to have yielded the tracks of undetermined tetrapods, and the tracks of a caseasaur, an herbivorous reptile known from deposits of this age near Penrith. Given the close proximity of these deposits, one should be forgiven for reasoning that Yorkshire may have supported plants and animals like this, at least in favoured spots.

The faunas of the Zechstein Sea are better preserved. The Marl Slate Formation is remarkable for the fine lamination and well preserved vertebrate fossils. Fish are frequently present (*Fig. 9.19*), and the remains of reptiles, including a lizard-like glider, are known from these deposits in Durham. The brachiopod named *Lingula* is also present. The nature of the deposit and the preservation of the vertebrates suggest a stagnant, **anoxic**, sea floor which supported little or no life; scavengers were unable to disrupt the carcasses of the dead animals which settled on the bottom. Renewed flooding of the basin brought oxygenated conditions and the deposition of the peripheral carbonates in normal marine conditions. Sometimes the carbonate sheets stretched out across the basin, providing an altogether more hospitable environment for life. Fossils include algae, bryozoans forming patch reefs, and brachiopods – amongst which is the splendidly named *Horridonia horridus* – a small productoid with a profusion of spines on the pedicle valve. Bivalves, scaphopods (tusk shells), and gastropods are also well known. Corals are not recorded from these strata.

.... and the almost perfect extinction

The history of life on earth has been punctuated by events called extinctions, when large numbers of species on the planet die out over what is perceived to be a relatively short period of time. Previously mention was made of the great Ordovician extinction (Chapter 5) the trigger for which has been linked to a major glaciation. Given that a small thickness of sediment may represent a large span of time, the definition of what constitutes 'rapid extinction' has become a topic of rigorous scientific debate, as has the matter of the trigger, or triggers, for such events. These debates continue.

Even the end-Permian extinction is not entirely straightforward, with some suggesting that there may have been a lesser event some 5 Ma earlier, with a continuum of extinction between them! Hypotheses have included an impact by a comet or other extraterrestrial object, and massive volcanic

eruptions, possibly connected to the impact, across parts of Siberia. The former is unsubstantiated while the latter's immense outpouring of carbon dioxide would certainly have increased the effects of global temperature rise, and the warming of the world's oceans. Ocean warming could have sparked the release of methane gas, still further increasing the warming process. An overheated ocean could have led to the collapse of the circulatory system, this in turn triggering full blown **anoxia** in the oceans, an event capable of wiping out the great range of species known to have become extinct. Intriguingly, this proposal also provides a possible explanation for the death of large numbers of land-based species. Hydrogen sulphide gas, a by-product of an anoxic ocean, would have delivered the *coup de grâce* to much of life on earth.

We do know that the Permian has the dubious honour of holding the record for the most catastrophic extinction the planet has witnessed. Estimates of the number of species wiped out at the close of the period have provided a figure of between 90 and 96% of all marine species with a shell or skeleton capable of being fossilised, and perhaps as many as 70% of all terrestrial species.

The end of an era …. but life does go on

Yes, quite literally, the catastrophic close of the Permian was the end of a geological era. The change from Palaeozoic, which had started with the Cambrian, to the Mesozoic saw little obvious change to the environments across Yorkshire. Had the strata of Yorkshire been deposited in marine environments, and contained a record of the life they supported, we would have detected this dramatic change. We should have been able to place a spike in the rock sequence and say, 'those are Permian and these are Triassic'. We cannot.

9.19 A palaeoniscid fish from the Marl Slate Formation which draped the early Permian land-surface, a first whiff of the sea across these ancient desert landscapes. The shafts sunk through these strata during the development of the Selby Coalfield led to the discovery of many specimens such as this one.

Despite the lack of marine faunas across this boundary in Yorkshire, consideration of the changes recorded in rocks elsewhere is relevant. The iconic trilobites had become more or less extinct before the end of the Permian and did not survive into the Triassic. The two main orders of coelenterates, the tabulate and rugose corals, did not cross the divide, and in view of the scenarios for the Permian extinction, one cannot help but draw parallels with the stressed coral reefs in today's warming oceans, a casualty of what is perceived to be the fast changing world climate.

Arguably the end Permian extinction of the corals is a chimaera, for while two orders of these important organisms were snuffed-out, this was not the end of their road. In Triassic sediments are found the scleractinian corals. If as we believe, all other corals had become extinct, where did this order of corals, to which all modern corals belong, spring from? Probably this has more to do with the fragmentary and incomplete nature of the fossil record which palaeontologists have to work from in describing the history of life on Earth.

Discoveries of scleractinian-like corals in Palaeozoic sediments are pointing to these corals having already evolved during the Palaeozoic, either from existing corals, or independently. With the amelioration of world climate and marine habitats in which life could once again flourish, the absence of any competition from 'the old orders' of corals provided a fantastic opportunity for these new 'kids on the block' to thrive and expand. There were competitors – such as the aberrant, cup shaped and lidded, bivalves

9.20 Exposures of Triassic strata are rare. Here the Mercia Mudstone Group, overlain by till, is exposed in the banks of the River Leven at Hutton Rudby, north-west of Northallerton. The contortions are probably caused by freezing and thawing during the Pleistocene, or possibly by ice moving over the surface.

called rudistids which formed reefs during the later Mesozoic where corals had before. The cephalopods lost the goniatite lineage in the Permian extinction, but the nautiloid cephalopods survived and were joined during the Triassic by the ceratoid cephalopods.

The great reddening

The Zechstein Basin was the product of thermal relaxation which caused sagging. During the Triassic, this same region underwent further subsidence, but this was increasingly in response to stretching of the crust and consequent faulting. The evaporating basin which had accumulated the great thicknesses of salt and related minerals now accumulated clastic sediments that merged with those of the underlying Permian, the Roxby Formation having a 'foot in both camps' so to speak. In contrast to the bulk of the Permian sediments, the vast majority of Triassic sediments are red. Initially the sediments are coarser and sands dominate, as seen fleetingly from the train on the approach to Doncaster from the south.

In the south of Yorkshire the sands contain scattered pebbles, hinting at the system of braided rivers flowing from south to north. Follow the same strata south into Nottinghamshire, and their lower beds are dominated by the conglomerates and gravels of the Bunter Pebble Bed facies. Their source is identified to the south of Britain, over northern France; in south Devon, the same beds are the famed Budleigh Salterton Pebble Beds. Interestingly, the development of the river systems which transported these deposits

northwards is thought to have been encouraged by the dramatic changes to the vegetation during the end-Permian extinction. Evidence has been found which indicates that as the Triassic progressed, the braided watercourses reverted to meandering rivers, contained by banks, across flood plains.

The Triassic strata are poorly exposed (*Fig. 9.20*), and what little we know of them is from rare sites where they have been exploited, and from boreholes. The latter are frequently drilled to extract water from what, with the Permian strata, form the UK's second most important series of aquifers. Triassic sediments provide a winning combination, juxtaposing water bearing sandstones, especially the Sherwood Sandstone Group, with impervious mudrock caps. Water may be essential for life, but aquifers can prove to be expensive 'barriers' when sinking mine shafts! Hatfield Main, near Doncaster, is one such example. Here the shaft sinkers, who had started in 1911, hit an aquifer. Conventional methods of staunching the flow failed, and alternative methods had to be employed to block the pore spaces in the sandstones – both costly and time consuming.

As a result of the various exposures and rock samples retrieved from boreholes, we know that the Triassic sediments in the vales, between the Pennines and North York Moors and extending south towards Doncaster and the Humber, pass from the sandy sediments of the early Triassic, into the marls and clays with evaporites of the Mercia Mudstone Group. These sediments were deposited in environments where sabkhas formed in shallow depressions fed by internal drainage systems. Though marine incursions have been mooted as the source of the halite, there is a strong argument which favours salts being concentrated from eroding Permian sediments, and possibly arriving on salt-laden winds from more remote ocean basins. Even today this latter effect is not unusual in the UK during periods of strong onshore winds, with attendant 'scorch' to salt-sensitive plants. Of course, in our relatively wet climate, such salts are diluted and flushed back into the oceans from whence they came. During the Triassic, winds would have been driven by the monsoonal climate.

A dramatic change took place around 230 Ma during deposition of the Mercia Mudstone Group. Deposits elsewhere in the UK indicate considerable increase in rainfall with greater diversity of plants and animals. In Yorkshire this interval lies between the Sidmouth Mudstone and Branscombe Mudstone formations; in the south of the region coarser sediments are present, equivalents of the Arden Sandstone Formation, and what were once known as the Waterstones. This name derives from their value as local aquifers. The short-lived shift to a wetter climate is thought to have been the outcome of increased warming of the earth's atmosphere, a state sometimes referred to as *greenhouse earth*.

The next time we see evidence of such a change is at the top of the Mercia Mudstone Group in what were once charmingly known as the Tea Green Marls. The dominantly red mudstones are replaced by grey and green dolomitic mudstones. This colour change suggests another period of amelioration in the remorselessly arid climate. In support of this view, the sediments are increasingly rich in organic material and contain sandy partings, indicative of water capable of transporting larger grain sizes. Because there was such a contrast between these sediments and the underlying red mudstones, they were at one time included with the overlying Penarth Group, named after the location in South Wales where they are especially well exposed. The ensuing Penarth Group are an increasingly varied and fossiliferous package of sediments, providing an early taste of the sea which will soon dominate Yorkshire and much of the British Isles.

Inevitably, in a county where only limited Triassic sediments are preserved, the question arises, how much of Yorkshire was covered by Triassic sediments? We do know that the beds thicken to the east into a more pronounced basin which underlies parts of the North Sea, and that halite is present just off the Yorkshire coast. There are extensive and economically important salt deposits in Cheshire which are of a similar age. While a more extensive cover is accepted, there is some debate as to whether the Pennine axis was covered by sediments during the Triassic or not.

Sophisticated techniques have been used to estimate the thickness of sediment of different periods that had once cloaked the Pennines. Grains of a mineral, apatite, from rocks buried by younger sediments, are examined to see what temperatures they have been exposed to during burial. This information, when combined with knowledge of the strata immediately adjacent to the Pennines, provides an estimated minimum and maximum thickness for the different strata. In the case of the Triassic, estimates for what might have been present are put at between 300 and 800 m. Though not always a precise art,

the information gathered is subjected to continuing scientific scrutiny and debate fuelled by research and serendipitous discoveries.

Plastered!

While the results of consuming too much bitter or pale ale produced from waters drawn from the Permian aquifers is known to have this effect, the Triassic really does contain the raw materials for plastering. Amongst the evaporites present is halite which has been proved in boreholes in the east of the Yorkshire, and which thickens out into the North Sea. Gypsum is also present at certain horizons and was previously worked at Brompton near Northallerton, and at Scrayingham north of Stamford Bridge.

A modern twist to the production of gypsum in Yorkshire has placed the industry in an intriguing quandary regarding supply of the natural raw material. While Yorkshire no longer produces natural gypsum, desulphogypsum is being produced in ever increasing quantities as a by-product of the desulphurisation of flue gasses at coal-fired power stations. The future of this product is bound up in shifting energy policies, the price and quality of coal, environmental targets and legislation. Last but not least, the process relies on planning legislation regarding the extraction of the considerable quantities of high quality limestone used to treat the flue gases in the first place. At present, the limestone comes from Derbyshire – and the irony of this is that while limestone extraction increases in one area, gypsum extraction decreases elsewhere. The desulphogypsum costs less per tonne than true gypsum. Given the importance of gypsum to the construction industry, both as a minor constituent in cement production, and in the manufacture of plaster board and plaster products, the industry sees a need to maintain, and therefore to 'turn on' a reliable and accessible natural supply, should market forces and environmental whim so demand.

Not a lot of life .... ?

Following the extinction at the end of the Permian, life appears to have been slow to recover. Compounding this paucity of life, Yorkshire lay close to the edge of the North Sea basin, and this environment of sabkhas would have been one of the least hospitable, perhaps just too harsh? Fossils found elsewhere in the UK may provide clues as to what could have occupied or moved across the Triassic landscapes of Yorkshire. The sandstone beds deposited during the wetter intervals mentioned above, provide 'enhanced' snapshots of life during this 52 Ma episode; the remarkable, if short-lived, flowering of life across arid regions after rain storms may provide an insight into these Triassic environments.

Plants included conifers, and horsetails, already present in the Carboniferous coal swamps and still extant today. Invertebrate life included molluscs and arthropods. New reptile groups were emerging. Herbivorous rhynchosaurs are known from skeletal remains found in Devon and the Midlands. Dinosaurs are found in Triassic sediments. Mammal-like reptiles appeared, and around 20 Ma before the close of the Triassic, the first true mammals are recorded. Their remains have been recovered from sites in Wales and at the eastern end of the Mendip Hills in Somerset.

Rare temporary exposure of the Penarth Group, deposited at the close of the Triassic, have yielded sparse invertebrate fossils hinting at what might have been. Where exposure is good, from Nottinghamshire southwards, the sediments of the Penarth group have yielded a diverse fauna including corals, rare brachiopods, bivalves and gastropods, insects and crustaceans, **cirripede** plates, echinoids and brittle stars. The famous 'Rhaetic Bone Bed' contains a rich assortment of fish scales, bones and teeth, including those of the freshwater lung fish *Ceratodus*, the teeth of amphibians, and the bones of reptiles. Amongst the latter, both marine reptiles, which would come to dominate the Mesozoic oceans, and dinosaurs are represented by bones, and there are also large numbers of **coprolites**. The Felixkirk borehole yielded vertebrate rich sediments pointing to the continuation of this horizon across Yorkshire. The possibility that this deposit represents the widespread impact of a substantial tropical storm cannot be ruled out.

In these strata, the conodont animals are supposed to make their last known appearance (but see below) and indeed the end of the Triassic is marked by yet another significant extinction event. Suggestions made to explain this have included the impact of an extraterrestrial object (Chapter 14), massive volcanism linked to the start of the opening of the Atlantic Ocean, sea-level changes, and methane-hydrate release. In all probability, as with other extinctions, no one event is likely to have been solely responsible for the demise of so much life on earth.

In or out?

A particularly taxing issue has been where the boundary of the Triassic and Jurassic is placed, and therefore, whether the lowest Liassic sediments are Triassic or Jurassic. For many years the adopted convention was that the appearance of the first ammonites, *Psiloceras planorbis* (*Fig. 9.21*) which succeeded the ancestral ceratoid ammonoids found in European sequences where marine sediments of this age are exposed, is used to define the start of the Jurassic. If this is so, ammonites should not occur in Triassic sediments in the UK. The scientific community had something of a shock when, a few years ago, a single tiny specimen, of what has been tentatively identified as an early ammonite, was discovered in the Triassic Westbury Formation of the Penarth Group in southern Britain.

The implication of this discovery, i.e. the moving of the Triassic – Jurassic boundary back in time, remains in limbo, waiting upon the recovery of additional specimens from these 'Triassic' rocks. If the discovery is supported by new evidence, this would of course mean that what are currently the uppermost Triassic sediments would become Jurassic! Until this is resolved, one might be forgiven for thinking that the *status quo* would be maintained with the all-important Triassic-Jurassic boundary immediately below the point where the ammonite *Psiloceras planorbis* first appears? Not so, for even these lowest Liassic sediments are up for grabs, as researchers have now found hitherto unrecognised ammonite faunas in the Lias, below those beds containing *Psiloceras*! And if all this wasn't confusing enough, rare conodont remains have been discovered in the pre-*planorbis* Lias. As noted above, conodonts became extinct in the Triassic; their discoverer has suggested that they might be reworked from older deposits. Who ever said that stratigraphy was dull?!

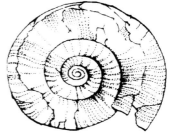

9.21 *Psiloceras planorbis* from the lowest strata of the Lias Group.

TEN

Life on the Edge

10.1 Easterside Hill in Bilsdale, viewed from Newgate Bank to the east. Hawnby Hill is seen in the distance to the left. Both hills are prominent outliers of strata above the Ravenscar Group. Easterside Hill is capped by the Middle Calcareous Grit of the Coralline Oolite Formation.

Time: Jurassic: 199 – 145 Ma
Latitude: 35°N – 40°N
Climate: Tropical with distinct seasons becoming almost Mediterranean for a time.
Environment: Marine, marginal-marine, and terrestrial.
Rocks: Grits, sandstones, siltstones, mudstones, limestones, ironstones.
Stratigraphy:
NORTH OF THE MARKET WEIGHTON HIGH, AND ACROSS THE CLEVELAND BASIN:
Lias Group: Redcar Mudstone, Staithes Sandstone, Cleveland Ironstone, Whitby Mudstone, and Blea Wyke Sandstone formations.
Dogger Formation (no parent group*).
Ravenscar Group: Saltwick, Eller Beck, Cloughton, Scarborough, and Scalby formations.
Great Oolite Group: Cornbrash Formation. Kellaways (north to near Malton), Osgodby and or Oxford Clay formations (no parent group*).
Corallian Group: Lower Calcareous Grit, Coralline Oolite, Upper Calacareous Grit formations.
Ampthill Clay and Kimmeridge Clay formations (no parent group*).
SOUTH OF THE MARKET WEIGHTON HIGH:
Lias Group: Scunthorpe and Charmouth mudstone, Marlstone Rock, and Whitby Mudstone formations.

Inferior Oolite Group: Lincolnshire Limestone Formation.
Great Oolite Group: Rutland and Blisworth Clay, and Cornbrash formations.
Ancholme Group: Kellaways, Oxford Clay, West Walton, Ampthill Clay, and Kimmeridge Clay formations.

Time: Cretaceous: 145 – 65 Ma
Latitude: 40° – 47°N
Climate: Increasingly arid.
Environment: Terrestrial (not preserved) and marine
Rocks: Gritty sandstones, mudstones and limestones, including the 'red chalk', which are frequently very pure. Flint.
Stratigraphy:
Speeton Clay Formation – coastal section and of limited extent inland, north of the Market Weighton High; Carstone Formation developed over and south of the Market Weighton High; Hunstanton Formation (= Red Chalk) (no parent group*).
Chalk Group
Grey Chalk Subgroup: Ferriby Chalk Formation;
White Chalk Subgroup: Welton, Burnham, Flamborough, and Rowe chalk formations.
(* No higher ranking stratigraphic unit, =Group, has been allocated for these formations)

Setting the Scene

As if balancing the great bulk of the Pennines, with their dales and moors in the west, are the North York Moors, taken here to include the Cleveland, Hambleton and Tabular hills, the Howardian Hills and Wolds in the east, lying between the Tees in the north and Humber in the south (*Fig.* 1.3). The Moors and the Wolds are set apart by the broad and frequently flat Vale of Pickering. Towards the western end of this broad vale, the terrain is increasingly hilly with the passage to the Vale of York blocked by the southern end of the Hambleton Hills, hook-like and curling away from the North York Moors, and the west-north-west to east-south-east line of the Howardian Hills. This pronounced barrier is broken by a faulted gap between these two ranges of hills, and to the south, the Howardian Hills are cut dramatically by the valley of the River Derwent flowing through Kirkham Gorge (Chapter 12). Trains alone follow the contours of this scenic defile on the route of the York to Scarborough line.

The North York Moors, Vale of Pickering and Howardian Hills are composed of Jurassic sediments, the Moors forming the other great wilderness of Yorkshire, both harsh and yet fragile in equal measure. The Wolds are composed of Cretaceous Chalk and are largely a landscape of extensive arable farms, and while neither they nor the Moors have the

altitude of the Pennines, in harsh winters both areas become extremely dangerous places to be caught out in, a point worth remembering in the context of Yorkshire's ice worlds (Chapter 12).

Apart from their potential hostility, there are a number of threads that connect the Pennines in the west and Moors to the east. One, a thin line on the map, is Wainwright's Coast to Coast long distance path, crossing from the Cumbrian coast in the west, across the Pennines, through the glaciated Permo-Triassic lowlands of the Vale of Mowbray, before climbing steeply (*Fig.* 10.2) to gain the heather clad tops and huge views of the North York Moors. Here the walker passes over strata representing a spectrum of environments, marine, marginal-marine and terrestrial, and may even unwittingly criss-cross the tracks of dinosaurs!

The conditions in which these sediments were deposited echo those of the Upper Carboniferous, with rivers feeding sediment from the north and west. The presence of terrestrial environments provides the context for vivid snapshots of evolving flora. Coastal and inland locations provide horizons that yield exquisitely preserved 167 Ma plant fossils, reminding us of the 300 Ma plant remains of the Pennine Coal Measures Group (Chapter 8). Plant remains are preserved in other ways as well, providing the raw materials for the jet industry, and sometimes where sufficient plant material accumulated, poor quality

10.2 The North York Moors dramatic and convoluted western escarpment seen from Roseberry Topping. In the immediate foreground are sandstones of the Saltwick Formation of the Ravenscar Group. The closest escarpment is that of Easby Moor. Beyond is the wooded escarpment below Hasty Bank.

coals formed and have been exploited for local use.

Iron-rich rocks, an interesting and important attribute of several parts of the Jurassic succession in the UK, have been won from mines cut into coastal cliffs, and hillsides. They previously contributed some of the raw materials for an all-important UK-based iron and steel industry. Iron and steelworks at Skinningrove on what was at the time the north Yorkshire coast, and around Teesside, used the local ores. In the process, these extractive industries have led to landscape modifications ranging from the workings themselves, to industrial structures such as blast furnaces, kilns and ingeniously engineered, contoured rail links – features which are now an integral part of the landscape known as the North York Moors.

The similarities between the Pennines and North York Moors are not coincidental. During the Jurassic there were clear parallels to be drawn with the Carboniferous. Once again sedimentation was strongly influenced by periodic movements of Yorkshire's foundations deep below the surface, and

10.3 Robin Hood's Bay, viewed from Ravenscar. The scars or reefs of Redcar Mudstone Formation (Lias Group) exposed at low water follow the sweep of the bay, tracing the outline of the anticline underlying Robin Hood's Bay. Those in the foreground are trending more or less east to west whereas those beyond are north-west to south-east, then north to south, and in the far distance north-east to south-west.

fluctuating sea-levels dictated what was deposited, where and when. Now, in the east of Yorkshire, the Market Weighton High (MWH – don't forget this abbreviation!), a buoyant block produced by a granite intrusion some 2500 m below the surface (Chapter 3) and more deeply buried than the Wensleydale Granite of the Askrigg Block, is known to have exerted a strong influence along an east-west axis. This is well illustrated in the synopsis of the stratigraphy, at the beginning of this Chapter, which shows how the Jurassic and early Cretaceous formations are more often than not, quite different across this divide.

The area immediately to the north of the MWH is punctuated by a swarm (or perhaps 'a spasm' would be more appropriate) of east-west faults of the Howardian-Flamborough Head Fault Zone, along the southern margin of the Cleveland Basin. This basin, part of an extensive feature which continued out into what is now the southern North Sea and into mainland Europe, had first shown signs of subsidence

during late Triassic times. This renewed jostling of bocks and basins was the result of the stresses generated regionally by the progressive opening of the North Atlantic, and igneous activity in the North Sea as Pangaea started to break-up (Chapter 2). Superimposed on these movements were changes in sea level causing both lesser and greater transgressions and regressions.

While such fluctuations during the Carboniferous were associated with glacial cycles, Jurassic fluctuations have proved very much more difficult to explain. The melting of mountain ice-caps and glaciers, if extant, would have caused a world-wide rise in sea-level, but evidence for this is hard to come by. Changes to ocean volumes would have had the potential to either displace or conversely 'absorb' huge volumes of water with an inevitable impact on the continental shelves and land of low-relief. The greater rate of subsidence of the Cleveland Basin through the Jurassic and into the Cretaceous, ensured that sediments frequently thickened towards the basin's shifting depocentre.

There is a curious truth in geology, *contra* to the saying 'what goes up, must come down', 'what sinks down – will almost invariably come back up', a process known as inversion, and usually linked to the variations between tension and compression caused by plate tectonic movements. So with the Cleveland

Dome, subsequent movements during the later Tertiary (Chapter 11) saw the thick pile of sediments, including those of the Cretaceous and Palaeogene which had accumulated in and over the Cleveland Basin, undergo uplift to form the series of associated anticlines which together form this structure.

Though this feature has seen significant erosion, some of the up-lifted sediments are of the Ravenscar Group, tough and 'element-defying', giving rise to the lofty sweeps, and at times rugged, scenery of the moors. The crest of the dome is marked by Urra Moor in the west, across Danby High, Glaisdale, Egton High, Sleights and Fylingdales moors towards Robin Hood's Bay in the east. Here an eroded lesser anticline gives rise to the characteristic arcs of Liassic strata on the foreshore, features best seen at a low spring tide (*Fig.*10.3 see also Chapter 8). To the south and down dip of the crest of the dome, the Upper Jurassic sediments form the Tabular Hills, before these strata finally dip beneath the Kimmeridge Clay of the Vale of Pickering.

Visualising this can be difficult, so adopting a culinary analogy, think of an onion which has been cut lengthwise. Lay one half on a chopping board, and imagine that the oldest parts are those layers nearest the middle – which in vegetative terms they are not! Now starting along the same axis as before, make an horizontal cut to remove a layer or two of the top and then cut obliquely down to just above the outer edge of the onion. The exposed surface will reveal the older strata on the flank, before they dip beneath progressively younger layers. This process of erosion has taken place on all sides of the Cleveland Dome.

Relationships

One of the great advantages for those who study the Jurassic and Cretaceous is the relative abundance of ammonites in the marine sediments (*Fig.* 10.4). The appearance of the ammonite *Psiloceras planorbis* signals the start of the Jurassic (Chapter 9). From this moment, right through until their disappearance at the end of the Cretaceous, ammonites, when present, provide the almost perfect means of linking rocks of the same age in Yorkshire and far beyond, the process called correlation. Sadly, they do not always occur when one would like them to; certain environments were more conducive to their presence and survival than others, and they are strictly marine!

10.4 Ammonites provide geologists with the key to correlating Jurassic and Cretaceous rocks in Yorkshire, the UK and around the World. These are examples of ammonites from Yorkshire. Jurassic: Lias Group, Whitby area: a. *Lytoceras* sp.; b. *Grammoceras* sp.; c. *Dactylioceras* sp.; d. *Harpoceras* sp.; Corallian Group, Malton: e. *Perisphinctes (Dichotomosphinctes) buckmani*. Cretaceous, Speeton Clay Formation, Speeton: f. *Olcostephanus (Polyptychites) polyptychus*.

Important parts of Yorkshire's Jurassic sequence are non-marine. By observing the different rocks, using ammonites and other fossils, and all the tools at their disposal, geologists have mapped the Jurassic and Cretaceous deposits of Yorkshire, though fine tuning and interpretation continues.

A glance at a map of the bedrock geology of the eastern half of Yorkshire reveals a curious relationship between the Cretaceous and the underlying Jurassic strata (*Fig.* 3.2a). Why does the Chalk rest on Cretaceous rocks in the north-east, but then as the edge of the outcrop is followed southwards, on progressively older Jurassic rocks? To help understand this conundrum, pretend the red and white chalks are a carpet which may be rolled back from west to east. What is uncovered is a bit like the floor of a very old

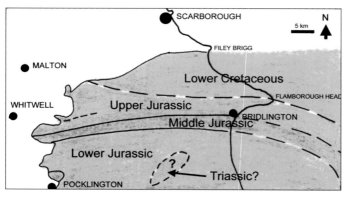

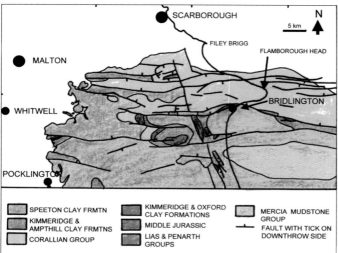

10.5a-b TOP (a) A 1980 interpretation of the geology below the 'Red Chalk' (Hunstanton Formation) across eastern Yorkshire. BOTTOM (b) A 1987 interpretation based on improved data.
(a) Modified from Kent 1980, *Proceedings of the Yorkshire Geological Society*, Vol. 42, 505-524, and (b) Kirby and Swallow, *Proceedings of the Yorkshire Geological Society*, Vol. 46, 301-309, both by permission of the Council of the Yorkshire Geological Society.

house, where a succession of owners laid new floors, some partly or completely covering earlier ones, as the house was extended and modified. The latest owner has smoothed off the various levels, put a thin screed (the Lower Cretaceous) over some of the surface to fill the odd hole, and then has carpeted (the Chalk) the whole lot!

In 1980 a provisional geological map showing the distribution of these beds below the Red Chalk was published. In 1987, using new data, part of this area was refigured. The combined image is reproduced here, demonstrating both the basic accuracy of the original interpretation, but equally, showing how

even within a few years, the data available is able to enhance a map so dramatically. (*Fig.* 10.5a-b).

Bearing the above in mind, we know that the Lias Group, the lowest part of the Jurassic succession, rests conformably on the Penarth Group at the top of the Triassic. Sediments overlying the Lias were laid down across the region, thinning out against, or from time to time disappearing completely over the top of the MWH. This was the result of the MWH, a bit like a small iceberg – just submerged but nevertheless buoyant. Towards the close of the Jurassic, there is clear evidence that more widespread uplift took place. Deposition of sediments ended except in the Cleveland Basin and the northern part of the **East Midlands Shelf**, an area running south from the MWH into Lincolnshire and down to the Wash. As a result of the uplift, there was erosion of the already attenuated Jurassic sediments over the MWH and adjacent areas, exposing progressively older strata. From the interpretations shown in *Fig.* 10.5a-b, we see that even Triassic sediments had been exposed before the Chalk was deposited.

After *c.*10 Ma, deposition recommenced in the Cleveland Basin, either on eroded Kimmeridge Clay Formation, or at a surface with sediments representing a period of minimal or no sedimentation at all. On this surface, the Speeton Clay Formation was laid down. This formation was confined to the Cleveland Basin, with its southern boundary apparently controlled by faults bordering the MWH. Erosion presumably continued over the MWH, while how far north the Speeton Clay was deposited is not known. Around the MWH, in the absence of the Speeton Clay, an impersistent ferruginous sand is sometimes present between the eroded Jurassic surface and the base of the Chalk Group, representing another marine transgression.

Finally, the Red Chalk of the Hunstanton Formation, taking the name from the sea-side town in north Norfolk where these beds are superbly exposed, begins to carpet the eroded early Cretaceous landscape of east Yorkshire, completing the process of covering the different Triassic and Jurassic strata across the MWH, and producing that strange relationship between the Chalk Group and the rocks below.

The transgression over the MWH heralds the inundation of large tracts of the British Isles by the Chalk seas, a process which took around 15-20 Ma to complete. Even during the deposition of the Chalk, there is a suggestion that the MWH

continued to influence deposition, and that the Chalk thins somewhat over this structure. Although the Cretaceous sediments have long gone from across the Cleveland Dome, we may suppose that they are likely to have been more or less conformable on top of the youngest Jurassic strata.

While the relationship of the Upper Cretaceous Chalk to the underlying Jurassic sediments may be the most striking feature on the map, there are other quirky features, especially within the Jurassic part of the Mesozoic succession. Even within formations which many view as remarkably consistent throughout, there are sometimes subtle changes in **lithology** or thickness that call for explanation. Often the answer lies in the seafloor, for even across the Cleveland Basin, subsidence did not occur at a constant rate, and there were periods of warping, caused by movements in the basement, during which previously deposited sediments suffered local erosion.

As already hinted, Jurassic and Cretaceous sediments were not confined to their present sub-crop and outcrop. The nature of the sediments on the edges of their exposure would contain tell-tale signs if land was close by. While the extent of the Jurassic and Cretaceous sediments has been much modified by later erosion (Chapters 11 & 12), and the story we have to tell is thereby constrained, the strata which remain and are exposed across eastern Yorkshire, enable geologists to paint vivid pictures of life and times between 199 and 65 Ma. For much of this period, Yorkshire was on the divide between marine and terrestrial conditions; the sediments and their fossils provide a record of 'life on the edge'.

10.6 The southern end of Robin Hood's Bay. Peak Steel, composed of Staithes Sandstone Formation, is the seaward reef just exposed to the left of the point below Ravenscar cliff. Towards the camera are rocks of the Redcar Mudstone Formation. The two formations are juxtaposed by movement on the Peak Fault (this Chapter).

Stormy Waters

The oldest Jurassic sediments belong to the Lias Group, and the coasts of Yorkshire and adjacent Cleveland provide excellent sections at the north-eastern end of their outcrop, an outcrop which William Smith had mapped all the way across England from the Dorset coast. Comparison between the two ends of the outcrop is both inevitable and illuminating. In Yorkshire, the greatest thickness of the Lias Group is on the coast where 447 m of sediments have been measured, though the succession thins towards the MWH. With a total thickness of 317 m, Dorset's sequence is startlingly thinner, and at times the sediments are very different.

The earliest sediments of the Lias Group are not exposed on the coastal fringes of Yorkshire or Cleveland, from where the Redcar Mudstone Formation takes its name, but have been penetrated by boreholes within the county. East and south from Redcar, various parts of the succession are exposed as far as Blea Wyke Point, just south of the evocatively named Peak Steel on the southern edge of Robin Hood's Bay (*Fig.* 10.6). Inland, inliers of Lias Group sediments floor valleys cut through the flanks of the east-west axis of the Cleveland Dome; examples on the southern limb are Bilsdale, Bransdale, Farndale and Rosedale, with Westerdale, Danby Dale, Great and Little Fryup dales (*Fig.* 10.7), Glaisdale and Esk Dale on the northern limb. Continuing with the onion analogy, this is the equivalent of cutting linear, v shaped cuts in the rounded surface of the onion. The deepest parts of the cuts represent valleys, producing limited exposures of the deepest layers of the onion. The western margins of the North York Moors, Howardian Hills and Wolds all stand above a narrow and poorly exposed strip of the Lias Group.

North of the MWH, the Lias Group is composed of five formations defined on the basis of their respective lithologies, these being in part controlled by the depth of the sea in which they were laid down. The late Triassic and early Jurassic marine transgression had set the scene; sea-levels were sufficiently high to flood extensive areas of land, and remained at high levels for around 10 Ma. During this time the Redcar Mudstone Formation, which broadly equates with the Blue Lias and Charmouth Mudstone formations of Dorset, was deposited. The Redcar Mudstone is predominantly composed of mudstones and siltstones, with calcareous sandstones and shelly limestones (*Fig.* 10.8a).

Remembering the concept of wading out into deeper waters and passing from shingle to muds (Chapter 7), these layers of coarser sediment should indicate shallow waters. In fact the **arenaceous** beds with distinctive sedimentary structures and trace

10.7 Little Fryup Dale viewed from the south. The valley floor cuts Lias Group sediments to form an inlier. At the end of this valley is the major east-west Esk Dale along which the Cleveland Dyke (Chapter 11) is occasionally exposed. The high point in the distance is Beacon Hill mostly composed of the Ravenscar Group, and capped by the Kellaways Formation.

10.8a-b ABOVE (a) The Siliceous Shales of the Redcar Mudstone Formation (Lias Group) at Boggle Hole, Robin Hood's Bay. BELOW (b) The trace fossil *Diplocraterion*, a vertical burrow in the Siliceous Shales; 20p piece for scale.

10.9a-b LEFT (a) The Staithes Sandstone Formation exposed immediately east of Staithes.
RIGHT (b) The Cleveland Ironstone Formation exposed on the foreshore and in the cliffs of Jet Wyke and Old Nab.

fossils, which are interspersed with mud, are regarded as the product of storms stirring up and winnowing the sediments on the floor of a shallow sea, and transporting coarser sediments from shorelines into deeper waters. Carbonate nodules occur, especially higher in the sequence. The more arenaceous nature of the Redcar Mudstone in Yorkshire contrasts with the predominantly fine grained muddy and calcareous sediments of the same age in Dorset, and hints at a dramatic change to come with the deposition of the overlying Staithes Sandstone Formation. Fossils do occur, but in the silts and sandy beds preservation is poor. The beautifully preserved trace fossils (*Fig. 10.8b*) that are common in parts of the succession more than compensate.

While these sediments were being deposited in northern Yorkshire, over the MWH the strata thinned before gradually thickening into North Lincolnshire. Here a mixture of mudstones and ironstones were being laid down. The Frodingham Ironstone was of major economic importance on the south side of the Humber, and fed the blast furnaces at Scunthorpe from 1864 until 1988. These strata belong to the Scunthorpe and Charmouth mudstone formations.

The overlying Staithes Sandstone and Cleveland Ironstone formations were deposited in shallowing water conditions across Yorkshire over a period of approximately 6 Ma (*Figs.* 10.9a-b). Initially siltstones and fine grained sandstones dominated, with an abundance of delicate sedimentary structures. These suggest storm surges, possibly related to hurricane activity, and as such provide interesting parallels with Dorset. In both successions, storm generated deposits are common, and within them the remains of rapidly buried, and superbly preserved, crinoids, sun-stars and brittle stars are found from time to time (*Fig. 10.10*), along with pockets or drifts of concentrated fossil shells, winnowed from the sediment during a storm. One might make a passing comparison with conditions along the eastern seaboard of the USA where occasionally the remnants of hurricanes,

10.10 '*Plumaster ophiuroides*', a rare sun-star found in strata at Skinningrave [*sic*] Bay in what was then Yorkshire. The specimen was figured by Thomas Wright (1863) in a *Monograph of the Palaeontographical Society.*

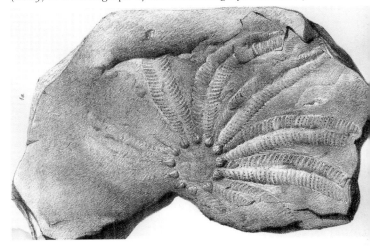

10.11 Saltwick Nab in the distance, viewed from the East Pier at Whitby. The foreshore and lower cliff mostly exposes the Whitby Mudstone Formation (Lias Group), overlain by the attenuated Dogger Formation, and the thick Ravenscar Group.

for the iron. The collective wisdom is that iron was carried in the run-off from the remaining subdued landmass which was undergoing tropical weathering. The ironstones consist of a mixture of different iron minerals, frequently oolitic, which are the signature of shallow water and high energy conditions. They contain a rich marine molluscan fauna where bivalves are especially prolific, including thick-shelled oysters and scallops. Exposed around the northern edge of the Cleveland Hills, in the valleys of the moors and along the coast, this formation has played a significant role in the industrial history of the region and country, with mines active until 1964. Output had peaked at around 6 million tonnes of ore per annum in 1875.

From superstition to the age of jet

The final chapter in the story of the Lias Group begins when deposition of the Cleveland Ironstone was terminated abruptly by an increase in the depth of the sea, and onset of the deposition of the Whitby Mudstone Formation. The exception was in northeast Yorkshire where the Main Seam ironstone continued to accumulate for a short while before being overwhelmed by mudstones. The Whitby Mudstone, though appreciably more muddy than what had gone before, is frequently silty, especially towards the top, and even sandy. Though greatly reduced in thickness, probably through subsequent erosion, this formation is recognised over and south of the MWH.

The foreshore and lower part of the cliffs from Whitby towards Robin Hood's Bay are composed of Whitby Mudstone (*Figs.* 10.11), and from these sediments, for generations local dealers in curios have collected nodules containing ammonites. In the past the ammonites were readily turned into the fabled 'snakestones' (*Fig.* 10.12). The name of the saint credited with turning snakes to stone was St Hilda,

downgraded to tropical storms, sweep up the coast. A number of these cycles have been recognised and they continue into the overlying Cleveland Ironstone Formation.

Each of the ironstones, there are six main ones, represent the acme of a phase of local regression, presumed to be the result of contemporary uplift, a thesis which finds support with evidence of the erosion of earlier horizons before the final Main Seam ironstone was laid down, unconformably, on top. Simultaneously, and counter-intuitively, global sea levels are thought to have been high, but clearly not sufficiently high to swamp the buoyant ironstone forming environments. They did flood the surrounding coastal shelves, helping staunch the flow of sediment into the basin, thereby fostering conditions for ironstone formation.

The unconformity across the North York Moors and in the Cleveland Hills occurs at the start of the deposition of the Marlstone Rock Formation, widely distributed in southern Britain and represented on the Dorset coast by what is now known as the Marlstone Member of the Beacon Limestone Formation. This horizon is relatively iron rich and in the Midlands has been commercially exploited as an iron ore, echoing the Main Band of the Cleveland Ironstone Formation. Such widespread deposition of iron-rich sediments suggests remarkably uniform environmental conditions, and requires a source

10.12 *Hildoceras bifrons*, from the Whitby Mudstone Formation, with a head carved to form a 'snakestone'.

founder in 657 AD, and one time Abbess of Whitby. Her name is for ever associated with these serpentine fossils through the naming of the genus *Hildoceras*.

Another important resource from these deposits was the jet, so much valued by Victorians, but with a far longer history. Worked jet and evidence of jet working is known from archaeological sites; jet has been found in Neolithic, Bronze Age and Roman contexts, and even though the great Victorian fashion for this sombre yet beautiful jewellery has long gone, a demand remains and is supplied by a much diminished industry based in Whitby. The local jet-workers took unpromising looking fossil logs mined or quarried from the local cliffs and cut, turned, carved and polished, set in silver and hung from chains, and in doing so produced a wide range of products (*Fig.* 10.13).

This semi-precious 'stone' is the product of the fossilisation of wood from auricarian trees. The Monkey Puzzle tree and Norfolk Island Pine belong to this family, though the latter is thought to be closest in appearance. Whereas most fossil wood once exposed tends to break up into small pieces, these logs do not. The trees from which the jet formed were probably casualties of severe storms over adjacent landmasses. They were washed down rivers, sometimes trapping sand grains on their fissured surfaces, before being swept out to sea. Eventually, waterlogged, they sunk to the sea floor to be buried in the marine muds. Though these trunks have been compressed over time, cell structure may still be seen with the aid of a microscope. The clays were rich in the remains of both tiny, and not so tiny creatures. As the sediments were buried to progressively greater depths and heated, so oil was generated from the organic material and gradually impregnated the already carbonised wood, imbuing a degree of plasticity and resilience. These attributes made this wood precious above all others and an industry was born.

Denizens of the deep

While the Redcar Mudstone may contain beautiful trace fossils, the formation is not a great source of eye catching body-fossils, i.e. shells and skeletons, though their importance to science when found should not be underestimated. By contrast, the Whitby Mudstone has yielded numerous specimens of both invertebrates and vertebrates which are scientifically

10.13 A Victorian jet pendant.

important, and exquisitely preserved. First and foremost, ammonites have long been collected, and both doctored and sold as curios as noted above, and studied. The latter course brings great rewards, for throughout the Jurassic and Cretaceous these coiled cephalopods provide an accurate method of defining where, in a succession one is, and for correlating that horizon with another, perhaps hundreds or even thousands of miles away. Though often distributed widely, ammonites also show provinciality; certain species are known from one area but not another, and therefore provide clues as to the connections between different oceans and shelf seas. For Yorkshire, the two oceans with influence were the Boreal to the north of Scotland and Tethys, *c.* 1800 miles to the south.

The related but very different looking **belemnites** (*Fig.* 10.14, *see following page*) are also abundant and again, much studied. Ranging from immensely long and thin, to short and stout, these fossils also provide clues to the palaeogeography, and are used for identifying different horizons within the strata. Primitive crabs first appear in the Jurassic; a specimen of *Eocarcinus praecursor* has come from these sediments.

Vertebrate fossils have long been known and are still much sort after by collectors and museums. Records of their discovery go back 250 years, and their collection was both stimulated and aided by quarrying for alum shale. Alum, an important ingredient in the dyeing

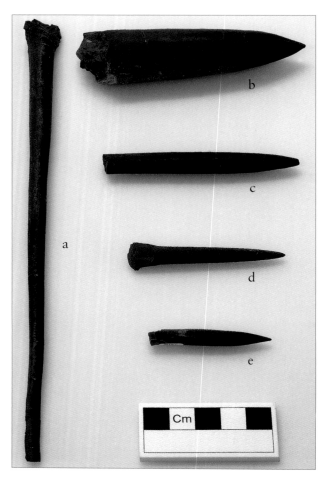

and tanning industries, was produced at several sites such as Ravenscar (*Fig.* 10.15a-b), Saltwick Nab (*Fig.* 10.16) and Kettleness on the coast, and also inland. Production started in the early 17th century and is characterised by heaps of burnt shale (*Fig.* 10.17). The coastal sites appear to have been the source for most of the specimens. Fish were plentiful and included sharks (*Fig.* 10.18), and others covered in shiny enamelled scales. One particular fish was 5 m or more in length, and though never recovered as a complete specimen, pieces of limestone with parts of the skeleton are found from time to time. This nektonic giant was called *Gyrosteus*.

Marine reptiles included crocodiles with narrow, rounded snouts like the present-day Indian gharial –

10.14 Belemnites are not uncommon fossils in marine Jurassic and Cretaceous rocks. They are frequently found in the Whitby Mudstone Formation. The figured specimens illustrate the variation between species from different parts of the succession. a. *Youngibelus tubularis*; b. *Acrocoelites (Odontobelus) levidensis*; c. *Simpsonibelus lentus*; d. *Acrocoelites (Acrocoelites) subtenuis*; e. *Simpsonibelus dorsalis*.

10.15a-b (a) The alum works manager's house between Stoupe Brow and Robin Hood's Bay. The house is built of local sandstones from the Ravenscar Group.
BELOW (b) Stoupe Brow and the quarried land below, north-west of Ravenscar. Alum Shale was worked from the 17th century along parts of the Yorkshire coast and the industry was an important one here.

10.16 Saltwick Nab east of Whitby. The red colour is due to the burnt shale created during the production of alum; this was another site where alum was produced on an industrial scale.

10.17 Burnt shale with characteristic red colour in the spoil heaps at Ravenscar. New style 10p with 24.5 mm diameter for scale.

10.18 Jurassic shark. Extraordinary preservation has led to the fossilization of the cartilaginous elements of the skull of a shark. The fossil was discovered on the Yorkshire coast by an amateur collector, Ian Ransby, in the 1990s. The large element is the lower jaw, viewed from a left and ventral aspect with the anterior pointing down. A few teeth are preserved on the surface of the nodule.

ABOVE 10.19 An artist's impression of a Jurassic seascape. Flying reptiles circle while a shark (Figure 10.18), dolphin-like ichthyosaurs, and a short-necked pliosauroid hunt for prey. A small shoal of belemnites looks especially vulnerable!

10.20a-b Small head and long neck – the plesiosauroid *Microcleidus homalospondylus* which occupied the sea over Yorkshire while the Alum Shale Member of the Whitby Mudstone Formation was being deposited. From Whitby. BELOW (a) The jaw is 0.34 m long; the sockets of the slender teeth are clearly visible; BELOW LEFT (b) The complete specimen (head, top right) as illustrated by Professor Richard Owen (1865) in a *Monograph of the Palaeontographical Society*.

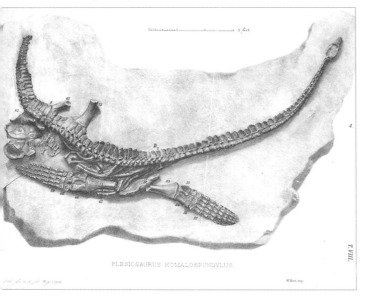

PLESIOSAURUS HOMALOSPONDYLUS.

T. VIII.

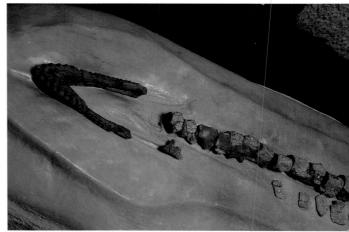

ideal for swinging around in the water when catching fish, the dolphin-like ichthyosaurs which attained considerable size – an 8 m long specimen has been found, and both plesiosauroids and pliosauroids (*Fig. 10.19*). The former had long necks and small heads, equipped with slender jutting and 'fragile' teeth, ideal for darting about and snatching at small prey (*Fig. 10.20a-b*). The latter had shorter and more robust necks supporting large heads with big mouths. They were armed with substantial teeth suitable for tackling pretty much anything that came their way. One of these has the name *Rhomaleosaurus zetlandicus* (*Fig. 10.21*), the species name honouring the Earl of Zetland from whose property the fossil had been collected. Wonderful, if rather gothic, illustrations of the marine environment in the early Jurassic, based on the interpretation of evidence found in Dorset and elsewhere, were published by De la Beche and Hawkins in the nineteenth century.

'Volcano' at root of environmental disaster?

At a time when we are becoming ever more preoccupied with the effects of climate change on the Earth, where the impacts of natural processes have to be 'crash – bang – wallop' affairs to gain attention, we remain blissfully unaware of the 'slow but sure' earth-processes which constantly drive change. These imperceptible processes have far reaching consequences, orders of magnitude greater than the cycles of floods, droughts, tornadoes, hurricanes, and the occasional tsunami.

Around 6 Ma after the start of the deposition of the Whitby Mudstone, 217 miles north-east of the Cleveland Basin, a plume of warm and plastic mantle started welling up beneath the crust of the central North Sea Basin, offshore from what is now the east coast of Scotland. The plume, still deep within the crust, was having a regional impact by gradually distorting the earth's surface, causing uplift on a regional scale; Yorkshire was not immune. Towards the top of the Lias Group in the Cleveland Basin we see these effects as there is evidence of regression, a shallowing of sea, marked by the deposition of the Blea Wyke Sandstone Formation.

This distant yet significant event continued to have consequences for the palaeogeography, sediments, and fauna and flora, across the Cleveland Basin and the southern North Sea, for approximately 14 Ma.

10.21 Large head and short neck – the pliosauroid *Rhomaleosaurus zetlandicus*. This is likely to have occupied the same niche, and hunted other plesiosaurs like the one in Figure 10.20. The skull is *c*.1 m long and was armed with an impressive array of very large and strong teeth; the broken shaft of one can be seen curving over the snout from the jaw. From Loftus Alum Mine, *c*.1852.

Only after an eruptive phase, marked by the volcanic rocks of the Rattray Formation found in the northern North Sea, does the dome start to collapse. During the course of this time, the plume indirectly wiped out the Lower Jurassic marine communities across the area, cut the links between the Boreal and Tethyan oceans, and turned the sea floor into land, creating new environments which remained largely free of marine influences for millions of years. Eventually these too were destroyed by a major marine transgression as the dome progressively collapsed and finally the southern and northern oceans were reunited.

Returning to the Blea Wyke Sandstone, sediment starvation led to the formation of ironstones in

10.22 Kilns on the northern side of Rosedale, north-west of Rosedale Abbey. The iron ores mined nearby were roasted in these kilns to improve their quality before they were transported by rail to Teesside's blast furnaces.

10.23 Part of a fallen block of the Dogger Formation on the Yorkshire coast. Characteristically an orangey-red or purplish colour and often with a conglomeratic layer as seen here. Occasionally the pebbles are pieces of worn ammonite which have been eroded from the folded and faulted rocks upon which the Dogger was deposited. Old style 50p piece with 30 mm diameter for scale.

Rosedale (*Fig.* 10.22). These have been the subject of much debate. Recent reassessment of the Blea Wyke Sandstone and the once important, partly magnetic, Rosedale Ironstone which lay above the Cleveland Ironstone, has led to a number of interesting conclusions. Firstly that the top of the Lias Group thins across the Cleveland Basin and that this thinning began earlier here than on the coast. Secondly the Rosedale Ironstone was not in two abandoned channels as previously thought, but was the remains of a more extensive deposit which had been divided by faulting active shortly after the sediments were deposited. The study confirmed that the existing strata had been subjected to folding and erosion prior to deposition of the overlying Dogger Formation.

At Ravenscar there is the important north-south Peak Fault, which has a bit of a twist – or possibly not?! On the seaward side of this fault there is a complete and thicker succession from the Whitby Mudstone Formation to the Ravenscar Group, the sediments accumulating in what is now recognised as a 3 mile wide, north-south trough. On the landward side of the fault, parts of the succession are missing or are less thick. This led to the suggestion that this was a fault that was active during the Jurassic, a view that fits nicely with what we now know of Rosedale. Another suggestion was that less than 65 Ma ago, a sideways movement, of as much as 5 miles, to the left took place, juxtaposing sediments which were originally laid down in quite different bits of the Cleveland Basin. An alternative suggestion is that most of the movement was vertical, and there was a

small lateral movement to the right! The jury is still out on this, and on the extent to which our North Sea plume had been involved in these disturbances.

The last gasp of the sea across the region deposited the Dogger. Never thick and sometimes absent, this formation is distinctive on the coast as an orange to purple-red, ferruginous sandstone, often pebbly at the base with occasional pieces of derived ammonite (*Fig.* 10.23). These were eroded from the underlying Lias Group at the base. Shallow water and lack of sediment was once again responsible for the iron enrichment.

Yorkshire's Jurassic Park

The regional uplift described above was now on course to create Yorkshire's very own Jurassic Park – hardly an environmental disaster for the plants and animals that would inhabit this new found land – not so good if you were an organism unable to 'up-sticks and off', following a retreating but not done-for, sea! Today, the successor of the Jurassic sea has carved magnificent cliff sections along the North York Moors coastline, providing unrivalled exposure of these quite amazing formations.

Environmental interpretations of the Ravenscar Group have been the focus of vigorous debate. A substantial number of research projects have looked at different aspects of these sediments and the consensus is that the Cleveland Basin was a coastal plain, across which both braided and channelled rivers flowed, draining higher ground to the north and west. The sandstones deposited frequently form important topographic features (*Figs* 2.1, 10.11).

The difference between being a terrestrial environment and a marine one came down to a fine balance between subsidence rates driven by tectonic activity and sea level changes. In addition, there was probably some subsidence related to the dewatering and compaction of the underlying strata. Evidently the rate of sedimentation was usually great enough to compensate for subsidence, and to keep the sea at bay. There are indications that occasional marine surges did occur; burrows, thought to have been produced by a variety of marine crustacean, are present in the Scalby Formation, and the rare formation of pyrite is likely to have been triggered by salt water penetration of the flood plain sediments.

Over the next 14 Ma there were three significant marine episodes. As these ended, there is sometimes evidence for small scale deltaic conditions as the rivers and their distributaries built back out across the flooded basin, interacting with the marine environment as they did so. The marine sediments are relatively easily identified by their distinctive faunas. They include the Eller Beck Formation, the Lebberston Member of the Cloughton Formation, and the Scarborough Formation. Only the latter has yielded rare ammonites, providing a valuable opportunity to correlate these strata with sequences elsewhere. Each formation is represented by distinctive combinations of sediment including oolites, fine grained limestones, sandstones, mudrocks and ironstones. The Lebberston Member is noteworthy for the two beds of oolitic limestone which outcrop to the south, one close to the northern edge, and the other on the southern flank of the MWH, and which are viewed as lateral equivalents. These are the Whitewell Oolite quarried from the edge of the Howardian Hills west of the Derwent valley, and the Cave Oolite from around South Cave between Market Weighton and the Humber.

The marine incursions originated from either the East Midlands Shelf (*Fig. 3.3*), spreading northwards over the MWH, or from the east, across the Southern North Sea and Europe. The extent of these events was very much controlled by 'localised' tectonic activity, activity which may or may not have been particularly important at the end of the last marine episode. Despite the ammonites, there has been much debate about a possible unconformity between the Scarborough and overlying Scalby formations (*Fig.* 10.24). The gap is said by some to be the equivalent of 8 ammonite zones which, depending on the figure adopted for the duration of an ammonite zone, could represent an interval of between 3.2 and 12.8 Ma. In tune with this, some suggest that the Scalby Formation was all laid down in around 1 Ma. Others have suggested intermittent sedimentation with periods of erosion over 3 – 4 Ma, and includes non-marine sediments equivalent to the lower part of the overlying Cornbrash Formation. Such are the problems when there are no ammonites! Certainly a gap of uncertain duration in the depositional record is greatly emphasised by the contrasting cross-bedded Moor Grit Member at the base of the Scalby Formation. This well cemented gritstone and coarse sandstone with varying amounts of mud, is superbly exposed at White Nab south of Scarborough. The bed is considered by some to represent a major flood. The Rudston Monolith (*Fig.* 10.25) may be from this horizon.

10.24 The wave-cut platform between White Nab and Scarborough is in the marine Scarborough Formation (Ravenscar Group). The cliffs are formed of the fluviatile Moor Grit and Long Nab members of the Scalby Formation (Ravenscar Group). The gables and roofs of the ill-fated Holbeck Hotel (Chapter 12 and figures 12.22a-b) are just visible silhouetted against the skyline to the left of centre.

10.25 The Rudston Monolith. This imposing prehistoric standing-stone is situated in the Churchyard at Rudston. The stone is thought to be from the Moor Grit Member of the Scalby Formation, and is most likely to have been brought here through human endeavour.

10.26 An inclined tree stump entombed in the flood-plain deposits of the Saltwick Formation (Ravenscar Group) east of Whitby in 1995. The way the strata has bent down around the stump may have been caused by the tree rotting and the surrounding sediment collapsing into the void left behind. Hammer *c.* 24 cm.

10.27 The Long Nab Member (Scalby Formation) at Burniston Steps, near Burniston. The aluminium ladder was being used to inspect a substantial bulge on the base of one of the sandstones – probably a sauropod track.

The Ravenscar Group is by any standards a remarkable geological entity. There is an approximately 125 m sequence of grits, sandstones, siltstones, mudstones, and occasional limestones associated with the marine episodes. The non-marine sequences include the Saltwick (*Fig.* 10.26), Cloughton (but not the Lebberston Member), and Scalby formations (*Fig.* 10.27). The cliffs of the coast display sections through spectacular river channels, often with slumped margins, and their courses and evolving structures are sometimes laid bare as sweeping arcs on the foreshore (*Fig.* 10.28a-b). The importance of these formations for the understanding of oil fields in the North Sea has long been recognised, and cored boreholes

10.28a-b BELOW LEFT (a) Crook Ness north of Scalby, near Scarborough. In the cliff, a channel is preserved in the Long Nab Member which is also exposed on the foreshore. The foreshore when viewed from above (BELOW) (b) shows arcuate rock bands dipping below the shore. These show the progressive migration of the ancient river channels over the flood plains across which they flowed.

have been drilled along the cliffs in order to form a better understanding of their sediments and the environments they represent. Some descriptions of these strata compare them to the Carboniferous Coal Measures, a parallel alluded to earlier, and certainly there are many aspects in common.

Within the terrestrial facies, plant beds, and the tracks and trackways of dinosaurs are frequently encountered (*Figs* 10.29, 10.32bc). Though the latter had not evolved during Carboniferous times, amphibians and early reptiles had, so perhaps we should be puzzled why examples of much earlier trackways have not been recorded from the Carboniferous of Yorkshire. Perhaps we have not been looking? The eroded coastal sections certainly increase the chances of spotting such trace fossils. Occasionally, deposits containing the shells of *Unio*, a freshwater mussel, are found, indicative of shallow freshwater pools on the flood plain or in the abandoned meanders of rivers.

Tracking dinosaurs

The potential importance of dinosaurs to sedimentological processes was flagged in 1970 when Dick Selley, writing in his refreshing style in *Ancient sedimentary environments*, said of slumps and slides, 'These slope failures can occur spontaneously or be triggered by earthquakes, storms, or herds of stampeding dinosaurs.' – though to what extent the last may have been tongue-in-cheek was not clear! Dinosaurs had evolved during the Triassic, and evidence of their one-time presence across the Cleveland Basin was recognised in the early 20th century. Further discoveries continued at a low level until the 1990s. In the late 1980s, the author of a paper on the **syn-sedimentary** deformation of sediments of this age, alluded to 'animal activity' as one of four triggering mechanisms. The author describes the other three in more detail, but 'animal activity' is taken no further. This was ironic, as examination of the coastal sections showed that there was impressive evidence for extensive **dinoturbation** (*Fig.* 10.30). The degree of deformation observed was likely to have been the result of at least several dinosaurs, even if evidence of a stampeding herd was lacking!

In the 1990s, the Department of Geology at the University of Sheffield, already initiated into dinosaur tracking from an earlier discovery, took the lead in a Yorkshire renaissance of dinosaur **ichnology** across the Cleveland Basin. They established the 'Sheffield

10.29 Tridactyl (three toed) dinosaur track preserved as an upstanding cast in the Long Nab Member, Scalby Formation, north of Scarborough.

Dinosaur Track Research Group', developing research projects, and involving teams from Earthwatch International over several seasons, conducting detailed surveys and research, and publishing their findings. The Group's research has established the Cleveland Basin as a megatracksite. Why should so much spectacular evidence be found here? The answer

10.30 Dinoturbation seen in the Long Nab Member, Scalby Formation, south east of Scarborough. The sediments have been hugely disrupted, the bulges having been produced by dinosaurs moving over waterlogged and or poorly consolidated sediment.

10.31 Swimming traces of dinosaurs preserved as casts on the base of a sandstone from the Saltwick Formation, Ravenscar Group, near Whitby. They may have been made by dinosaurs trying to escape a marine storm surge or river flood. Hammer *c.* 24 cm.

is that both Yorkshire and the dinosaurs were in the right place at the right time! They have shown how different species of dinosaur and other reptiles ranged across extensive flood plains, walked beside rivers, trampled unconsolidated sands and clays, and even

10.32a-c (a) An elephant track in once wet sediment in Kenya. Lens cap for scale. (b) A sauropod dinosaur's track preserved in iron-rich sediment south-east of Scarborough; compass arrow 6 cm for scale. The similarities between (a) and (b) are clear. (c) A cast of the right hind-limb of a large sauropod. The cast of a tridactyl print, probably made later, is preserved within it. The shallow rim seen around parts of this cast is the mould of a thin layer of sediment displaced by the foot. 10 cm scale bar.

swam in what is presumed to have been attempts to save their lives from floods (*Fig.* 10.31).

The formation and preservation of trace fossils such as these requires a combination of events, sediments with the right properties, and burial soon after their formation. The tracks left by bird, dog, man and bicycle in the soft mud and silt dumped on on an urban tow-path by a river in flood are a good example of the processes involved. Fortunately there was no one around to hose down the mud when dinosaurs stalked Yorkshire *c.*166 Ma. The threat to tracks in the Ravenscar Group came from destruction from weathering and the growth of vegetation, or if buried, from the ever-migrating rivers in their meandering channels. Doubtless, over several million years, these natural processes destroyed countless trackways, while providing fresh surfaces for new ones! Those dinosaurs that survived the flood would have had fresh layers of mud, silt and sand to walk across with startling results (*Fig.* 10.32b-c).

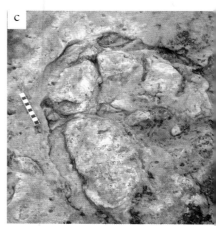

Tracks and trackways are present throughout the non-marine parts of the Ravenscar Group, and are even occasionally recorded from the most marginal of the marine units. The tracks, commonly preserved as casts, show a variety of complex preservational variations making interpretation challenging. Despite this, the Sheffield team have been able to distinguish two species of sauropod and a stegosaur (quadrupedal dinosaurs), two theropods (carnivorous dinosaurs), and two ornithopods (bird-hipped, plant eating dinosaurs), in addition to the tracks of a crocodile and a turtle. Track sizes range from a tiny 3 cm, to a staggering 1m for tracks made by a sauropod.

What of the track-making dinosaurs and where are their remains? Despite decades of active fieldwork by generations of geologists and collectors along eroding cliffs, very rarely have their bones been found. The explanation for this absence has usually been placed at the door of the sediments over which the animals moved. They would have been far from ideal for the fossilisation of bone. A dividend, or bonus, of the renaissance in dinosaur studies has seen a considerable increase in the number of specimens found (*Fig.* 10.33). Doubtless further intensive study will yield further skeletal evidence, so like in the early days of television, the picture we can have can only get better!

10.33 Despite all the evidence for their presence afforded by tracks, the bones of vertebrates are rare in the rocks of the Ravenscar Group. However, remains are occasionally found. In this example, an eroded section across dark brown bone (dinosaur?) is visible; Saltwick Formation.

A Jurassic Kew

The fossil record of plants in these sediments is remarkable and world renowned. Collections have been made from over 600 plant beds, and from these collections, over 300 species have been identified (*Figs.* 10.34, 10.35 *see following page*). Amongst these are rare liverworts, the foliage of ferns which include forms identifiable in today's flora, ginkgos, conifers, cycads, and the extinct cycad-like Bennettitales. The Bennettitales and the gymnosperm Caytoniales are plant fossils which have taxed palaeobotanists, for the former has a flower-like organ, and the latter, leaves which appear angiosperm-like. Angiosperms are the modern flowering plants which evolved during the Cretaceous, so their discovery in Jurassic rocks, if ever confirmed, would push back the boundaries of plant evolution. Plant seeds and other reproductive structures are also found.

In addition to these plant remains, which include delicate plant cuticles, one of the more iconic though

10.34 Plant fossils from the Ravenscar Group of Yorkshire as illustrated on plate X of John Phillips, 1829, *Illustrations of the Geology of Yorkshire; or, a description of the strata and organic remains of the Yorkshire Coast accompanied by a geological map, sections, and plates of the fossil plants and animals.* York.

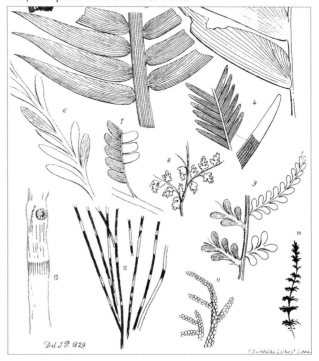

10.36 Rootlets, probably of *Equisetum* in floodplain sandstone from the Saltwick Formation near Ravenscar. New style 10p with 24.5 mm diameter for scale.

10.35a-e Plant fossils from the collection of the York Museums Trust.
(a) *Cladophlebis* sp. (fern);
(b) *Ptilophyllum pecten*;
(c) *Zamites gigas*;
(d) *Williamsonia gigas*; (b-c is cycad-like bennettitalean foliage, and d a female flower of the same);
(e) *Ginkgo* foliage. The Jurassic *Ginkgo* is the ancestor of our Maidenhair Tree.
All specimens from the Ravenscar Group. They vary in size from 8 cms (centre left) to 12 cms (top right).

relatively common fossils is the finely sculpted and sediment filled stem of *Equisetum columnare*, the second or specific name being allocated for obvious reasons. The horsetails (related to, but smaller than, *Calamites* in the Pennine Coal Measures Group) grew around the edges of the rivers, and owe their preservation to the filling of the broken, hollow stems of dead plants with silts and sands. Casts of *in situ* stems are known, having filled with sediment during floods. Horizons with rootlets of horsetails provide evidence for them colonising flood-plains (*Fig. 10.36*).

Palaeobotanists rely on a variety of accumulations of different plant remains, variously preserved, and in different environments, in order to elucidate the flora. These deposits have also allowed researchers to explore the relationships of the plants and suggest the communities and habitats within which they flourished (*Fig. 10.37*). Studies of the growth rings of fossil conifer wood from these deposits, and comparison of the fossil plants with modern floras, have provided valuable information on the likely climate at the time. The evidence points to a seasonal climate, which had started to develop during the deposition of the latter part of the Lias Group, with wet winters and dry summers. This climate became more pronounced, but not truly Mediterranean, during the latter part of the Ravenscar Group. The scenario of increasing seasonality with summer aridity is supported by the presence of small pieces of charcoal, sometimes exquisitely preserving plant structures, the result of

10.37 A Jurassic Kew. An artist's reconstruction of a Jurassic landscape and how the higher ground across parts of Yorkshire may have looked during the deposition of the Ravenscar Group.

wildfires started by lightning strikes.

This Jurassic flora was rich and provided a veritable cornucopia for herbivorous dinosaurs – and doubtless many other creatures too, directly and indirectly. During a field trip several years ago, a leaf was found with what appeared to be dinosaur bite marks.

All at sea again

Overlying the Scalby Formation with dinosaur track-bearing sandstones, at the top of the Ravenscar Group, the Cornbrash Formation heralds the return of the sea to Yorkshire; life was no longer to be quite so 'on the edge'. The North Sea High, which had formed over the mantle plume, isolated both northern and southern oceans for around 14 Ma. The culmination of this event was a series of volcanic eruptions which occurred while the Ravenscar Group was being deposited, signalling the start of the dome's collapse.

10.38 Members of The Yorkshire Geological Society on a field excursion discussing sedimentary structures in a disued quarry near Oldstead, below the Hambleton Hills, on the south-west margin of the North York Moors, June 2007. Amongst the company were the then President of the Society, Martin Whyte (third from the right), and two past Presidents, Mike Romano and John Powell (second from the right and furthest left respectively).

10.39 The Observatory in the gardens of the Yorkshire Museum, York, was built 1832-33 using stone quarried in the Hackness Hills. The same source of stone was used for the Rotunda Museum in Scarborough.

By around 164 Ma, the sea had returned from a broadly southerly direction across the Cleveland Basin, and by around 160 Ma the Boreal – Tethys connection had been re-established across the Mid North Sea High.

Across Yorkshire, for the remaining 19 Ma of the Jurassic, successive episodes of transgression and regression, of minor folding and faulting, provided the wide range of seafloor configurations and environments in which a remarkable range of sediments would accumulate. Sea cliffs provide fantastic opportunities for detailed study, but give what is an essentially 2-d view. As for the Ravenscar Group, the 3-d view is only gained by detailed study of the inland outcrops, often through limited and even treacherous access to overgrown and obscure exposures. Making sense of the sedimentological subtleties of the Jurassic is far from easy, especially when superimposed on the continuing fluctuations in global sea level. Refreshingly, as with so much to do with Yorkshire's geological history, there is evidence of continuing debate fostered by both the British Geological Survey and the Yorkshire Geological Society, at indoor meetings, while looking at outcrops in the field (*Fig.* 10.38), and through publication.

To the north of the MWH, the attenuated Cornbrash Formation with limestones and clays is overlain by the Osgodby Formation which is exposed on the coast at Cayton Bay, north-west of Filey Brigg, and

in the valleys of the southern dip-slope of the North York Moors. The beds are particularly interesting on two scores. Firstly, the fine grained sandstones with their evidence of non-deposition and even erosion, are the Cleveland Basin's equivalent of the more **argillaceous** Kellaways and lower part of the Oxford Clay formations to the south. Secondly, these fine grained **bioturbated** sandstones were quarried on the Hackness Estate where Sir John Johnstone, a leading local intellectual, employed William 'Strata' Smith as land agent (Chapter 1).

It is no coincidence that Smith's brainchild, the Rotunda Museum (1828-29) in Scarborough (*Fig.* 1.7), was constructed from this beautiful stone. The uncle (Smith) – nephew (Phillips) (*Figs.* 1.5-1.6) connections with the Yorkshire Philosophical Society where John Phillips was Curator were almost certainly behind the same stone being used for the Neo-Classical Yorkshire Museum (1829-30), and the small astronomical observatory (*Fig* 10.39) built in the Museum Gardens (1832-33). Restoration work carried out to the latter in the late 1980s, used a Triassic Sandstone from Grinshill in Shropshire.

When the Osgodby Formation strata were being deposited, sediments to the south show a mingling of Boreal and Tethyean faunas, signalling the final collapse of the Mid North Sea High. Eventually, but only for a relatively short span of time, the more muddy facies of the Oxford Clay did take hold across the region, though Yorkshire was never visited with the organic-rich mudrocks that have made parts of this formation so valuable for brick-making; pits

10.40 The view inland from Filey Brigg. To the right in the distance are Grisethorpe and Lebbertson cliffs, and to the left the cliffs of Filey Bay (Figure 12.3a). In the foreground are strata of the Corallian Group.

10.41 The irregular shape of a Coral Rag patch-reef in disused quarry workings west of Scarborough. Malton Oolite Member of the Coralline Oolite Formation.

in this formation in the south Midlands were the source of the huge numbers of bricks required for post World War II reconstruction in southern Britain. Soon the Cleveland Basin's short-lived sequence of clays became increasingly silty, the first evidence of the shallow water sedimentation of the Corallian Group.

Where corals lie

From Filey Brigg's jutting reefs in the east (*Fig.* 10.40), strata of the Corallian Group run west, cladding the dip slope of the North York Moors with a variety of calcareous sandstones, and limestones. On the western edge of their outcrop these beds form the great cliffs of the Hambleton Hills to the north and south of Sutton Bank (*Fig.* 4.5). These strata then turn southeast, forming the Howardian Hills to Malton, finally disappearing beneath the Chalk around 7 miles to the south. As seen in *Figure* 10.5a-b, the Corallian is believed to be present in the faulted **subcrop** beneath the Chalk of the Wolds. In the south of the Cleveland Basin, the MWH is seen to influence the nature of the sediments.

The interdigitation and variability of these strata, coupled with localised gaps in the succession, all point to a shallow marine basin with migrating oolite shoals, and intervening areas of quieter water deposition where carbonate mud accumulated. Within the oolitic limestones, coral patch reefs are occasionally developed (*Fig.* 10.41) and with one of these, Yorkshire boasts the earliest example found

in these strata anywhere in the UK. Sponges are occasionally found in the sediment starved waters that existed early in the deposition of these beds. There is no surprise that in such conditions these strata would sometimes contain a diverse fauna, including bivalves, gastropods – some of large size, a wealth of ammonites, and echinoids. Trace fossils are present, a not uncommon example being a branching mass of tubes across weathered surfaces, revealing the one-time presence of burrowing crustaceans.

The unexpected is sometimes found, and by serendipity saved for future generations to marvel at. In the Yorkshire Museum's palaeontological collection is a tooth, at once both fearsome and beautiful, once belonging to a megalosaur-like dinosaur (*Fig.* 10.42, *see following page*). The remains of dinosaurs are occasionally found out of context in marine deposits, though one is left to speculate on the fate of this particular predator that led to its formidable tooth being incorporated in an oolitic limestone near Malton. If only we knew the whereabouts of the rest of this theropod!

Comparison has been made between these sediments with their evidence of tropical fauna, and conditions in the Bahamas today. The Corallian Group closed with environments in which sands dominate, ferruginous in the east, and elsewhere frequently calcareous. Corallian Group strata have yielded useful building stones which grace villages and houses built along the outcrops and nearby. Today, a few quarries produce crushed stone.

10.42 The serrated edges are clearly visible on this example of a tooth of carnivorous dinosaur. The tooth, labelled as *Megalosaurus*, was found in marine rocks (Corallian Group) near Malton. The tooth is 114 mm long.

Mud, mud, glorious mud!

While a Bahamian paradise existed over much of the Cleveland Basin and for an unknown extent to the west and north, to the south of the influential MWH, the Corallian Group sediments were absent, represented only by mudrocks and siltstones of the West Walton Formation within the Ancholme Group. The Ampthill Clay Formation is present both to the north, overlying Corallian strata, and south of the divide, overlying the West Walton Formation, before passing upwards into the Kimmeridge Clay Formation which is the uppermost part of the Jurassic sequence in Yorkshire. Buried beneath extensive superficial deposits, the Kimmeridge Clay is never well exposed in the Vale of Pickering. Cliff sections and brick pits (*Fig.* 10.43) provide small windows through which to glimpse this other-world; boreholes have added detail to our knowledge. Fossils include bivalves, and ammonites which are valued for the usual reasons, but may confuse by looking very like stratigraphically

unrelated varieties!

The formation is much studied on account of its significance as a source rock for hydrocarbons in the northern North Sea; studies have included calculations of the amounts of organic productivity of the Kimmeridge ocean. There are frequent organic rich-horizons, which accumulated in anoxic conditions on the sea floor, deposits which contributed to the banding effect seen in parts of the Kimmeridge Clay. The banding is believed to result from climatic variations brought about by a 3° change in the incidence of the sun's radiation to the Earth, as the Earth's axis of rotation went through 38 ka cycles, shorter than today's at 41 ka. This is called orbital obliquity. In addition the Earth has a slow wobble about the same axis of rotation called orbital precession. A complete 'wobble-cycle' currently takes 23 ka but was a little shorter during the late Jurassic. These mechanisms are collectively known as orbital forcing. Ocean productivity and climate at this time were all linked in to this cosmic clockwork. Using this information, scientists studying these rocks in Dorset, where they are especially well exposed, suggest that the full thickness of the Kimmeridge Clay Formation took *c*.7.5 million years to accumulate.

Despite poor exposure, the remains of extinct marine reptiles have been collected from the cliff sections, though uncertainty may creep in as to whether these were from the Kimmeridge Clay or overlying Speeton Clay formations. The contact between the two is sometimes visible in the cliffs at Speeton, marking the transition from Jurassic to Cretaceous.

10.44 The Speeton Clay Formation forms rapidly eroding cliffs on the southern side of Filey Bay, near Reighton Sands.

The long goodbye

There is an irony in the often obscured exposures of the Jurassic – Cretaceous boundary, for this junction is one of those special ones representing a long interval. Erosion of more or less of the earlier Kimmeridge sediment may have taken place, but there is every reason to suppose that a bit like in the story of Sleeping Beauty, 'time stood still'. Nothing much was deposited, nothing much was eroded – and this for an estimated 9-10 Ma, a very long zizz by any standards! In fact the upper part of the Kimmeridge Clay is missing, and there are no strata which match the Portland Group and the lower part of the Purbeck Limestone Group of Dorset. This was a period of tension-triggered uplift probably caused by another spasm in the opening of the Atlantic Ocean, a process which would dramatically impact on the palaeogeography of Britain for a long time to come. A bed of phosphatic nodules known as the Coprolite Bed marks the boundary, and was mined in the 19th century as a source of phosphate. Reworked fossils from the Kimmeridge Clay are present, accounting for some at least of the missing strata.

The Speeton Clay Formation (*Fig.* 10.44) though initially organic-rich like the preceding Kimmeridge Clay, soon becomes a sequence of clays and calcareous clays with occasional **septarian nodules** and **glauconite**. Representing a period of around 28 Ma, the formation has a number of breaks in sedimentation, and thin bands of volcanic ash called bentonites have been recognised. The ashes provide valuable datum lines for correlation with offshore North Sea boreholes, and two provide a rare link with horizons in the Purbeck Limestone of Dorset.

Like the Kimmeridge Clay the Speeton Clay exhibits rhythmic banding which is linked to orbital forcing. The 100 m thick sequence is often very fossiliferous, with bivalves, ammonites (*Figs.* 10.4f, 10.46), belemnites and brachiopods. The sieving of samples of the clays through a fine mesh will procure a whole wealth of tiny invertebrate microfossils, along with, if you are lucky, the teeth of sharks and rays. The latter may be very small (down to <1 mm wide), but they come at a time of change between the late Jurassic forms and the appearance of the ancestors of modern sharks around 112 Ma. By contrast, rare remains of larger vertebrates have been found. Both ichthyosaurs and a headless plesiosaur have been collected, and the limb bones of an iguanodontid dinosaur, identified as *Iguanodon atherfieldensis* were found in 1960. The association of a femur, tibia and fibula would confirm the presence of land not too far away, and close enough for the bones' connective tissue not to have decayed before they sank to the sea floor.

The Speeton Clay sediments pass conformably into the red chalk of the Hunstanton Formation. Over the MWH, where no Speeton Clay had been deposited, and southwards, a thin and patchy ferruginous sand called the Carstone Formation rests unconformably on the eroded Jurassic surface, filling hollows at the northern extreme of its outcrop. The presumption is that while the Speeton Clay was accumulating in the shallow sea over the Cleveland Basin, an unknown thickness of Carstone accumulated to the south of a

10.45 'The Red Chalk' (Hunstanton Formation) is exposed at the foot of the western end of Bempton Cliffs. Wave worn lumps of the stratigraphically higher White Chalk Subgroup litter the foreshore.

fault controlled basin-margin.

The Hunstanton Formation's red chalk (*Fig.* 10.45) is seen from Norfolk through to Yorkshire, a harbinger of the more familiar white chalk cliffs of Flamborough and beyond. Elsewhere, argillaceous and arenaceous sediments are being deposited. The Red Chalk, as it was formerly known, is in stark contrast to the underlying slipped clays to the north, and the precipitous white Bempton Cliffs (*Fig.* 11.1) to the south. The red colour is thought to be derived from pre-existing iron-oxide rich sediments. A small belemnite by the name of *Neohibolites*, which occurs in these beds, has done its bit for science by being subjected to isotopic analysis. This has revealed that the red chalk sea may have periodically reached an average annual temperature of around 16.4°C – compared with 11.5 °C off south west England today.

The white cliffs of Flamborough

Well perhaps 'Bempton' would be more accurate, but whichever, here is yet more thrilling coastal scenery in Yorkshire, and this time composed of the largely brilliant white limestones collectively known as the Chalk, or more correctly the Chalk Group. The spectacular cliffs between Bridlington and Speeton, temporary home to millions of nesting seabirds each year, are the seaside culmination of the great sweep of rolling chalkland scenery, the Wolds. To the east and south, the Chalk Group, with a thickness of over 530 m, dips down below the Plain of Holderness (Chapter 12), and here the uppermost unit, the Rowe Chalk Formation, discovered in a borehole is named after

the amateur geologist Arthur Walter Rowe (1858 – 1926) who did so much to elucidate this group.

The cliffs have provided extensive, if hazardous, sections for the study of these strata. At one time the Chalk was viewed as rather monotonous and was neatly packaged as 'Lower', 'Middle' and 'Upper', for decades appearing as such on the maps of the British Geological Survey in their three shades of green. Suddenly, all change – and a new terminology was introduced in order to provide a more effective system for mapping this far from monotonous deposit!

There was much debate about the new terminology, and the summary at the beginning of this chapter gives the one that has been adopted. This change in nomenclature echoed the rapidity with which white

10.46 Cretaceous fossils of Yorkshire as illustrated on plate I of John Phillips, 1829, *Illustrations of the Geology of Yorkshire; or, a description of the strata and organic remains of the Yorkshire Coast accompanied by a geological map, sections, and plates of the fossil plants and animals.* York. Above the line are fossils from the Chalk including several sponges (1-12) and the nektonic crinoid *Marsupites*; below the line are ammonites from the Speeton Clay.

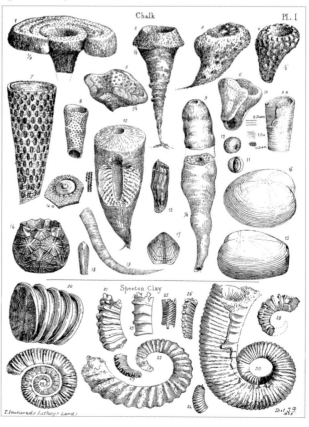

Chalk deposition set in across the UK, a response to rising sea level and the reduction in sediments derived from the land; there was less land exposed, and the climate was becoming increasingly arid. The Chalk sea eventually covered the Pennines, with possibly as much as 600 m of Chalk deposited, while the Cleveland Basin may have accumulated between 700 m and possibly 1000 m.

Chalk is mostly a very pure limestone composed of the remains of both microscopic, and fragmented macroscopic organisms, with which the warm chalk sea teemed. Take a sample of soft Chalk (Yorkshire chalks tend to be hard!), and scrub it vigorously with a nail brush in a bowl of water. Careful dilution of the milky white water, flushing out the finest white mud, will leave a residue amongst which, with the help of a hand lens, will be seen the remains of some of these fossils. Particularly abundant and important, but only visible under high powered microscopes, are the rings of plates, several of which form the spherical skeleton of the planktonic algae called coccoliths. The remains of complete organisms are also present in

10.47. RIGHT Part of an artist's reconstruction of the environment in which the Chalk was deposited. The image shows a selection of the varied fauna which either burrowed in, was attached to, or rested on the sea floor. In addition we are also able to glimpse some of those invertebrates and vertebrates which moved more or less freely through the overlying water column.

10.48 BELOW Rhythmic banding revealed in the face of a Chalk pit south-west of Fridaythorpe.

the Chalk, sometimes in abundance, and include the whole spectrum of marine invertebrates (*Fig.* 10.47). Sponges are especially common in one horizon, in fact so prolific that the bed is named after them (*Fig.* 10.46). In contrast to the great crinoid 'forests' of the Carboniferous seas (Chapter 8), nektonic crinoids which lack stems are better known.

With the organic remains are varying amounts of clay, sometimes making the Chalk marly, and in some parts of the sequence contributing to rhythmic banding (*Fig.* 10.48) like that observed in the Kimmeridge Clay. Not all marls are the product of orbital forcing; some have a geochemical signature which betrays their origin as volcanic ash falls,

10.49 A massive, circular paramoudra-like, flint in the Chalk cliff near Flamborough Head. *Yorkshire Rocks and Landscape* (13 cm x 19.5 cm) published by the Yorkshire Geological Society for scale.

10.50 Chalk in use as a building stone. The old Flamborough Lighthouse, an octagonal Chalk tower built in 1674 at the behest of Sir John Clayton. Twenty tonnes of Chalk was used in 1996 during a major restoration of the tower, and especially of the badly damaged north side.

possibly from either the North Atlantic or North Sea; could their widespread distribution point to the more remote source? A particularly prominent marker horizon in Yorkshire and the North Sea is called the Black Band. Deposited at a time of anoxic conditions on the sea floor, the bed is rich in organic matter and sediment derived from landmasses. Some have suggested this may in some way be connected to rapid sea-floor spreading and associated sub-marine volcanism within the Atlantic.

The Chalk Group also exhibits hardgrounds formed when deposition was interrupted, and the sea floor became **lithified** before being buried beneath more sediment. The chalk ooze was frequently burrowed, and the burrows are often preserved as **flint** casts. Exceptional amongst flints and associated burrows are the vertical pipe-like flints known as paramoudras. These strange formations are explained through the physiochemical relationship between silicon bearing fluids and the sediments in and around vertical burrows found in the axial core of a paramoudra (*Fig.* 10.49). They are especially well known in Norfolk where local geologists founded the Paramoudra Club. The Chalk is sometimes sufficiently hard to find use as a building stone (*Figs* 10.50).

How did the Cretaceous end?

The uppermost part of the Chalk Group is no longer present in Yorkshire, presumed eroded. Chalk deposition carried on in parts of the North Sea beyond the end of the Cretaceous. There and in Denmark, Paleogene Chalk is present. In Denmark, there are exposures with a fine clay band marking the Cretaceous – Paleogene boundary, and these have unusually high concentrations of the rare element iridium. This encouraged speculation that the extinction at the end of the Cretaceous, usually quoted as the one that killed the dinosaurs, large marine reptiles, ammonites – and a good deal else besides, was caused by a large extraterrestrial object hitting the Earth. Some are now suggesting multiple impacts, and in this context, a disputed crater of a similar age, 80 miles off the Yorkshire coast (Chapter 14), has been of more than local interest. Volcanism and falling sea levels have also been suggested as causes of extinction. There is little evidence that the debate over this, which has ebbed and flowed for decades, will end any time soon.

ELEVEN

Landscape Evolution

11.1. This picture nicely illustrates just some of the landscape-creating forces which Yorkshire has been, and still is subjected to. The sea has played a significant role over 542 Ma, depositing sediment in ocean basins and cutting new cliff lines as land has been uplifted. Ice sheets have remotely controlled sea-levels on several occasions, and more recently encroached on Yorkshire, sculpting the land surfaces and depositing glacial till over the more ancient rocks (Chapter 12). Just north of Flamborough Head, Thornwick Nab is in the foreground, and Bempton Cliffs stretch into the distance. Chalk Group strata are overlain by Pleistocene till.

Time: Paleogene – Neogene: 65 – 2.65 Ma
Latitude: 47° – 53°N
Climate: Sub-tropical becoming very warm at 56 Ma, then starts to cool, a process which climaxes in the Pleistocene glaciations.
Environment: Probably marine – marginal marine, then terrestrial.
Rocks: No sediments recognised. Basalt intrusion.

What happened next?

Whether with a full stop or exclamation mark, the Cretaceous was over. In Yorkshire, with the exception of the intrusion of the Cleveland Dyke, we lose the record of the rocks for over 65 Ma, slightly less than the time interval recorded in Chapter 6. We are confronted by virtually no evidence for a great deal that happens. A number of questions inevitably arise. After the Chalk, when did deposition cease? Sediments of this age are present offshore in the North Sea, so were they deposited over Yorkshire? How soon did the erosion of these previously deposited rocks begin? What did our landscape look like during this time?

When the Chalk sea was at its zenith, the Pennines were covered, so we can conclude that at some point towards the end of the Cretaceous or possibly during the early Paleogene, Yorkshire would have been a more or less flat surface. This surface then becomes the superficially blank canvas on which our landscape evolves.

Beneath the 'canvas', the presence of the deep structures are as relevant now as before, and with the ever present influence of plate tectonic activity, provide us with a framework upon which to speculate on the evolution of this region. Playing their part were the continued opening of the Atlantic, an igneous plume and associated doming in Greenland, and possible uplift associated with igneous activity in the Irish Sea and along the west coast of Scotland. The first hint of Britain's easterly tilt may have been imparted during this time (see also Chapter 12), which would have subsequently played a part in defining how extensive was the marine influence across Yorkshire during the Cenozoic.

In order to discover how much sediment might have been deposited, scientists resort to a variety of geophysical and geochemical techniques (Chapter 9).

11.2 Staple Nook, Bempton Cliffs. A photograph taken of the contortions in the Chalk by James W. Davis no later than 1885 and published by the Yorkshire Geological Society in that year.

The data from these investigations suggests that up to 1,000 m of Paleogene sediment was deposited across the Cleveland Basin. This is fascinating, for here is an area once thought to have been above sea level now regarded as a major depositional basin. The same study suggests much less Paleogene sediment was deposited to the south of the Market Weighton High. There is consensus that during this time, deposition is unlikely to have impinged on the Pennines, and that the whole of Yorkshire was undergoing erosion by around 23 Ma. From then on, all the Paleogene and Cretaceous sediments, and in some areas the uppermost Jurassic, were being eroded. Studies indicate that as much as 2,500 m of post-Middle Jurassic (i.e. Jurassic, Cretaceous and Paleogene) sediments have been removed from across the top of the Cleveland Dome in the last 23 Ma.

A further impact on the 'canvas' was the Alpine Orogeny caused by the closure of Tethys, as northward moving Africa and India collided with Laurasia (*Fig.* 2.5). The Chalk exposed along this coastline provides evidence of this, with dramatic folds and faults in the area of Selwicks Bay and at Staple Nook (*Fig.* 11.2). Disentanglement of this web of tectonic structures exposed along this coast had to wait until the end of the 20th century, and only then was the true complexity revealed. Reactivation of the east-west faults of the fault zone separating the MWH and Cleveland Basin had left their mark, but in addition there had been four distinct phases of deformation during the last 65 Ma. These were a consequence of compression associated with the Alpine Orogeny, and tension in its aftermath. These forces, coupled with tilting and uplift of the Cleveland Dome, had acted on the Howardian-Flamborough Head Fault Zone, which intersected the north-south Peak Trough (Chapter 10), and terminated offshore against the 'north-south' trending Dowsing Fault (*Fig.* 3.3).

Our 21st century landscape may provide clues as to how Yorkshire looked. While considerably modified by successive glacial and interglacial episodes, there will be echoes of an already mature and sculpted surface, with an established but perhaps low pattern of relief, and associated drainage pattern (see Chapter 12). Were there extant or developing cave systems in the limestone of the Dales? We might be able to visualise a landscape which while elevated, boasted a less dramatic relief than today. As the Cleveland Basin underwent inversion to form the Cleveland Dome, and as the Pennines gradually rose, drainage systems already initiated will have been modified and possibly redirected.

Next we have to filter out the effects of 2.65 Ma of Pleistocene climatic fluctuation in order to see what might have been (Chapter 12). Valleys were deepened and spurs truncated (*Fig.* 12.9). The precipitous escarpments of the North York Moors (*Figs.* 4.5 & 9.1) above the Vale of Mowbray were left as a memorial commemorating the extent of a former landscape, and rare **phreatic** caves within the associated limestones have a whole new tale to tell. Researchers have pointed out that these caves, *c.*250 m above Kirkdale Cave (Chapter 12) which is in the same formation, may be relics of a significantly earlier phase of cave development, when the landscape and water-tables were very different to those of today. The landslides on destabilised fell, mountain and hillsides (*Figs.* 11.3 & 12.19), and deeply incised river gorges (*Fig.* 12.11) are all artefacts of the waxing and waning of a succession of ice sheets and the instability they created.

11.3 Landslipping on a north-facing slope south of Wigtwizzle, south-west of Stocksbridge, near Sheffield.

A five(?) day fiery wonder!

Are we to imagine that living creatures across Yorkshire experienced earthquakes? Quite possibly, for as the igneous province along the west coast of Scotland fired up during the Paleocene, the Cleveland Dyke was intruded. This basaltic intrusion runs in a great 267 mile (430 km) arc, almost unbroken at the surface, from the Isle of Mull volcanic centre, to just short of the Yorkshire coast. In the Yorkshire region, a maximum thickness of 25 m is sometimes attained. Research has led **petrologists** to suggest that a volume of 85 km³ of magma was intruded in between 1 and 5 days, at the astonishing rate of between 1 and 5 metres a second! The once buried dyke, exposed by erosion, has been extensively worked for roadstone in quarries and cuttings over the North York Moors (*Figs*. 2.1 & 11.4). As a result of this economic interest, apart from holes, a scatter of loose rubble, and an emphatic geophysical anomaly, for those with the equipment to detect such things, there is little left to see of this 5 day, or less, igneous wonder.

Niches to fill! Opportunities for life!

The end-Cretaceous extinction is over, and while not as devastating as that at the end of the Permian,

11.4 Shallow depressions are all that remain of the site of the quarrying operations which took place along the outcrop of the Cleveland Dyke on the northern edge of Sleights Moor, above Sleights near Whitby.

there were some important absences as a result. No dinosaurs, no flying reptiles, no plesiosaurs or ichthyosaurs. Here were big opportunities for survivors with genetic good fortune on their side!

While no fossils from this period are known from Yorkshire, we do know that this was a period of dramatic evolutionary developments in which climate played a part. Modern plants were now developing fast, and amongst the forms to be found would be many familiar to us today, including the grasses. The latter were to have a significant impact on mammalian evolution. With the dinosaurs no more, the mammals, though still relatively small as the period opens, were well placed to become all-powerful. We must imagine that they both lived in and moved across the landscapes of Yorkshire. Birds, which had continued to evolve during the Cretaceous, are found as fossils in the sediments of south-east England and their presence is certain. Here in Yorkshire there was a pristine, almost modern world awaiting its evolutionary fate.

TWELVE
Ice Worlds and the Yorkshire Underground

12.1 A Norber erratic. One of many Silurian (Windermere Supergroup) blocks plucked from the floor of Crummack Dale and left perched on a Carboniferous (Great Scar Limestone Group) limestone pavement. The protected limestone plinth stands proud of the surrounding limestone providing a gauge of the rate of limestone dissolution since the ice retreated.

> **Time:** Early Pleistocene: 2.65 Ma – 700 ka; Mid Pleistocene: 700 – 128 ka; Late Pleistocene 128 – 10 ka; Holocene 10 ka – present.
> **Latitude:** 53° 57'N
> **Climate:** Ranges from cool or cold 'glacial' to warm 'interglacial'.
> **Environment:** Glaciated through tundra to open grassland and forest. Lakes and rivers.
> **Stratigraphy:** Often complex and only slowly being understood. (*Table* 12.1)
> **Rocks:** Shattered rocks, till (boulder clay), clays, varved clays, silts, sands, gravels, peat.

Setting the Scene

Though 2.65 Ma is little more than a blink in the 540 Ma history of Yorkshire covered in this book, the landscapes and deposits which resulted from the Pleistocene roller-coaster ride that Yorkshire experienced can be summarised in two words, *incredibly complex*. Cyclicity was touched on previously in the context of Carboniferous sediments (Chapters 7 & 8) and banded sediments in the late Jurassic and Cretaceous (Chapter 10). Driving that cyclicity was orbital forcing caused by continuing changes to the Earth's axial tilt and wobble. Now implicated with them, in the later Pleistocene, is a 100 ka cycle during which the yearly orbit of the Earth around the Sun slowly changes from less to more elliptical. These three forcing mechanisms are components of Milankovitch Cycles which are widely linked to Pleistocene climatic fluctuations. However, puzzles remain, as the 100 ka cycle of glaciations recorded over the last 1 Ma does not fit in with the peaks of orbital forcing as might be expected. Carbon dioxide and other greenhouse gases are in the dock and the jury is out.

Yorkshire during the Pleistocene was once viewed, along with the rest of the British Isles, as having experienced seven cold and seven warm episodes known as stages. In fact, studies of Pleistocene temperature have shown that within these episodes there were frequent fluctuations. These have been numbered from 1-100 and form the Marine (Oxygen) Isotope Stages abbreviated to MIS (*Table* 12.1). Glacial phases did not inevitably bring full-blown glaciation,

and the old interglacials were not constantly warm. The out-of-sync and sudden switches from warm to cold and *vice versa* are almost certainly down to factors other than Milankovitch Cycles. In addition to the discovery that the Pleistocene climate was far more highly strung than first realised, researchers have discovered that deposits once thought to represent a particular stage, do not. The Pleistocene is undergoing a renaissance.

A variety of processes, glacial, **periglacial** and **glaciofluvial** were all active to a greater or lesser extent during cold phases and these were interspersed with conditions with which we are more familiar today. Yorkshire's landscape, seen and unseen, owes a huge debt to the effects of ice, and the associated freezing and thawing processes. Generations of geologists and geomorphologists have struggled with the evidence, and still the early part of the story (2.65 Ma – 700 ka) is poorly understood. Even the timing of the start of the Pleistocene is contentious. The internationally agreed date is set at 1.8 Ma, while 2.65 Ma is preferred by many researchers in the UK. This marks the moment when there is clear evidence of ocean cooling, of sea ice transporting derived rock debris, and of floral changes in Europe. These all attest to the onset of global cooling, and the eventual creation of an 'ice house' Earth.

The landscapes, initiated by erosion of the surfaces uplifted and folded during the Paleogene and early Neogene (Chapter 11), were modified by successive glaciations. The effects of ice and melt-water could be dramatic both in the uplands and lowlands. Rivers cut new courses, and with much reduced sea-levels during the cold phases, high volumes of sediment charged water, would erode deep channels along the coastal margins, in search of sea-level.

Much of Yorkshire's bedrock geology, once well exposed, is now shrouded beneath superficial deposits, sediments laid down by ice and huge volumes of melt-water (*Figs* 3.2a-b). Till (previously known as boulder clay), clays, silts, sands and gravels are commonplace. Some of these deposits may date back several hundred thousand years, perhaps longer, but mostly they are no older than the **Devensian** (117 – 10 ka). Dating tills is notoriously difficult and usually relies on their relationship to underlying or overlying interglacial deposits. These are datable – often through the fossils they contain; these may be plant remains and especially pollen and seeds, beetles – which are particularly useful as they responded

PLEISTOCENE TABLE

Period	Marine (Oxygen) Isotope Stage (MIS)	Subdivisions (=Stages) where named		Dates	Yorkshire sites/events mentioned in the text	Climate in Yorkshire
Holocene	1	Holocene		10 ka - present		Temperate
Late Pleistocene	2	Late Devensian (including Dimlington Stadial (26-13 ka) and Loch Lomond Stadial (11-10 ka)		26 - 10 ka	Whernside re-advance (Loch Lomond Stadial). Man arrives; Vale of York Ice sheet (Dimlington Stadial) Lake Humber and Vale of York moraines. Norber erratics.	Cold. Largely ice covered during Dimlington Stadial = Late Glacial Maximum
	3	Middle Devensian		50 - 26 - ka		
	4	Early Devensian		117 - 50 ka	Stump Cross Cavern wolverine (c. 80 ka)	
	5a					
	5b					
	5c					
	5d					
	5e	Ipswichian Interglacial		128 - 117 ka	Sewerby Raised Beach; Leeds hippos; Kirkdale Cave hyaenas den; Victoria Cave hippo (120 ka)	Warmer than present
Middle Pleistocene	6	cold episode		362.5 - 128 ka		Cold
	7	'Aveley Interglacial'			Bielsbeck fauna (c. 200 ka)	Warmer than present
	8	cold episode				Cold
	9	'Purfleet Interglacial'				Warmer than present
	10	cold episode				Cold
	11	Hoxnian Interglacial		410 - 362.5 ka		Warm
	12	Anglian glaciation		470 - 410 ka	Tunnel valleys form in South Yorkshire	Cold. Yorkshire fully-glaciated
	13	interglacial	'Cromerian complex'	700 - 470 ka	Victoria Cave, Settle, formed before 500 ka	A series of 4 warm and 3 cold episodes
	14	cold episode				
	15	interglacial				
	16	cold episode				
	17	interglacial				
	18	cold episode				
	19	interglacial				
Early Pleistocene	100 - 20	Undifferentiated in this account		2.65 Ma - 700 ka		Oscillating warmer and cooler phases, with progressive climatic deterioration

Table 12.1 The Pleistocene and Holocene in Yorkshire; timescale, subdivisions, events, and climate.

12.2a-b A Shap Granite glacial erratic displayed in the Museum Gardens, Yorkshire Museum, York. Shap Granite is a distinctive pink granite with large phenocrysts (larger irregular crystals set in a finer groundmass) of pink feldspar. Erratics such as this were transported by ice from the eastern edge of the Lake District, across the Stainmore Pass and into Yorkshire.

quickly to changing climate, and the teeth of voles. Even correlating scattered deposits of till is taxing, relying on distinctive signatures they may have derived from the rocks the ice rode over and pulverised; colours may provide clues, reds indicating a Triassic source, and greys and blacks – Carboniferous or Jurassic. Rock fragments containing fossils also give pointers to the source of the till.

In Yorkshire, boulders of the distinctive Shap Granite (*Fig. 12.2a-b*) are well known from the Vale of York and along the North Sea coast. They provide clear evidence that glaciers during the last glacial maximum (26 – 13 ka), were travelling from the eastern margin of the Lake District, over the Pennines into Yorkshire via the Stainmore Pass. On the east side of the Pennines, the flow then divided, part heading down the vales of Mowbray and York and the other stream heading eastwards before joining southward flowing North Sea ice, moving down the coastal side of the North York Moors. Evidence supporting this came in the form of erratics like the one of Shap granite found in a gravel pit at Seamer south of Scarborough. Scatters of boulders and cobbles like this help us discern the routes taken by these immense rivers of ice. Scandinavian rocks found along the east coast tell of ice coming from across the North Sea. Agates, washed from the cliffs of till (*Fig. 12.3a-b*)

on east coast beaches, are from sources in North East England. Pebbly beaches are commonly a treasure trove of the unexpected and beautiful, a bewildering array of pebbles representing all manner of rock types, challenging the most experienced geologists.

Reading the runes

The ruthlessness of ice, sometimes hundreds of metres thick, gouging and grinding while riding over the landscape, meant that the sedimentary evidence of earlier glaciations and interglacials was largely removed by later glaciations. Sometimes, beyond Yorkshire, we are provided with useful clues, which may be read like the characters of an ancient script on a worn piece of stone, informing us of what may have happened. Ice transported rocks from the north of England are found in datable, pre Anglian (*Table 12.1*) gravel deposits in East Anglia. In the south of England, there is undisputed evidence that probably the most extensive ice sheet of the Pleistocene reached the northern outskirts of London during the Anglian (470-410 ka); clearly this ice sheet must have covered much if not all of Yorkshire. Tills presumed to be of this age are found in South Yorkshire beyond the limit reached by the ice sheet during the last glacial maximum.

Another relict of the Anglian ice sheets are tunnel valleys in South Yorkshire, produced by pressurised, sediment loaded, sub-glacial rivers carving out narrow valleys. These were then filled with later deposits, and in some cases have been re-excavated. The Hoxnian (*Table 12.1*) interglacial (410-362.5 ka) is not recognised in Yorkshire. Along the Holderness coast, the Basement Till is exposed on the foreshore,

12.3a-b ABOVE (a) A thick deposit of dramatically weathered till overlying horizontally bedded Hambleton Oolite (Coralline Oolite Formation) immediately west of Filey Brigg in Filey Bay. RIGHT (b) Close up of till with irregular and poorly sorted rock fragments. Speeton Cliffs, near Reighton Sands. Hammer 24 cm long.

12.4 Sewerby Cliff north of Bridlington, where the Ipswichian cliff line and raised beach deposits (middle distance) are intersected by today's coastline. In the distance are the cliffs at South Landing; Flamborough Head is hidden from view.

and is believed to represent a Middle Pleistocene glaciation from between 362.5 and 128 ka. Inland, and emphasising the complexity of these glacial episodes, is the Bielsbeck site south-west of Market Weighton. Here the mammal bones which include lion, straight-tusked elephant, steppe mammoth, rhinoceros, bear, wolf, bison, red deer and horse, date from around 200 ka and represent the Aveley Interglacial (*Table* 12.1).

The ensuing Ipswichian (*Table* 12.1) warm phase (128-117 ka) witnessed sea-levels rise as the glaciers and ice caps melted. This resulted in the formation of a new and higher cliff line and beach. This now 'fossil cliff' is cut in the Chalk and is exposed in the present-day Sewerby Cliff (*Fig.* 12.4), north of Bridlington. The cliff can be traced inland, passing west of Hull to Hessle, and south into Lincolnshire. The difficulties that have been confronted by even experienced geologists in understanding a feature such as this is clear to see from the 1925 account of the *Geology of Yorkshire*. Kendall and Wroot regarded the feature as 'preglacial', not appreciating the number of glaciations which had occurred. They also highlight the debate, still continuing, about estuarine shells found sandwiched between different glacial deposits. Could such occurrences result from ice moving over,

ABOVE 12.6 Buckland entering the Kirkdale Cavern, from a caricature by W. B. Conybeare. Reproduced in E. O. Gordon, 1894, *The Life and Correspondence of William Buckland, D.D., F.R.S.*

LEFT 12.5 Kirkdale Cave, near Kirkdale on the northern edge of the Vale of Pickering. The cave, in the Coralline Oolite Formation (Corallian Group) was home to hyaenas during the Ipswichian (Table 12.1). The front portion of the cave was quarried away and the entrance to all that remains is part way up the quarry face.

BELOW 12.7a-b Bones recovered from Kirkdale Cave in the 19th century. (a) Limb bone of a mammal which has been broken and bitten by hyaenas; the pitted surfaces of the bone is characteristic. (b) The lower right jaw of a hyaena from the Kirkdale Cave.

a

b
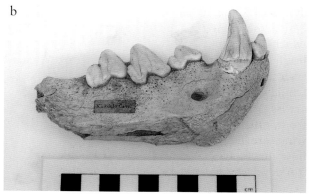

and incorporating coastal sediments? The question is still apposite to those studying these sediments today.

Ipswichian deposits have provided windows on life during an interglacial warm phase. The remains of mammals are known from the raised beach deposits at Sewerby, and include hyaena, straight-tusked elephant, hippopotamus, rhinoceros, bison, bear, giant deer, and water vole. The famed Kirkdale Cave (*Fig. 12.5*), on the edge of the Vale of Pickering, was uncovered during quarrying operations for roadstone. The first evidence of this discovery came when in June 1821 a visitor to the area spotted bones and teeth mixed with roadstone at Kirbymoorside. Enquiry led to the quarry at Kirkdale which during a subsequent excavation yielded an astonishing array of vertebrate remains, providing evidence for 18, possibly 22, different species including wolf, fox, brown bear, stoat, lion, spotted hyaena, straight tusked elephant, hippopotamus, rhinoceros, bison, red, fallow, and giant deer, hare, mouse, and three species of vole.

William Buckland (*Fig. 12.6*) was lured north from Oxford to investigate this remarkable discovery. After excavation of the site, he declared that the cracked bones with their characteristic puncture marks (*Fig. 12.7a*) were the remains of the victims of hyaenas which had occupied the cave (*Fig. 12.7b*). In 1823, Buckland published an account of the deposit, *Reliquiae diluvianae*, in which he stated that the bone-rich deposit pre-dated the then accepted Biblical flood; some had considered this scriptural flood responsible for the deposit, while others thought the bones post-

12.8 An ice smoothed surface of strata in the Windermere Supergroup forms part of a track across the floor of Crummack Dale.

freeze-thaw action, and the formation of at least small glaciers around the highest peaks. The dating of a scree in the southern Dales, indicates that during the last glacial maximum, rock surfaces were exposed. This suggests that Pen-y-ghent, Ingleborough, Whernside, and perhaps other high-ground, may have been icy summits poking through a sea of ice, at least during the waning of this ice sheet.

Near Austwick, we are provided with graphic evidence of both the power and route taken by a glacier. On a grassy limestone pavement at Norber, above Crummack Dale are a group of perched **erratics** (*Fig. 12.1*). The ice flowing down the valley below has plucked great chunks from the Lower Palaeozoic valley floor, stranding them high above on the Carboniferous limestone. Here, they now rest on residual plinths, providing a fascinating insight into the nature of the ice cover and the rates of dissolution of the limestones over the last *c.*13 ka. In the valley below, a track runs across an ice smoothed surface (*Fig.* 12.8. The Wharfedale glacier both truncated and undercut a spur of limestone to form the memorable Kilnsey Crag (*Fig. 12.9*).

On the high ground the ice, generated during successive cold phases, stripped bare areas of

dated this catastrophic event. The Kirkdale discovery had a remarkable impact on the scientific community, furthering the formation of local philosophical societies (Chapter 1). Such discoveries continued to challenge accepted wisdom and belief, as happened when the remains of three hippopotami found in Ipswichian gravels in the Armley district of Leeds in 1851, were initially reported to the local museum curator as too big to 'be Christians' bones'!

Some late Ice Age impacts

The positioning of weather monitoring equipment beside the A166 at the summit of Garrowby Hill, which at 807 m is the highest point on the Wolds, testifies to the potential for extreme conditions at such altitudes. During the Pleistocene, modest cooling would have soon begun to affect the high ground across Yorkshire, though the position of the polar front, attendant pressure systems and the prevailing winds are likely to have greatly influenced where, and how much, snow fell. During cold phases, whether Yorkshire was glaciated or not, there would have been penetrating frost, with the shattering of rock through

12.9 Kilnsey Crag in Wharfedale. This extraordinary, gravity defying, feature is the result of a limestone spur being truncated, and undercut, by the Wharfedale glacier.

12.10 Gordale Scar, near Malham. The dramatic nature of this feature is captured by James Ward (*See Contents page*). A chasm, initiated along the line of the Middle Craven Fault, has been created by the erosive power of melt-water from the Devensian ice sheet to the north.

limestone, exposing the surface to dissolution and forming glaciokarst landscapes. Magnificent limestone pavements have resulted around Ingleborough, in Ribblesdale (*Fig. 7.1*), and at Malham Cove. The latter feature is believed to be the product of glacial induced retreat of the limestone escarpment created by the Mid-Craven Fault a little to the south. Water flowing down the valley and a resurgence cave at the foot of the cliff are thought likely to have further modified this spectacular feature. Goredale Scar (*Fig. 12.10*), a short distance to the east, is not the product of cave collapse, but of the rapid retreat and destruction of a limestone scarp, originating along the same fault as Malham Cove, caused by melt water from the Devensian ice sheet. The true power of such rivers is only fully appreciated when visiting present-day ice sheets and glaciers.

The Dales glaciers, fed by the ice caps over much of the high ground, moved out and down valleys onto the wider vales. In the west, ice moved down onto the coastal plains of Lancashire, while in the east, joined ice flowing from north of the Tees and from Stainmore. In the valleys and vales, sediment carried at the base of the glacier was released and plastered over existing landscapes, producing a range of features, including mounds of till, sand and gravel called drumlins. They provide valuable evidence for the direction of ice movement.

Also present are the casts of the ice tunnels once occupied by sub-glacial rivers known to achieve lengths of up to 50 km, and terraces where gravels and sands were deposited by streams flowing alongside the edge of the ice. Kettle holes are a particular feature of lowland glaciation, produced where substantial blocks of ice, embedded or buried in the glaciofluvial deposits, have thawed to produce a small lake. The organic deposits found in such features are often datable and potentially valuable for understanding the climate and environment.

Across the Vale of York, the Dimlington Stadial's (*Table 12.1*) great ice sheet produced a 'witches kitchen of chaos', triggering events which in our relatively ordered and ice-free existence, we would find hard to visualise! Perhaps the nearest we come to such a scenario is the nightmare of major road-works where every day, you find your route through the mayhem, gravel and mud, has been changed on a truly colossal scale. Comparison may be useful with the effects of rapid thaw, after a snowy winter, coupled with heavy rain as witnessed in 1947. Severe flooding ensued. During the Dimlington Stadial, in the summer months, water flowed from under moving ice sheets to form constantly shifting braided river systems and deltas. The same ice diverted rivers. The Nidd's northerly route was blocked by ice, forcing a southerly detour during which Knaresborough's gorge was cut, and through which the Nidd now flows (*Fig. 12.11*).

Moraines form when an ice sheet's margin moves nowhere, leading to the deposition of sinuous mounds of till and gravels. The Dimlington Stadial saw the ice sheet reach its most southerly point, theoretically marked by the Escrick Moraine to the south of York (*Fig 12.12*). There is a school of thought that takes the view that before this moraine formed, a broad tongue of floating ice surged south, reaching the latitude of Doncaster, constrained to the east by the Lower Lias escarpment west of Scunthorpe. If correct, the ice floated on what has been called Lake

12.11 Knaresborough Gorge through which the River Nidd flows. This was created when the Vale of York ice blocked the course of the proto-Nidd. The latter proceeded to cut a new course. Knaresborough was built along part of that gorge.

Humber, formed when North Sea ice plugged the River Humber's exit, much deepened by melt-water cutting-down into a basin at a time of low sea-level. Strandlines, combined with dating evidence, indicate that Lake Humber was at around 33 m above current sea-level *c.* 22 ka, and around 8.5 m after the sea-ice barrier melted and was replaced by moraines. The North Sea ice was responsible for the extensive tills over Holderness, seen today in the rapidly eroding cliffs along this coast.

A further two morainic barrages across the Vale of York mark the sporadic retreat of the Vale of York ice. The York Moraine was utilised by the Romans as the site for York and as a crucial crossing point of the Ouse, where its course is incised through the glacial debris. The most northerly is the Tollerton Moraine. The occurrence of lake sediments north of the Escrick and York moraines suggests that Lake Humber extended northwards as the ice sheet retreated.

At one time, these lakes were not the only ones thought to have formed. In the early 20th century, the more or less north-south Newton Dale was interpreted as a melt-water channel, carrying water from Esk Dale (*Fig.* 12.13), blocked by North Sea ice at Whitby, southwards over the largely ice-free North

12.13 The valley of the Murk Esk to the right, and in the distance Esk Dale running to the coast at Whitby, viewed from Randy Rigg near Beck Hole.

12.12 Barely visible on the floor of the Vale of York is the Escrick Moraine from which this photograph was taken looking to the north. The moraine forms a low ridge composed of till, sands and gravels marking the point at which the static Vale of York ice sheet decayed. On Figure 3.2b this feature is the arcuate line which runs in a north-easterly direction across the Vale, south of York.

York Moors, cutting a hugely impressive valley. Today the valley is occupied by the Pickering Beck, a fluvial misfit if ever there was one. Continuing research has led to an alternative interpretation. Lack of evidence for a lake has led to the view that snow and ice filling the topographic lows of the moors, would have fed sub-glacial streams and rivers, which, charged with sediment, cut and enlarged this channel.

Whatever mechanism was the cause, the pulses of water, gorged with sediments, scoured from the ever deepening valley en route, swept on to pour into Lake Pickering, forming a delta to the south of the

moor-side town of Pickering. Water in this glacial lake was ponded by a sea-ice barrage at its eastern end, escaping through the scenic channel, not entirely accurately known as Kirkham Gorge, before flowing into Lake Humber in the southern part of the Vale of York.

The less deep, but equally dramatic, dry valleys across the Wolds (*Frontispiece*) are also relics of the last glaciation. While not covered by the ice sheets of the Vale of York and North Sea, the Wolds accumulated snow and ice. The normally pervious chalk was frozen by permafrost. Superficial melting and renewed freezing generated chalk-sludge, which, with melt water from the snow, and ice unable to soak into the substrata, would have helped carved out these finely sculpted valleys, with lines reminiscent of the sparse but sweeping curves of the White Horse of Uffington in Oxfordshire.

The effects of arctic conditions, combined with strong winds and freeze-thaw, contributed to a variety of features and landscapes. The fine dust and sand whipped up by the wind, polished stones littering the un-vegetated surfaces to produce **ventifacts**. The same strong winds were responsible at least in part, for blasting out the soft sand and grit loosened by the cycles of freezing and thawing around Brimham Rocks (*Fig.* 8.12), and then shaping the gritstone tors (Chapter 8). Wind and melt-water also consorted in the formation of the Bridestones in Dalby Forest.

A different product of the Pleistocene, and little known outside mineralogical circles, is the mineral scarbroite which was named after Scarborough from where the mineral was first described by William Venables Vernon, later William Venables Vernon Harcourt, in 1829. Found in fissures cutting Jurassic sediments, this aluminium carbonate is thought to have formed during intense weathering of local sediments under periglacial conditions. Study of specimens from the site has yielded other minerals including the related form, hydroscarbroite.

A brief glimpse of the Yorkshire Underground

Cave systems within the Great Scar Limestone Group (Chapter 7) of the Dales are extensive. They formed wherever water was able to develop the smallest passage along and across bedding planes. There has been much debate over their inception. Why should some horizons be more susceptible to 'horizontal' cave development than others? Some cave systems are of great complexity, with their form controlled by the dip of the strata, the sediments, joints and faults in the limestones; the cathedral-like chamber of Gaping Gill and its associated cave system on the slopes of Ingleborough is a good example (*Figs.* 7.8 & 12.17). In all this, the eroded Lower Palaeozoic surface on which the limestones rest must have had some control. Another important question concerns when they first formed (Chapter 9).

The crystalline flowstone coating cave walls and forming hanging stalactites or mounding stalagmites, are all varieties of **speleothem**. They form when carbon dioxide is lost from the water, and the dissolved calcium carbonate is precipitated, processes which have been active during the warm phases, and obviously post-date the caves in which they occur. Samples from speleothems have been used for **uranium series dating** techniques. Many of the tube-like phreatic caves have been shown to be older than 350 ka; Victoria Cave near Settle is at least 500 ka, and contained the remains of hippopotamus embedded in speleothem dated at 120 ka. At Stumpcross Cavern, flowstone dated at 80 ka had entombed the remains of large variety of the weasel family called a wolverine, a representative of a cold-stage fauna.

Pre-existing or early Pleistocene caves are likely to have been modified, enlarged and extended during the Pleistocene. They owe much to the erosive power of sub-glacial, sediment charged, high pressure water coursing through the perforated limestones of the fells. Research indicates that recurrent lowering of valley floors during glaciations, with consequent reduction of the water table, led to the draining of the higher phreatic systems, after which speleothem formation would occur. Occasionally speleothem formations are found in flooded systems where glacial deposits have blocked resurgences. Conversely, subsequent glaciations could, through glacial blocking of resurgences, produce another phreatic phase of development with sub-glacial water being forced back up passages to higher levels, as has been identified in caves between Chapel-le-Dale and Kingdale, near Ingleton. Questions remain over the true date of inception of the earliest caves in the Yorkshire Dales and elsewhere (Chapters 9 & 11).

Clues as to the presence of cave systems come from the shake holes which are a common sight across the hillsides of the Dales (*Fig.* 12.14). Till or other sedimentary cover deposited over previously or newly perforated limestone surfaces has been gradually

12.14 Shake holes between Ingleborough and White Scars north-east of Ingleton. These features are produced where the superficial deposits draping limestone are gradually washed and or collapse into the narrow shafts which link to the cave systems below the surface. The linear nature of some of these is likely to be due to structural features in the underlying limestones, such as fractures or faults. The large hole in the left middle distance is Quaking Pot.

12.15 Below Simon Fell to the east of Ingleborough, a stream disappears into part of the Long Churn Caves and Alum Pot system.

undermined; sometimes there is nothing to see at the bottom of these shallow conical depressions, but on other occasions, water is to be seen trickling into a doline or pothole; sometimes a river suddenly disappears (*Fig. 12.15*); the Buttertubs (*Fig. 12.16, see following page*) between Hawes and Thwaite are fine examples. Initially, such shafts may be too narrow to explore, but gradually they enlarge, forming **vadose** cave systems above the water table, much less tube like than their phreatic cousins. Cave systems within the Dales extend for many miles, with both active and abandoned phreatic, and vadose systems. The Gaping

Gill (*Fig.* 12.17) and Ingleborough cave system is a complex network of passages which has an explored length exceeding 10 miles. A little to the west and south of Gaping Gill is Pillar Pot, mentioned here as a fine example of the survey work carried out by the Gritstone Club, this one being recorded in 1922. Their achievement was all the greater when the lack of modern sophisticated clothing and equipment is taken into account.

While cave systems are well documented in the Dales, much less has been written about cave systems elsewhere in Yorkshire. Mention has been made of the dissolution of Permian carbonate rocks and evaporites (Chapter 9), but perhaps more startling has been the discovery of what appear to be phreatic caves in the Coralline Oolite Formation near Boltby, on the edge of the Hambelton Hills (Chapter 11).

The landscape bounces back – the shocking truth

The significance of the weight of glacial ice over our country has long been appreciated and viewed as the creator of a see-saw Britain. While glaciated, the northern half of Britain was being depressed and the southern half buoyed up, followed by uplift in the north as the ice thawed, and a commensurate sinking in the south; this process is known as isostasy. Such processes are closely linked with the tectonic structure and elasticity of the UK.

For a number of years there has been a growing awareness of the importance of the impact of erosion on isostatic re-adjustment within a limited area, and the impact this has regionally. The more sediment removed during an erosive cycle, the more pronounced would be the local re-adjustment. Researchers have

12.18 Degrading blanket bog near Tan Hill south of the Stainmore Pass. Healthy blanket bogs are important carbon sinks.

demonstrated that the Cotswold escarpment has probably risen by around 8 m per ka over a period of 50 ka, and that this was largely triggered by the Anglian glacial event, and maintained by subsequent climatic fluctuations during the remainder of the Pleistocene, each resulting in significant erosion within the area's drainage systems. They have suggested that the UK as a whole owes its present relief to the climatic fluctuations initiated at the close of the Pliocene, 2.65 Ma. Yorkshire's landscape and cave systems must be viewed in the light of this fascinating research.

There is every reason to expect these isostatic adjustments to be a factor in some of the occasional earthquakes which jolt the UK. Yorkshire is not immune from such shocks, with epicentres both within and beyond the county boundary. Unsurprisingly, earthquake records are concentrated along the faulted western margin of the Pennines and Askrigg Block. Perhaps more surprising is the absence of earthquake records for the east-west trending Craven Fault belt and the Howardian – Flamborough Head Fault Zone.

When did those feet in ancient time?

The groundbreaking *Ancient Human Occupation of Britain* project (2001-2010) has so far extended the sporadic record of human occupation back to at least 700 ka, based on discoveries in East Anglia. Even though there was a wealth of animal-life during the Ipswichian, represented at various sites in Yorkshire, the remains of humans have not been recorded anywhere in Britain at this time. This Ipswichian

absence is entirely consistent with the conclusion of the project's scientists, that the occupation of Britain was not continuous. They believe that modern humans arrived around 13 ka, maintaining a toe-hold during the Loch Lomond Stadial (11-10 ka, *Table 12.1*), a climatic hiccup, when, just as everything seemed to be warming up again, glaciers started to re-advance. Even in Yorkshire, there was sufficient snow accumulation to trigger the formation of small glaciers on Whernside, and adjacent peaks over the county boundary. One thousand years may not seem long, but put yourself in our ancestors shoes; no central heating and mean temperatures several degrees lower than today's! Around this time, the world famous Starr Carr Mesolithic site on the edge of the Vale of Pickering was occupied for a period of around 350 years.

Post glacial post-script

As the Loch Lomond Stadial ended and the climate warmed once again, the **Flandrian Stage** began. Extensive, rain-fed, blanket bogs began to develop over the higher ground (*Fig. 12.18*) and there are important examples which date back some 9 ka within Yorkshire. These fragile deposits are threatened by changing land use and climate. In these higher altitude sites, a few plants normally associated with colder climes found refuge, along with others content to be in the different ecological niches provided by

12.19 The Hills. An area of extensive landslipping at the south-western end of Great Fryup Dale where relatively porous Ravenscar Group strata overly the Dogger and Whitby Mudstone formations.

12.20 A quarry on the edge of the Wolds near East Knapton exposing strata of the White Chalk Subgroup which has undergone rotational movement. Above and behind are superficial deposits which have accumulated on and possibly behind the rotated block.

the limestone pavements. In parallel, plants continued their colonisation of the low-altitude wastelands created during glaciation and glacial retreat. Rivers developed from braided to incised, and extensive landslides modified the profiles of hills.

Such events are often recognisable (*Fig. 11.3*) and a particularly good example is seen at the head of Great Fryup Dale (*Fig. 12.19*) on the northern side of the Cleveland Dome. Here both sides of the valley have suffered extensive failure, probably as the Devensian came to an end and valley ice and permafrost thawed. Landslipping was probably exacerbated by water passing down through Ravenscar Group sediments to meet the Dogger and impervious Alum Shale of the Whitby Mudstone Formation all dipping gently to the north and into the valley. Another interesting example was observed during the 1990s near East Knapton on the northern margin of the Wolds. Chalk, with a capping of layered Chalk sludge or Head from the Wolds escarpment, had undergone rotational slipping, possibly while the sludge was accumulating (*Fig. 12.20*).

Rising sea-level began to modify the coast, interacting with rivers and creating features such as Spurn Head. This impressive spit is now being

12.21 Coastal landslipping at Speeton. Devensian till becomes semi-liquified during periods of rainfall and cascades over the cliffs of Speeton Clay Formation onto the foreshore.

12.22a-b (a) An advert from the late 1930s for the fashionable Holbeck Hall, Scarborough, providing accommodation for 60. (b) The dramatic landslide which saw the abrupt evacuation and closure of the hotel in 1993. The hotel was subsequently demolished, the remains of the extensive grounds landscaped, and the toe of the slip afforded massive rock armour protection. (See also Figure 10.24).

SCARBOROUGH HOLBECK HALL

Accommodation for sixty

Six acres of lovely gardens overlooking the sea. Close to the golf course, bathing pool and Yorkshire Tennis Club. The quietest and most exclusive site in Scarborough. Own garage in grounds. **Terms 4-7 guineas per week.** July, August and September 5-8 guineas per week. Tel. 1999. Grams—Holbeck Hall, Scarborough. *Resident Manageress—Mrs. Goodman.*

overwhelmed by further rises in sea-level, the effects of which are speeding the erosion of the soft sediments, and especially superficial deposits, which make up large parts of the Yorkshire coast (*Fig. 12.21*). Coastal instability is not confined to this part of the coast, as those living above South Bay in Scarborough will remember. In June 1993, part of the clifftop Holbeck Hall Hotel suddenly descended towards the shore when the superficial deposits on which the building stood failed in spectacular fashion (*Fig. 12.22a-b*). Inland the silts and organic rich sediments which were deposited in pro-glacial lakes along with associated deposits of peat are subject to compaction, sometimes posing problems for houses built on them.

Into these post-glacial and pristine conditions came the latest in a succession of peoples, looking to establish settlements. At once, even these relatively small populations started to have an impact on the

12.23a-b Examples of land-use and settlement in the remoter Yorkshire Dales. TOP (a) Hill farming on the edge of the open moors; the east flank of west Stones Dale below Black Moor, north of Swaledale. BOTTOM (b) The southern flank of Swaledale just west of Reeth. The River Swale here forms a braid plain. Beyond the Swale, stone walls are only the latest imposition on the landscape; the linear features revealed in the light of the raking late afternoon sun date from earlier periods of settlement and land use.

environments they occupied, even though to a very great extent, they were forced to live within their environment's means (*Fig. 12.23a-b*). Our brave new world has changed all that. With the aid of technology, we appear to be living way beyond the means of our environments. For how much longer this fragile planet will tolerate our occupation, is debatable.

THIRTEEN
Yorkshire Water

13.1 Aysgarth Falls in Wensleydale. The alternating soft and hard layers present in the Yoredale Group strata provide the framework which the River Ure has developed into this much visited series of waterfalls.

Setting the Scene

Water and the geological history of Yorkshire are inseparable. Much of the geological column consists of water-lain sediment. Economically important minerals were emplaced by hot aqueous solutions emanating from great depths. Water power was hugely important for their extraction. Brines were the source of the great deposits of salt, and other evaporites, which formed during the Permo-Trias. Water as a liquid and as ice has sculpted Yorkshire above and below ground, and continues to do so. Water has both given and taken life on a truly colossal scale, as is witnessed by the fossil record dispersed throughout much of the county's strata.

The trouble with water

In 1995, drought was headline news; in parts of Yorkshire, Pennine reservoirs at a low ebb revealed long-flooded landscapes, tankers transported water from areas of relative plenty and standpipes stood at the ready. By way of contrast, there is a long record of severe floods afflicting swathes of Yorkshire, with cities, towns and villages taking direct hits from muddy torrents (*Fig.* 13.2). On 19th June 2005, parts of the North York Moors received as much rain in hours as would normally fall in weeks; 70 mm was recorded at Hawnby in three hours, and much of that fell in 30 minutes! Buildings, bridges and roads were

13.2 'Flood defences full'; the River Ouse at the bottom of Marygate, York, in 1992 with the flood gates closed, protecting riverside property.

13.3. Shaken Bridge, near Hawnby, across the River Rye, a casualty of the severe flooding on June 19 2005. The road has been diverted over a temporary bridge, while the aptly named 'Shaken Bridge', badly damaged on the downstream side, is shored-up and rebuilt.

damaged (*Fig.* 13.3), and landslides triggered as the narrow valleys struggled to cope with the deluge. Gone are the barely perceptible changes we are used to, this is the crash, bang, wallop of catastrophe, a timely reminder as we face up to the probability of more frequent, high intensity rainfall. This was graphically underlined in 2007 when parts of Hull and South Yorkshire were inundated, and the Ulley Reservoir's dam, close to Rotherham, was believed to be in danger of collapse.

These events may seem remote from 'geology', and yet during events such as these, more sediment is moved than has been for years, and rivers and landscapes are exposed to sudden and dramatic change; here is

13.4 The Hole of Horcum west of the Pickering to Whitby road. Springs thrown out at the junction of Lower Calcareous Grit and the underlying Oxford Clay formations are responsible for this dramatic landscape feature.

13.5 Beezley Falls on the River Doe, part of 'The Scenery' or Waterfalls Walk, north of Ingleton.

the evolution of the landscape in fast-forward mode. Spring lines appear where water is thrown out by impervious strata, or when the water table reaches ground level, usually during persistent rainfall. If the strata are unsupported and dipping towards a void they are especially prone to landslipping. The Hole of Horcum (*Fig.* 13.4) is a spectacular example of a deep basin of a valley excavated by water issuing from the spring-line at the junction of the pervious sandstones of the Lower Calcareous Grit Formation that overly the impervious Oxford Clay Formation. In the spring of 2008, the collapse of cliffs, at Cayton Bay south of Scarborough, left property teetering on the edge of the cliff. Water within the strata is blamed for this latest manifestation of what has been an ongoing problem (Chapter 12).

Water for therapy

Water in combination with the Lower Palaeozoic rocks and sequences of sandstones, shales, and limestones, provide the essential ingredients for the numerous waterfalls found across the Dales. Beezley Falls (*Fig.* 13.5), Hardraw Force (*Fig.* 7.13), Kisdon

13.6 Wain Wath Force, in the distance, looking anything but forceful during a dry summer. The expanses of yellow-brown limestone give a clue to the volume of water which is more normally carried by the River Swale.

13.7 The Strid near Bolton Abbey. The River Wharfe, draining an extensive Dales catchment, surges through a narrow defile carved along joints in grits of the Millstone Grit Group. The channel is thought to be in the order of 10m (33 ft) deep. There is much evidence of the formation of potholes. These are produced by the eddying waters swirling rock fragments around holes in the rock, and at times of high flow when the waters are charged with sediment.

Force, Aysgarth Falls (*Fig.* 13.1), Thornton Force (*Fig.* 5.1) and Wain Wath Force (*Fig.* 13.6) are all well known examples. The Strid (*Fig.* 13.7) is a deep channel cut by the swirling and churning Wharfe near Bolton Abbey, and the How Stean Gorge has an Alpine quality, saluted in the alternative name of Little Switzerland. This gorge owes its existence to

13.8 The pitted and potholed limestone exposed on the bed of the River Swale below Wain Wath Force.

13.9 A late 1930s advertisement, from a popular guide, for the spa town of Harrogate.

the down cutting effect of sediment-charged water, a process which was especially effective during and immediately after the last glacial episode. More subtle dissolution of limestones takes place in river beds, leaving an array of beautifully sculptured surfaces when the rivers are low (*Fig.* 13.8).

In the late 20th century, the rapid closure of coal mines which while operating had pumped and treated contaminated water from their underground workings, led to significant pollution as they flooded. Innovative treatment schemes have been commissioned with great success. Woolley, south of Wakefield, in West Yorkshire boasts a 1.4 hectare wetland, now owned and managed by the Coal Authority, which plays its part in treating polluted mine water from a substantial part of the West Yorkshire Coalfield. Every second the scheme receives and discharges up to 150 litres of mine water, containing 15 mg/l of iron, which after treatment is reduced to less than 1 mg/l.

The quality of some water, abstracted from boreholes, is especially valuable to the brewing industry (Chapter 9), but while brewing has its place, Yorkshire's waters have also been held in high esteem for providing a variety of 'cures'. Appropriately one was renowned for providing an antidote for 'over-indulgence', being described as 'most efficacious in functional disorders of the liver'. A spring containing high levels of magnesium sulphate, rising in South Bay at Scarborough, was rather ominously reported to 'loosen the belly'. The presence of mineral springs could lead to the appending of the term 'spa' to a place name, as for Thorp Arch Spa on the River Wharfe close to Boston Spa, and a little upstream, Langwith

Spa near Collingham. Harlow Carr, on the outskirts of Harrogate has mineral springs, but above all these, must come Harrogate, for as a popular guide declares, 'The Mineral Waters, the *raison d'être* of the town, possess in various degrees the curative properties of nearly every known spring in Europe.'(*Fig.* 13.9).

13.10 The Dropping Well at Knaresborough, a coloured engraving dating from 1829.

Harrogate provided a fashionable and cultured venue for those seeking the treatment of ailments such as, bronchitis, gout, skin diseases, disorders of the liver, kidneys and stomach, and nervous exhaustion. All in all, they provided a key part of a measured regime that might be known today as a 'detox'.

There is fascinating geology behind this occurrence and much work has been carried out to understand the nature and origin of the waters. The 94 springs recorded within 2 miles of Harrogate are associated with a fault running along the axis of the Harrogate Anticline. From as early as 1908, the British Geological Survey recognised 4 types of water: saline sulphur, alkaline sulphur, saline iron, and chalybeate. A local guide adds magnesia to this list. Geochemistry, and a constant temperature of 14°c for the most saline water, is all indicative of a relatively shallow origin for the water which originated as rainfall. The salinity of some of the spring water is probably derived from Permian evaporites with which the water came into contact on its journey from surface to 'depth' and back again.

Petrifying fates

One of the more bizarre sights in Yorkshire, is the miscellaneous collection of objects hanging beneath a great curtain of tufaceous limestone at Knaresborough's 'Dropping Well' (*Fig. 13.10*). The calcium carbonate rich solutions responsible for this are the product of the Permian sediments through which the water has passed, and echo the very processes seen in the fantastical speleothems seen in cave systems. Rippling down the smooth tufa face, the water trickles over children's toys, clothing, umbrellas – even a plastic dinosaur – left by visitors for as many months as necessary to suffer their petrifying fate!

While on the subject of petrifying fates, and watery ones at that, mention of the catastrophic Storegga Slide off the coast of Norway is appropriate. A little over 8 ka, a piece of sea floor the size of Scotland, detached from the shallower continental shelf off Norway, to slide down into the deeper water of the Norwegian Sea. An earthquake and or the release of methane gas trapped in the sediments are suspected as the culprits triggering this event. The waves produced by such an enormous displacement of water had a significant impact along much of the east coast.

To imagine Yorkshire did not witness at least the 'ripples' of this event is inconceivable. A thin seam of sand in the Holocene sediments along the east coast of Britain flags this sudden marine incursion over the low-lying coastal strip. This deposit in the area around the Firth of Forth records the tsunami reaching 49 miles inland at a height of 4 m above sea level. There is strong evidence to suggest that submarine landslides will happen again, emphasising that we live on a dynamic and ever changing planet.

FOURTEEN

Visitors from Outer Space

14.1. The Middlesborough Meteorite landed on the property of the North Eastern Railway Company near Middlesbrough on 14th March 1881. Deemed 'lost property' by the company, and having landed in what was then within Yorkshire, the meteorite was presented to the Yorkshire Museum. The meteorite measured approximately 16 x 12.75 cm with a height of 7.75 cm and weighed about 1.6 kg.

14.2 Hale Bop, a remarkably bright comet which was visible during 1996-7. Here the comet is seen in the night sky over York in 1997, a cosmic reminder of the Earth's origins (Chapter 2).

Setting the Scene

The violent, cosmic origins of the Earth were touched on in chapter 2. Apart from creating the planet, these processes along with subsequent, and even consequent, collisions, and the companion planets' positions within the Solar System, have provided a legacy of physical attributes which influence the Earth to this day. Climatic fluctuations are seen as the result of Milankovitch Cycles (Chapters 10 and 12), and echoes of this cosmic past have both touched, and continue to pass through Yorkshire!

Just passing through – the search for the illusive WIMP

Since 1987, the U.K. Dark Matter Collaboration (UKDMC) has used cavities in rock salt deep in the Boulby Mine (*Fig.* 9.16) on the Yorkshire county boundary, in their search for evidence of Dark Matter in the form of Weakly Interacting Massive Particles or WIMPs. WIMPs are predicted to hit the Earth's surface at the rate of a million/cm²/second. Detecting them is quite another matter! Astrophysicists use the 1,100 m of sediment above their detection chamber, to filter-out much of the background 'noise' produced by other ground penetrating cosmic particles. ZEPLIN III is the latest incarnation of this project, which with increasingly sensitive detectors still seeks evidence of the illusive WIMP!

Rumours

WIMPs may be abundant (?) – but meteorites, and evidence of their impacts, are not. In recent years, Triassic sediments in the west of Britain, where exposure is exceptionally good, have been scrutinised and yielded evidence which may support two impact events. The Branscombe Mudstone Formation has yielded **shocked quartz**, and tiny spherules of molten rock created in the colossal forces and high temperatures associated with a big impact. Within the Lilstock Formation, there is evidence of an extensive deposit generated by the earthquake/shock waves generated. Though evidence for these events is lacking in Yorkshire, there is every reason to believe that the county would have felt the effects in some shape or form.

The Isle of Axholme, lying just over the county boundary in Lincolnshire, is reported to have concealed evidence of a significant event that occurred much more recently. According to an account, in a popular publication of 1834, excavations to a depth of 1.52 m below the surface revealed burnt and flattened trees, all orientated in a north-westerly direction. Subsequently, comparison has been made with the effect produced by the airburst of a comet (*Fig.* 14.2) or meteorite over the Tunguska region of Russia in June 1908, in which hundreds of km² of forest were devastated. If this represents such an event, Yorkshire's landscape would not have been left unscathed.

Crater subject to impact assessment

Approximately 80 miles off the Yorkshire coast there is a circular crater-like feature with stepped sides (*Fig. 14.3*), known as the Silverpit Crater. The crater is buried beneath more recent sediments and was first observed on seismic surveys carried out in the search for hydrocarbons. Described in the journal *Nature*, the sub-marine, sub-surface crater was tentatively identified as the North Sea's first impact structure. The central crater is almost 2 miles in diameter, which when the stepped sides are taken into account, extends outwards to a maximum diameter of *c.*12 miles. The relationship of the sedimentary layers to each other indicates formation between 72 and 45 Ma. Despite the range of dates, this has led to much speculation that there is a link between this crater and the suggested end-Cretaceous impact and extinction. Superficially this ties in with a scenario that has the incoming 'end Cretaceous' asteroid being torn apart by gravity, to form a chain of smaller pieces which fell across the Earth. The presence of a number of craters that do fall within a certain range of latitude, amongst which is Silverpit, gives credence to this hypothesis. Such an occurrence was witnessed in July 1994, when Periodic Comet Shoemaker-Levy 9 broke up on its approach to Jupiter, forming what was described as 'a string of pearls', resulting in a series of observable impacts across the planet's surface over seven days.

In time honoured fashion, there has been vigorous debate over the origin of the Silverpit Crater, and agreement has not yet been reached! The position of such a feature in an area where there is both salt and faults, invites the suggestion that **halokinesis** coupled with fault movement may have been responsible for the observed feature. Despite such suggestions, the discoverers have pointed out that there are features preserved, like a cone in the centre of the crater, which do support the impact theory, and this origin remains a distinct possibility (*see Figure 14.3 caption*).

Taking a hit

Whether or not a large piece of cosmic debris created the Silverpit Crater or flattened the trees of the Isle of Axholme, we do have records of meteorites landing within the county over the last 200 or so years. One of the earliest recorded falls of a meteorite in England occurred at around 15.00 on 13th December 1795,

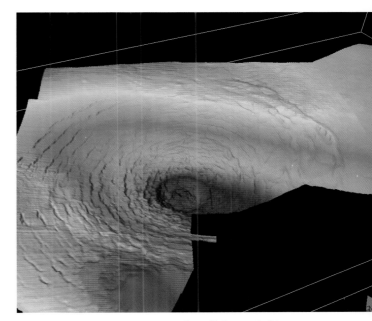

14.3 The Silverpit Crater, 80 miles off the Yorkshire coast in the North Sea. A false colour image produced from seismic data shows the deepest part of the crater (purple) with a projecting cone in the middle. The imaged surface is the top of the Chalk. A late Cretaceous age for the disputed crater was suggested. Recently published evidence uses the spatial relationships of the overlying deposits to suggest that the feature really is an impact crater, and is more likely to have been formed approximately 20 Ma after the Chalk was deposited at around 45 Ma.

when a **chondrite** landed near Wold Newton. The meteorite, variously known as the Wold Cottage meteorite and the Yorkshire meteorite, was sizeable, measuring 0.71 m by 0.76 m and weighing 25.4 kg. The impact occurred with such force that soil was hurled about, striking an agricultural worker nearby. The arrival of this small bolide had been preceded by a loud explosion. The owner of the land was local Magistrate, Major Edward Topham, who several years later had a monument placed on the site of the impact. In 1804, the specimen was sold to James Sowerby (Chapter 5), for the knock-down sum of 10 guineas and the promise of a copy of his *British Mineralogy* - once published. Sowerby gained much from the possession of this specimen, and was painted alongside the meteorite in 1816 by Thomas Heaphey (*Fig. 14.4, see following page*). Topham did eventually receive his specially bound copy of the new work, while Sowerby continued to lop pieces off the meteorite to exchange for other specimens he sought

for his collection and to illustrate his published works on the natural sciences. In 1837, the meteorite, now reduced to 20.6 kg, was purchased by the British Museum for the sum of £250.

Yorkshire was once again in the firing line when on the 14th March 1881, at around 15.35, north-east Yorkshire's citizens were witness to an unusual booming sound. A small group of workmen carrying out maintenance on rail tracks just outside Middlesbrough were somewhat startled when a 'rushing or roaring' noise heralded a sudden thud close by! Investigation revealed a hole, at the bottom of which was a cobble sized stone, black with radial fluting on the surface, and 'new milk warm'. The intact 1.6 kg meteorite (*Fig. 14.1*) dates from the formation of the Solar System around 4,500 Ma. The meteorite was duly recovered and as what the North Eastern Railway Company described as 'Lost Property', from Yorkshire, was donated to the Yorkshire Museum, along with a plaster replica of hole it had made! (*Fig. 14.5*)

The most recent discovery in 2005 of a meteorite, chanced upon beside a track by a meteorite collector while walking in the Hambleton Hills near Kilburn, is especially interesting. The specimen, weighing 17.6 kg, is of an exceedingly rare type, categorised as a FeS-rich **pallasite**, of which only one other in the world is known to scientists. An unusual combination of iron sulphide with significant amounts of nickel is pointing to the discovery of a new mineral species. How did the specimen come to be beside a track? One theory is that the meteorite may have fallen as long ago as 1783 when the region witnessed a meteorite which was tracked from the Shetland Islands to France. The report suggests that the meteorite exploded over Yorkshire. Later, a farmer may have moved the rock from the surface to the margin of the field, out of the way of precious plough blades! How many more meteorites might be out there waiting to be found – and more critically, how many more lurking in space have 'Yorkshire's name' on them?!

FIFTEEN

An Uncertain Conclusion

15.1 Tufa, a variety of limestone, actively accumulating beside the waterfall at Gordale Scar. Limestones have acted as carbon traps over the millions of years of Earth history. These deposits are playing a small part in reducing CO_2 in the Earth's atmosphere.

The preceding pages are an account of the complex geology of Yorkshire. Some matters of contention have been noted, for as was pointed out in the introduction, there remains much of which we are uncertain. A few speculative comments have been made. There are great opportunities for discovery, and to bring new insights to our understanding of Yorkshire and far beyond. The frequently repetitive but subtly different patterns of events and processes bring us echoes of the long history of Yorkshire, they are etched on and in the landscapes around us, and may with patience be interpreted, read, and perhaps – acted on.

Yorkshire's location on the face of the planet will continue to change through time, just as we have seen over the last 542 million years. Volcanicity is certain to return to Britain's much modified shores, and climate will continue to change, doubtless influenced by Milankovitch Cycles, global natural catastrophies such as super-eruptions, and our profligate way of life. Beyond our cocooning, but fast changing atmosphere, the influences of both the Solar System, and the Universe will continue to be profound. The recurrent patterns of events and processes seen through geological time, and recorded in the rocks, assure us that Yorkshire's future will be at least as dramatic as its past!

Glossary

ACRITARCH. The organic remains of single celled microscopic plants, believed to be chiefly algae.

ANGULAR UNCONFORMITY see Unconformity.

ANHYDRITE. An *evaporite* mineral frequently found in *sabkha* deposits. Anhydrous calcium sulphate. See also *Gypsum*.

ANOXIA see Anoxic.

ANOXIC. The term used to describe conditions where oxygen is absent; also anoxia.

ANTICLINE. Strata which have been folded into an arch shape. They range in size from a few metres to tens of kilometres.

ARENACEOUS. Rocks composed of, or containing a high proportion of mineral particles ranging in size 1/16 mm to 2mm, e.g. a sandstone.

ARGILLACEOUS. Rocks composed of, or containing a high proportion of mineral particles less than 1/16 mm.

ARKOSE. A sandstone in which the silicate minerals called feldspars are a significant component.

ASTEROIDS. Cosmic rock-rubble which escaped incorporation into the planets during the formation of the solar system, and now forms the asteroid belt around the Sun. Often of very large size, they are occasionally 'dislodged' from their orbit, and may eventually collide with one of the planets that did form. Collisions between asteroids within the asteroid belt are thought to have created many of the *meteorites* which have been found on the Earth.

ARTHROPOD. A phylum of segmented animals with chitinous or calcareous exoskeletons and jointed limbs. Includes *trilobites*, insects, crustaceans and *cirripedes*.

ASTHENOSPHERE. A layer of the Earth's crust 100-200 km below surface, perhaps to greater depths. A hot plastic layer which radiates heat outwards and upon which the lithosphere rests.

BALTICA. A continent whose origins go back 1,800 Ma. As an independent land mass, Baltica collided with Avalonia, of which Yorkshire was a part, during the late Ordovician.

BASEMENT. The folded and eroded rocks upon which the *Carboniferous sediments* rest across Yorkshire.

BASIC IGNEOUS ROCKS. *Igneous* rocks which contain little or no quartz, but do contain feldspar, and are normally rich in dark coloured iron and magnesium bearing minerals.

BASIN. An area which undergoes subsidence and will therefore accumulate greater thicknesses of sediment.

BEDROCK GEOLOGY. The *in situ* rock formations which are exposed at the surface, or are covered by *superficial deposits*.

BELEMNITES. Bullet shaped internal shells made of *calcite* belonging to an extinct group of animals related to the modern cuttlefish.

BIOTURBATED. The disturbance of *sediments* and original *sedimentary structures* by living organisms. The structures created are *trace fossils*.

BLOCK. An area, often bounded by faults, which is buoyant compared to the surrounding areas. They may be underlain by a *granite intrusion*.

BOREAL OCEAN. The ocean which lay to the north of Britain and Europe during the late *Palaeozoic* and *Mesozoic*.

BOREHOLE. A mechanically drilled hole used to gain an understanding of buried rocks, and to explore for minerals, including coal, oil, gas and water. Diamond studded drill bits are used to take cores, otherwise tungsten tipped drill bits produce rock chips. *Wireline logging* is used to provide as much information as possible from this expensive method of exploration. Shallow exploration holes in unconsolidated sediment are drilled by hand, using an auger.

BRACHIOPODS. Marine invertebrates protected by two valves. The resemblance of brachioipods to roman oil lamps led to them being called lamp shells.

BRAIDED RIVERS. Rivers, often youthful, which are unconstrained by banks, flowing in a mass of shifting channels across unconsolidated and poorly or un-vegetated *sediments*.

BRECCIA. A sedimentary rock composed of angular fragments of pre-existing rocks cemented by fine grained *sediment* or a mineral such as *calcite*.

BRYOZOANS. Small colonial animals which form skeletons of calcium carbonate (*Calcite*) which may encrust solid surfaces or grow in branching tree-like forms.

CALCITE. A crystalline form of calcium carbonate which is an important rock-forming mineral. Limestones are predominantly made of calcite as are the hard-parts of many invertebrates like *belemnites*, *brachiopods*, and *bryozoans*.

CALEDONIAN OROGENY. 220 Ma during which repeated collisions between different tectonic plates, with associated ocean closure, built successive generations of mountains, often accompanied by igneous activity, across large parts of what is now Britain.

CAMBRIAN. (542-488 Ma). A period of geological time.

CARBONATES. Sediments composed of calcium carbonate (see *Calcite*) which form many different types of limestone.

CARBONIFEROUS. (359-299 Ma). A period of geological time during which the limestones, shales and grits of the Dales and Pennines, and the coal seams of south Yorkshire were laid down.

CENOZOIC. (65 Ma to present day). A geological era which encompasses the *Paleogene* and *Neogene* periods.

CEPHALOPOD. Marine invertebrates with tentacles and chambered shells which may be straight or coiled. Ammonoids including orthocones, goniatites, ceratites, and ammonites, Also nautiloids and belemnites.

CHERT. A fine grained rock composed of the mineral *Quartz*. Cherts are hard and dense, ranging in colour from black to brown or yellow. Flint is a purer variety of chert found in the Chalk.

CHONDRITE. A category of stony *meteorite*, containing tiny spherular grains called chondrules. They date from the earliest days of the Solar System, composed of the same dust and molten particles that the planets formed from.

CIRRIPEDES. The barnacles which are a member of the phylum *arthropoda*.

CLASTIC SEDIMENT see *Sediment*.

CLEAVAGE. The preferred surface along which a *metamorphic* rock splits and which is not normally the original bedding plane. Slate, a metamorphosed mudrock, shows a pronounced cleavage, giving rise to the term 'slatey cleavage'.

CLEVELAND HIGH. An area which during the late Palaeozoic to Cenozoic underwent phases of both uplift, and subsidence forming the Cleveland Basin. During the Permian the high separated the Yorkshire and Durham parts of the Zechstein Sea.

COAL BED METHANE. Natural gas present in coal seams, filling the mass of tiny fractures in the coal. Increasingly seen as a potential energy resource if present in sufficient quantity.

CONCHOSTRACANS. Small crustaceans occupying a pair of hinged shells. Similar to a small bivalve.

CONGLOMERATE. A sedimentary rock composed of rounded fragments (pebbles) of pre-existing rocks cemented by fine grained *sediment*.

CONODONT ANIMAL. A 'worm-like' primitive vertebrate with elaborate and tiny jaw apparatus'. The latter are valuable for both correlation and from their colour, calculating how deeply a rock has been buried. Known from rocks dating from the *Cambrian* to the late *Triassic* and recorded in earliest *Jurassic* (possibly derived).

CONTINENTAL DEPOSITS. Sediments deposited on land.

COPROLITES. The fossilised droppings of both invertebrate and vertebrate animals.

CORAL. Sea-anemone-like organisms, which have a hard internal skeleton of calcium carbonate (see *Calcite*). They may be solitary or form colonies.

CRAVEN FAULT SYSTEM. A group of related faults around the western and southern margins of the Askrigg Block. They have been important controls on sedimentation at different times, and on today's scenery.

CRETACEOUS. (145 – 65 Ma). A period of geological time during which the Speeton Clay and Chalk were deposited across parts of Yorkshire.

CRINOIDS. Also known as sea-lilies, they are marine animals related to *echinoids*. They have a many armed food-gathering cup, which in fixed varieties is supported on a stalk.

CROSS-BEDDING. The inclined sediments accumulating on the face of a migrating dune of sediment. Sediments with these structures provide information on the direction of the wind or water current.

DELTAIC. Relating to deltas which form as sediment is deposited when rivers discharge into a lake or the sea. Each channel will form a mini-delta called a lobe.

DEPOCENTRE. That part of a *basin* which accumulates the greatest thickness of sediment.

DEVENSIAN STAGE. The latest episode of the *Pleistocene*, which lasted from around 117,000 to around 10,000 years ago.

DEVONIAN. (416 – 359 Ma). A period of geological time during which the *basement* of Yorkshire was subjected to uplift and erosion. No Devonian *Old Red Sandstone* sediments are preserved in the county.

DINOTURBATION. The disturbance of *sediments* and any original *sedimentary structures* by dinosaurs. Such disturbance is a form of *trace fossil*.

DOLOMITE. A *limestone* composed mainly or entirely of the mineral dolomite (calcium magnesium carbonate), rather than *calcite* (calcium carbonate). Limestones composed of calcium carbonate are sometimes altered to a dolomite, a process called dolomitisation.

DOLOMITISATION. See *dolomite*.

DOWNTHROW see *fault*.

DRIFT MINE. A mine where access is by way of an horizontal or inclined tunnel from the surface.

DYKE. An *igneous intrusion* where the molten rock is intruded into a linear or curvilinear vertical fracture.

EAST MIDLANDS SHELF. An area of relatively shallow water which extended from the Market Weighton High southwards into the east Midlands and onto the Anglo Brabant Landmass. The latter extended from southern East Anglia into the Low Countries.

EOCENE see *Paleogene*.

ERRATIC. A piece of rock transported by ice, and either incorporated into a deposit, or left as an isolated feature, in a foreign context.

EUSTATIC. Sea-level rise on a global scale.

EVAPORITES. The more soluble minerals or rocks formed when water containing dissolved salts is evaporated.

FACIES. A rock type or group of rock types and any fossils they contain that characterise a particular process or environment.

FAULT. A fracture through bedrock and or superficial

deposits which allows vertical or horizontal movement to take place. Movement may be measured in kilometres. Downthrow is on the side of the fault which has been displaced downwards. Faults may become active again after a period of inactivity (=reactivation), and may move in the opposite direction (=reversal).

FLANDRIAN STAGE. The first and only division of the *Holocene*, starting when the *Devensian* ended around 10,000 years ago.

FLATS. Ore deposits which are horizontal or almost so. They usually form between layers of bedrock or result from the replacement of the bedrock by the mineral deposit.

FLINT see *Chert*.

FLUVIATILE. Of rivers.

FORAMINIFERA. The collective name for what are normally marine, single celled, animals. They generally secrete a calcareous shell, known as a test, which may have one or more chambers.

GANGUE. The minerals which are regarded as waste in an ore deposit. In sufficient quantity, a gangue mineral may become a commercial deposit in its own right.

GEOPHYSICAL SURVEYS. Increasingly sophisticated techniques used to examine subsurface structures. See *Seismic surveys*.

GEOTHERMAL ENERGY. The energy harnessed from heat present in the earth's crust.

GLACIOFLUVIAL. Relating to processes and features resulting from the action of glacial melt-water.

GLAUCONITE. A mineral of complex composition often occurring as sand sized grains which vary from light green to almost black. Their presence in rocks is usually an indication of deposition in the sea.

GONDWANA. An ancient super-continent in the southern hemisphere. Antarctica, S. America, Africa, Australia and India were all part of this great landmass.

GRABEN. The downfaulted trough, which may be a *rift valley*, between two faults which are more or less parallel. A half-graben occurs when movement on just one fault creates a depression in which sediment will accumulate.

GRANITE. A medium to coarse grained *igneous* rock formed from *magma* which has cooled slowly beneath the surface of the Earth. The minerals quartz and feldspar are dominant, along with mica and minor amounts of other minerals.

GRAPTOLITES. Colonial marine organisms with a flexible 'skeleton' made of chitin. These fossils are found in Palaeozoic sediments.

GREYWACKE. A sedimentary rock consisting of poorly sorted grit and sand sized particles in a muddy matrix. They are formed when unstable sediment cascades down to the abyssal depths of the ocean from the continental shelf or slope as a turbidity current.

GYPSUM. An *evaporite* mineral precipitated in water and intertidal environments. Frequently found in *sabkha* deposits. Hydrated calcium sulphate. See also *Anhydrite*.

HALF-GRABEN see *Graben*.

HALOKINESIS. The deformation and movement of salt (halite) creating major structures.

HEAVY MINERALS. Minerals such as garnet, rutile, sillimanite and zircon, used to identify the source areas of the sediments in which they are found. Helpfully, because of their greater weight, they are separable from the more abundant light minerals which include quartz, feldspar and mica.

HIGH see *Block*.

HOLOCENE. (c. 10,000 years ago to present day) The period of geological time during which man became resident in Yorkshire, occupying a landscape which continued, and continues even now, to be modified by the movement, erosion and deposition of sediment.

HORIZON. A specific layer within a sequence of sediments.

HYDROGEOLOGY. The application of geology in relation to water resources.

ICHNOLOGY. The study of *trace fossils*.

IGNEOUS. The term which describes rocks which have formed when *magma* cooled.

ILLITE. A variety of mica which along with other clay minerals make up *mudrocks*.

INLIER. An exposure of older bedrock surrounded by younger rocks. The opposite of an *outlier*.

INTRUSION. A body of *igneous* rock which has forced its way into overlying or adjacent rocks; these may be *igneous*, *sedimentary*, or *metamorphic*. Minor intrusions include *dykes*, and major intrusions large bodies such as *granite* batholiths.

INVERSION. The reversal of the process of basin subsidence, so a *basin* becomes a dome shaped *anticline*. Also applicable to reverse movement on *faults*.

ISLAND ARCS. Arcuate chains of volcanic islands which are formed by ascending magma, created when a descending oceanic plate is thrust under, and descends beneath another oceanic plate abutting a continental plate.

ISOTOPE GEOLOGY. The study of chemical elements and their isotopes to gain an understanding of different aspects of Earth history. Examples include calculating the age of the Earth through the decay of radioactive isotopes, the amount of CO_2 in the atmosphere while the Greenland ice sheet grew, and the concentration of the heavy form of oxygen in the shells of foramanifera which provides evidence of glaciations.

JURASSIC. (199-145 Ma). A period of geological time when large marine reptiles swam in seas over Yorkshire, and later, dinosaurs walked and even swam across parts of the county.

KARST. Scenery composed of limestone which has undergone deep weathering and is characterised by limestone pavements and cave formation. Sandstones may also show karst features.

LAMPROPHYRE. A variety of medium grained *igneous* rock usually encountered in minor *intrusions*.

LAURENTIA. A continental plate which collided with *Baltica* during the *Devonian*, forming *Laurussia*.

LAURUSSIA . Also known as Euramerica, formed when

Laurentia progressively collided with *Baltica*.

LIMESTONE. A sedimentary rock composed of calcium carbonate (see *Calcite*) or *dolomite*. Limestones are produced by chemical or biological processes.

LITHIFIED. Literally, turned to stone.

LITHOLOGY. The composition and fabric of a rock as deduced in the field.

LITHOSTRATIGRAPHY. The ordering and correlation of strata based on their *lithology*.

LOBE see *Deltaic*.

LOWER PALAEOZOIC see *Palaeozoic*.

MAGMA. A molten rock which has not yet solidified from a liquid or plastic state to form an *igneous* rock.

MAGMATISM. The formation and dissipation of *magma*.

MEGATRACKSITE. An area defined by the extent of the track-bearing strata, and in which not less than 1000 tracks, or 100 trackways, made by terrestrial vertebrates are preserved.

MESOZOIC. (251-65 Ma). A geological era, encompassing the Triassic, Jurassic and Cretaceous periods.

METAMORPHIC. Rocks which have been altered by pressure and or heat. Existing minerals may be reformed and new minerals made.

METAMORPHOSED/METAMORPHISM see *Metamorphic*.

METEORITE. A piece of extraterrestrial debris which reaches the surface of the Earth is called a meteorite. Meteorites fall into three groups, irons, composed of nickel-iron alloys, stony irons composed of more or less equal proportions of silicate minerals and nickel-iron alloys, and stones which are composed predominantly of silicate minerals but may contain significant amounts of nickel-iron alloys.

MICA. A relatively soft mineral, the crystals of which may be split into very thin sheets. Present in some *igneous* and *metamorphic* rocks, and immature sediments forming from them.

MICACEOUS. Describes rocks in which *mica* is common.

MICROCONTINENT. A descriptive term for a small continental plate in plate tectonics.

MICROFOSSILS. Collective term for a wide variety of plant and animal fossils of very small size, requiring optical or electronic microscopy for their identification and study. They include the *foraminifera*, *ostracods*, radiolaria, *conodonts*, pollen, and spores. They often play an important part in the dating and correlation of strata.

MINERALISATION. The process where minerals form within the bedrock. The initial mineralisation is termed primary. Alteration of these minerals, e.g. by weathering, leads to the formation of secondary minerals.

MIOCENE see *Neogene*.

MORAINE. Sediment, transported by a glacier or ice sheet, which is released and accumulates in arcuate or linear mounds as the ice remains in one position while decaying.

MUDROCKS. Sediments composed of fine particles with a size less than 1/16 mm.

NEKTONIC. Free swimming organisms within a body of water.

NEOGENE. (23 Ma – present). A period of geological time which incorporates the Miocene (23 – 5.33 Ma), Pliocene (5.33 – 2.65 Ma), *Pleistocene*, and *Holocene*. Only sediments of the latter two have been recognised in Yorkshire.

NODULES. Sediment which has been cemented, often forming in sub-spherical to spherical masses. *Septarian nodules* are a variety.

OLD RED SANDSTONE. The non-marine *facies* of the *Devonian*.

OLIGOCENE see *Paleogene*.

OOLITE. A sedimentary rock composed of small spheres of calcium carbonate (see *Calcite*) called ooliths. These look like the coarse fish roes one can purchase from the fishmonger. The word oolith comes from the Greek 'ooid' which means egg, and 'lithos' meaning stone. The spheres form as thin shells of calcium carbonate are deposited around a sand grain or shell fragment.

ORDOVICIAN. (488 – 443 Ma) A period of geological time during which some of the oldest rocks exposed in Yorkshire were deposited.

OROGENIC. See *Orogeny*.

OROGENY. A period of time during which mountain building occurs. This is the product of *plate tectonics*. An orogeny may last for tens of millions of years.

OSTRACODS. Very small members of the phylum Arthropoda. They are protected by bivalved shells and occupy a wide variety of aquatic environments.

OUTLIER. An exposure of younger strata surrounded by older rocks. The opposite of *inlier*.

PALEOCENE see *Paleogene*.

PALEOGENE. (65 – 23 Ma). A period of geological time which incorporates the Paleocene (65 – 56 Ma), Eocene (56 – 34 ma) and Oligocene (34 – 23 Ma). No sediments of this time span have been recognised in Yorkshire, though an *igneous intrusion* is present.

PALAEOGEOGRAPHY. The physical lay-out and attributes of continents, oceans and islands, etc. during geological time.

PALAEOZOIC. (542 - 251 Ma). A geological era, encompassing the *Cambrian*, *Ordovician*, *Silurian*, *Devonian*, *Carboniferous* and *Permian* periods.

PALLASITE. A category of stony-iron *meteorite* which contains crystals of a silicate mineral, olivine, embedded in a mixture of iron and nickel.

PERIGLACIAL. Relating to processes and landforms close to, but not covered by ice sheets or glaciers. Such areas would be subjected to very low temperatures.

PERMIAN. (299 – 251 Ma) A period of geological time during which rock and sandy desert conditions early on, were followed by carbonates and *evaporites* deposited in the Zechstein Sea.

PETROLOGIST. A geologist who specialises in the study of the composition, history and significance of different rocks.

PETROLOGICAL MICROSCOPE. A microscope which is

equipped to allow thin sections of rocks to be examined in plain polarised light and in crossed polarised light, revealing the different minerals and their relationship to each other.

PHANEROZOIC EON. The last 542 Ma of earth history. Divided into three eras, the *Palaeozoic*, *Mesozoic*, and the *Cenozoic*.

PHREATIC. Relating to caves formed below the water-table.

PLANKTONIC. Floating within a body of water.

PLATE TECTONICS. The Earth is composed of a number of plates composed of denser oceanic crust and less dense continental crust. The plates are either pushed or pulled across the surface of the Earth. They may disappear beneath, collide with, or be forced over other plates. As a result of these processes, larger continents, mountains, and *island arcs* may be formed. Continents may break up to form smaller plates.

PLAY. A geographical area where the combination of source rocks, migration routes, reservoir rocks and suitable cap-rock formations provide the potential for the discovery of hydrocarbons, i.e. oil and natural gas.

PLEISTOCENE. (2.65 Ma to present) The period of time over which the earth has experienced the most recent in a long history of glaciations, dating back to the *Pre-Camrian*. Very important in terms of landscape evolution in Yorkshire. See also *Neogene*.

PLIOCENE. See *Neogene*.

PRE-CAMBRIAN. A period of geological time, older than 542 Ma, during which some of the oldest exposed bedrock in Yorkshire may have been deposited.

PRIMARY MINERALISATION see *Mineralisation*.

QUARTZ. An abundant mineral composed of silica. The major constituent of most sands. Flint and *Chert* are related.

QUARTZ MICRODIORITE. A variety of medium grained *igneous* rock usually encountered in minor *intrusions*.

QUARTZITE. A rock consisting of grains of *quartz*-sand which have been welded together with more quartz deposited from solution, or by grains fusing together along shared surfaces when the grain boundaries may vanish.

RADIOACTIVE ISOTOPES see *isotope geology*.

REFLECTOR. A buried rock which reflects shock waves, produced by either an explosive charge or vibrating lorry on the surface, back to the surface during a *seismic survey*. They provide mappable features enabling the interpretation of sub-surface structures and geology.

REGRESSION. A fall in sea level normally associated with *eustatic* fluctuations in sea level.

RELATIVE HUMIDITY. The term used to describe the amount of water vapour present in a body of air.

RIFT VALLEY. A valley the sides of which are one or more *faults*, the valley floor being downthrown as a *graben*.

SABKHA. Mud-flats fringing an inland lake or the sea, which are subjected to high temperatures with consequent evaporation. *Evaporites* form below and over the the surface of the mud. The name is from the Middle East where they are relatively common.

Table of sediment particle sizes and names		
Particle diameter	Name	Rock type formed
>256 mm	Boulder	Conglomerates and breccias (rudites)
64-256 mm	Cobble	
4-64 mm	Pebble	
2-4 mm	Granule	
1/16-2 mm	Sand (very fine to very coarse)	Sands and sandstones (arenites)
1/256-1/16 mm	Silt (very fine to coarse)	Mudrocks (argillites)
<1/256 mm	Clay	

SEATEARTH. The preserved sediment in which plants grew, especially well known in Yorkshire from the Upper *Carboniferous*.

SEDIMENTARY STRUCTURE. Evidence of processes which were affecting sediments as they were deposited and before they were lithified.

SEDIMENTS. Particles of rock or mineral grains ranging from very small (muds), through silts and sands to larger pebbles, cobbles etc. *See Table above*. Sediments generated from older rocks are known as clastic sediments. See also *limestone*.

SEISMIC SURVEY. A method used for investigating the hidden geology below the surface using shock waves produce by explosives or a special truck which vibrates the ground. See also *reflector*.

SEPTARIAN NODULES. Localised enrichment of clays with calcium carbonate (see *Calcite*) leads to the formation of spheres or flattened spheres. Loss of water causes a network of concentric and radial fractures to form which may fill with calcite and or other minerals, giving rise to a chambered or septate appearance.

SHOCKED QUARTZ. *Quartz* grains which when viewed under a *petrological microscope* show distinctive patterns produced by a high energy impact associated with an *asteroid*.

SILL. An *igneous intrusion* where the molten rock is intruded into horizontal bedding planes or fractures.

SILURIAN. (444 – 416 Ma). A period of geological time during which considerable thicknesses of turbidite, sandstone and mudstone were deposited across Yorkshire.

SLATEY CLEAVAGE see *Cleavage*.

SOURCE ROCKS. The sediments from which hydrocarbons originate. They include coal seams and mudrocks which contain a large proportion of organic material.

SPECIES. The standard unit used in the classificatory system of both extinct and extant plants and animals. Similar species are grouped into genera (singular, genus).

SPELEOTHEMS. A wide range of cave deposits, including stalagmites and stalactites, which form when water rich in dissolved calcium carbonate undergoes evaporation.

STRATIGRAPHER see *Stratigraphy*.

STRATIGRAPHY. The science of the relationships between layers of rock of different ages. A stratigrapher is a person involved in the study stratigraphy.

SUBCROP. The continuation of an outcrop beneath an *unconformity*.

SUPERCONTINENT. Through geological time, *plate tectonic* processes have both brought the continental plates together to form supercontinents, e.g. *Gondwana* and Pangaea. Supercontinents are then broken into smaller ones, e.g. *Baltica* and *Laurentia* and dispersed across the Earth.

SUPERFICIAL DEPOSITS. Usually unconsolidated deposits, e.g. gravels, sands and clays, of the most recent *Neogene*, including the *Pleistocene* and *Holocene*.

SYNCLINE. Strata which have been folded into a trough shape. They range from a few metres to tens of kilometres.

SYN-SEDIMENTARY. Refers to events which took place at more or less the same time as the sediments were deposited.

TECTONIC. Relating to movement of the rocks; a tectonic regime relates to a particular pattern of tectonic activity which in turn produces tectonic structures, e.g. a *syncline*.

TECTONIC REGIME see *tectonic*.

TECTONIC STRUCTURES see *tectonic*.

THIN SECTION. A piece of rock, glued to a glass slide, and ground down until light can be seen through the rock. These are studied under a *petrological microscope* in order to identify the minerals present, and to understand their relationship to each other and the history of the rock.

TORNQUIST'S SEA. A *Palaeozoic* ocean which lay between Avalonia and *Baltica*, and which finally closed during the *Silurian*.

TRACE FOSSILS. Evidence left in *sediments* by many activities of animals such as movement, feeding and protection.

TRANSGRESSION. When sea level rises and more land is covered by the sea; fringing seas become deeper.

TRIASSIC. (251 – 199 Ma) A period of geological time when Yorkshire was largely an arid desert; *evaporites* were deposited. Occasional wetter episodes are recorded.

TRILOBITES. Members of the phylum *Arthropoda*. They range from the *Cambrian* to the *Permian* when they were important members of the marine fauna occupying many different ecological niches. Distinctive body plan consisting of head, thorax and pygidium.

TROUGH see *Basin*.

TUFFS. Rocks made of the volcanic ash and other debris from an eruption, which having been carried aerially, are deposited on land or in water.

UNCONFORMITY. The contact between rocks where sedimentation has not been continuous. A considerable gap in time may be represented. The unconformity may be obvious with folded and eroded rocks overlain by horizontal *sediments* giving an angular unconformity, or bedding may be similar above and below giving a non-angular unconformity when only the preserved *zone fossils* (Chapter 3) allow detection.

URANIUM SERIES DATING. A method of dating deposits of *speleothems* up to 500 ka, using the rate at which uranium decays.

VADOSE. Relating to cave systems which have formed above the water table.

VARISCAN OROGENY. A period of folding and mountain building across southern Britain, associated with the northward movement of Gondwana towards Laurussia (formed from Avalonia and Baltica), which started during the Devonian and lasted until the close of the Carboniferous, with the formation of the supercontinent Pangaea.

VEINS. Fractures running through rocks which have been in-filled with minerals. These may be of economic importance.

VENT AGGLOMERATES. Angular fragments of country rock and cooled magma which are found filling the vents of a volcano.

VENTIFACT. A stone exposed on the ground which is polished by the wind carrying small particles of sediment. These stones are often faceted to form a triangular cross section, with all three surfaces polished. Ventifacts are common in both hot and cold deserts.

WADI. A steep sided valley, formed by flash floods, in arid regions.

WIRELINE LOGGING. A sophisticated method of studying rocks which a *borehole* has passed through. Ideally, the cylinders containing power supply and equipment, and the sensors are lowered down the hole on a single or multi-strand cable. They are then brought back to the surface while continuously recording resistivity, conductivity, gamma radiation (high gamma is an indicator of organic-rich horizons = potential as source for oil and gas), formation pressure, and a variety of other information. These details tell much about the nature of the strata, and help correlate between different boreholes.

ZONE FOSSIL. A fossil which is unique to a specific part of a sequence of rocks. The fossil therefore has the potential to link that horizon in different places.

Museums – Portals to the Past

Yorkshire boasts numerous museums and galleries each with many good reasons for visiting them. Displays of geology and related industries are of course especially good reasons, and valuable for anyone attempting to come to grips with the geological history of an area. Some museums' displays cover Yorkshire and even beyond, others are of a more local nature. The displays are frequently populated with fabulous specimens, giving a sense of the rich diversity of minerals, rocks and fossils which lie beneath our feet. Some show how the county's mineral wealth has been exploited through history. Others contain exceptionally rare fossils, like the Carboniferous amphibian in Cliffe Castle Museum in Keighley, so delightfully described on their web site as 'a 2 m long fossil newt!'. Others exhibit outrageously spectacular skeletons of the great marine reptiles, as in the Whitby and Yorkshire museums. Yorkshire specimens have travelled far and wide, and there is always a chance that a museum near you may have displays or collections with specimens from this geologically rich county.

Displays provide the interface between the visitor and the collections, for many museums are treasure houses holding the collected endeavors of amateur and professional geologists, students, and of sharp-eyed members of the public, ranging back for over 180 years. Museums and their staff are there to provide long-term security and access to the iconic and the unique, along with the humdrum but key specimens that help geologists flesh out the story of the Earth. These collections are reference points for future generations, and in line with this, collections will usually be made available for study, by appointment. Some museums run identification services, and other geologically related activities. Check out their web sites (see below) for more information.

All the museums with geological displays, and or collections, are listed below with their addresses and the URLS for their web sites. The latter usually provides details of admission charges (some are free), opening times, access, temporary exhibitions, and events, along with contact addresses. URLS do change from time to time so if one of these fails to link you to their server, either type a key word into your search engine, or go to the 24 Hour Museum of the National Virtual Museum (http://www.24hourmuseum. org.uk/mapsea.html) which may provide help where other routes have failed.

Basic details have been given. Providing such detail is fraught with problems, not least because they tend to become out-dated. As a rule, even those claiming to be open all year will be closed on Christmas Day and Boxing Day, and most if not all on New Year's Day. If you are travelling any distance to visit a particular museum, check the opening times by visiting their web site, or telephoning first. Afternoon opening may be for no more than 2 hours!

BAILDON: Bracken Hall Countryside Centre, Glen Road, Baildon, Shipley, W. Yorkshire, BD17 5EA. Displays of local geology. Open throughout year but not every day. http://www.bradfordmuseums.org

BATLEY: Bagshaw Museum, Wilton Park, Batley, W. Yorkshire, WF17 0AS. Limited collections of local geology, especially Carboniferous. Open all year. Due to reopen 09.2008. http://www.kirklees.gov.uk/community/museums/museums.shtml

BRIDLINGTON: SEWERBY HALL, Church Lane, Sewerby, Bridlington, East Riding of Yorkshire, YO15 1EA. Small display of local geology. Open from a nweek before Easter until the end of half term in October. http://www.eastriding.gov.uk/sewerby/index2.html

DONCASTER: Doncaster Museum & Art Gallery, Chequer Road, Doncaster, DN1 2AE. Displays featuring local Carboniferous, Permian, Triassic and Quaternary/Holocene geology, and collections of local geology, especially Carboniferous. Open all year. http://www.doncaster.gov.uk/Services/Art_Gallery_and_Museum.asp

FILEY: Filey Museum, 8/10 Queen Street, Filey, N. Yorkshire, YO14 9HB. Displays of local and other Yorkshire fossils. Open from Good Friday to the last Sunday in October, Sunday to Friday from 11 a.m. to 5 p.m., Saturdays 2 p.m. to 5 p.m. http://www.fileymuseum.co.uk

GRASSINGTON: Upper Wharfedale Folk Museum, The Square, Grassington, Skipton, N. Yorkshire, BD23 5AQ. Displays about local lead mining, local minerals, rocks and fossils. Open from Easter to October 31st daily 2.00 p.m. to 4.30 p.m. Open on some weekends during the winter season. Please contact Grassington Tourist Information Centre for the latest information.

HARROGATE: Royal Pump Room Museum, Royal Parade, Harrogate, N.Yorkshire, HG1 2RY. Display on the development of the 19th century Spa. Take the waters! Open all year. http://www.harrogate.gov.uk/museums

HAWES: Dales Countryside Museum, Station Yard,

Hawes, N. Yorkshire, DL8 3NT. Local displays, and collections connected with lead mining. Open all year. http://www.yorkshiredales.org.uk/dales_countryside_museum

HUDDERSFIELD: Tolson Museum, Ravensknowle Park, Wakefield Road, Huddersfield, W. Yorkshire, HD5 8DJ. Good collections of local Carboniferous rocks and fossils. Open all year. http://www.kirklees.gov.uk/community/museums/museums.shtml

HULL: Hull and East Riding Museum, Hull Museums and Art Gallery, 36 High Street, Hull, HU1 1NQ. Limited permanent displays on geology of the area, and collections of local minerals, rocks, and fossils. Open all year. Monday – Friday 10 a.m. – 5 p.m and Sundays 1.30 – 4.30 p.m. www.hullcc.gov.uk

HUTTON-LE-HOLE: Ryedale Folk Museum, Hutton-le-Hole, N. Yorkshire, YO6 6UA. Displays about local North Yorkshire Moors extractive industries; Open daily from mid-January to mid-December. http://www.ryedalefolkmuseum.co.uk

KEIGHLEY: Cliffe Castle Museum, Spring Gardens Lane, Keighley, W. Yorkshire, BD20 6LH. Displays and collections of local geology. Rich in Upper Carboniferous plants and Palaeozoic invertebrates. Open all year, but closed Mondays except Bank Holidays. http://www.bradfordmuseums.org

LEEDS: Leeds Museum Discovery Centre, Carlisle Road, Leeds, LS10 1LB. Collections include local and Yorkshire geology, especially Carboniferous and Jurassic plants, Carboniferous Limestone fossils, and minerals. Open Monday to Friday by appointment, 10.00 – 16.00. www.leeds.gov.uk/Leisure_and_culture/Museums_and_galleries/page.aspx

PATELEY BRIDGE: Nidderdale Museum, Council Offices, King Street, Pateley Bridge, N. Yorkshire, HG3 5LE. Displays about life in Nidderdale with a section about local quarrying & mining; small collection of local geology. Open afternoons Easter to end October & winter Saturdays & Sundays. http://www.nidderdalemuseum.com

REETH: Swaledale Museum, The Green, Reeth, N. Yorkshire, DL11 6QT. Displays on local geology with samples of minerals and rocks. Collections of material associated with the lead industry; Open from Easter to end October Wednesday to Friday, Sunday and Bank Holiday Mondays 10.30 a.m. – 5.30 p.m. Able to open at other times by appointment. http://www.swaledalemuseum.org/

RICHMOND: Richmondshire Museum, Ryders Wynd, Richmond, N. Yorkshire, DL10 4JA. Displays on local lead mining. Open from April 1st to the end of October. http://www.communigate.co.uk/ne/richmondshiremuseum

ROTHERHAM: Clifton Park Museum, Clifton Lane, Rotherham, S. Yorkshire, S65 2AA. Displays and collections of local geology, especially Upper Carboniferous Plants. Open all year, but closed Fridays & 25 December to 1 January inclusive. http://www.rotherham.gov.uk/graphics/Learning/Museums/EDSCliftonParkMuseum.htm

SCARBOROUGH: Rotunda Museum, the William Smith Museum of Geology, Vernon Road, Scarborough, N. Yorkshire, YO11 2PW. Displays of local geology which echo, and build on, William 'Strata' Smith's 1829 grand design. Collections of local and Yorkshire material. Open Tuesday to Sunday (and bank holiday Monday) 10am – 5pm. http://www.rotundamuseum.org.uk

SETTLE: Museum of North Craven Life, The Folly, Victoria Street, Settle, N. Yorkshire, BD24 9EY. Small displays of local fossils and minerals, and on mining, quarrying and building stones. There is a model of the Ebbing & Flowing Well of Giggleswick Scar. Open all Bank Holiday weekends, and from Easter to end of October, Tuesday, Saturday and Sunday from 10.30 a.m. – 4.30 p.m. http://www.ncbpt.org.uk/folly

SHEFFIELD: Weston Park Museum, Weston Park, Sheffield, S. Yorkshire, S10 2TP. Displays and collections of local geology especially Coal Measure Group plants of S. Yorkshire and minerals from the South Pennine orefield. Open all year. http://www.sheffieldgalleries.org.uk

SKIPTON: Craven Museum & Gallery, Town Hall, High Street, Skipton, N. Yorkshire, BD23 1AH. Displays of local geology and lead mining. Open April to September everyday except Tuesday 10 a.m. – 4 p.m. Open October to March, Monday, Wednesday, Thursday Friday, 12 p.m. – 4 p.m. and Saturday 10 a.m. – 4 p.m. http://www.cravendc.gov.uk/Craven/Visitors/Craven+Museum+and+Gallery/

WAKEFIELD: National Coal Mining Museum for England, Caphouse Colliery, New Road, Overton, nr Wakefield, W. Yorkshire, WF4 4RH. Caphouse Colliery has what is believed to be the oldest regularly used coal mine shaft in Britain. Displays on the search for coal, the geology of the coalfields, coal mining history, science and technology. Collections of items associated with the mining industry for the whole of England, and a small collection of Coal Measure specimens from the Yorkshire Coalfield, some of which are on display. Open all year. http://www.ncm.org.uk

WHITBY: Whitby Museum, Pannett Park, Whitby, N. Yorkshire, YO21 1RE. Displays of local geology including Jurassic marine reptiles, Zechstein evaporites, and Whitby jet jewellery. Collections of local geology especially fossils. Open all year. http://www.whitbymuseum.org.uk/

YORK: Yorkshire Museum, Museum Gardens, York, N. Yorkshire, YO1 7FR. Displays on regional geology and Jurassic marine environment. Large regional collections of minerals, rocks, and fossils. Open all year. http://www.yorkshiremuseum.org.uk/Page/Index.aspx

Geological Societies

'LOCAL' GEOLOGICAL SOCIETIES AND GROUPS

Craven and Pendle Geological Society
(http://www.cpgs.org.uk)
Cumberland Geological Society
(http://www.cumberland-geol-soc.org.uk)
East Midlands Geological Society
(http://www.emgs.org.uk)
Huddersfield Geology Group
(http://www.huddersfieldgeology.org.uk/)
Hull Geological Society
(http://www.hullgeolsoc.org.uk/)
Leeds Geological Association
(www.leedsgeolassoc.freeserve.co.uk)
Manchester Geological Association
(www.mangeolassoc.org.uk)
North-Eastern Geological Society
(www.northeast-geolsoc.50megs.com)
Rotunda Geology Group
(www.rotundamuseum.org.uk)

Sorby Natural History Society (Sorby Geological Group)
www.sorby.org.uk/grpgeo.shtml)
University of Sheffield Sorby Geology Group
(http://www.sorbygeology.group.shef.ac.uk/index.html)
York Geology Club
(http://www.communigate.co.uk/york/yorkgeologyclub/)
Yorkshire Geological Society
(http://www.yorksgeolsoc.org.uk/)

NATIONAL GEOLOGICAL SOCIETIES AND ASSOCIATIONS

The Geological Society of London
(http://www.geolsoc.org.uk/index.html)
The Geologists' Association
(http://www.geologists.org.uk/)
The Palaeontographical Society
(http://www.nhm.ac.uk/hosted_sites/palsoc/)
The Paleontological Association
(http://www.palass.org/)

Further Reading

As noted in the acknowledgments, the writing of this book would have been impossible without the legacy of more than 200 years of research and publication which has resulted in a rich geological literature on Yorkshire. The references given below are not exhaustive, but will provide additional references for those with particular interests.

The Yorkshire Geological Society www.yorksgeolsoc. org.uk is especially concerned with the publication of research on Yorkshire and across northern England, and occasionally further afield. A number of other organisations publish journals or monographs on a regular basis, and these not infrequently carry papers which touch wholly or partly on the geology of Yorkshire (*See Geological Societies on the previous page*).

Multi-author volume covering all geological periods

Brenchley, P. J. and Rawson P.F., (Editors), 2006. *The geology of England and Wales*. 2nd edition. Geological Society. An excellent compilation giving an up-to-date review of the geological history of England and Wales.

County-wide Geology books

Bell, R., 1996. *Yorkshire Rock*. British Geological Survey.

Kendall, P. F. and Wroot, H. E., 1924. *Geology of Yorkshire, an illustration of the evolution of Northern England*. Privately printed Vienna.

Rayner, D. and Hemingway, J. E., (Editors), 1974. *The geology and mineral resources of Yorkshire*. Yorkshire Geological Society.

Scrutton, C. and Powell, J., (Editors), 2006. *Yorkshire rocks and landscape, a field guide*. 3rd edition. Yorkshire Geological Society.

Coastal Geology

Rawson, P. F., and Wright, J. K., The Yorkshire Coast. *Geologists' Association Guide*, No. 34. [Includes some inland sites across the North York Moors].

Bibliographic Sources

Shepherd, T., 1915. Bibliography of Yorkshire geology. *Proceedings of the Yorkshire Geological Society*, 18, i-xxxvi, 1-629.

British Geological Survey publications

The British Geological Survey (BGS) have been at the fore-front of the mapping and description of the geology of Britain since the 19th century, and amongst their extensive portfolio of maps, memoirs, guides and reports are many which describe aspects of Yorkshire's geology. Their full catalogue may be viewed at www.geologyshop.com

Yorkshire is covered by 40 individual maps (also known as sheets) which are listed by map number and name in the Table on the following page. Prior to 2004, BGS maps were published in the following formats: Solid (S), Drift (D), Solid & Drift (S&D), and Solid with Drift (SwD). Since 2004 the maps have been published in the following versions: Bedrock (B), Superficial Deposits (Sup), and Bedrock and Superficial Deposits (B&Sup). Unless stated to be at the scale of 1:63,360, all maps are published at the scale of 1:50,000. They are available as flat or folded. Individual maps may or may not be in print.

Accounts of the geology have been published to complement most of these maps:

• = A Memoir, Sheet Description, or Brief Sheet Explanation has been published, but may be out of print.

■ = The map is covered or partly covered by the *Geology of the Northern Pennine Orefield Volume II: Stainmore to Craven*, K. C. Dunham, 1985.

Memoirs provide the most comprehensive accounts of the geology of districts covered by 1:50,000 (or 1:63,360) geological maps; however, the publication date may differ significantly from that of the complementary map. Sheet Descriptions provide a similar account for the most recently published 1:50,000 maps. Brief Sheet Explanations provide a concise account of the geology shown on the contemporary 1:50,000 maps.

Yorkshire and the adjacent areas are described in two of a series of guides titled 'British Regional Geology':

The Pennines and adjacent areas. Aitkenhead, N. *et al.*, 2002.

Eastern England from the Tees to the Wash. Kent , P., 1980.

Further information on the availability, formats and cost of all publications can be obtained from The Sales Desk, British Geological Survey, Kingsley Dunham Centre, Keyworth, Nottingham. NG12 5GG. Tel. 0115 936 3241 or by visiting www.geologyshop.com

Map number	Title, publication date and whether 'Provisional'. Scale 1:50,00 unless stated	Description
E031	Brough under Stainmore (S&D and SwD: 1974)	●■
E032	Barnard Castle (S&D and SwD: 1969 both at 1:63,360)	●■
E033	Stockton (S&D, 1987)	
E034	Guisborough (S&D: 1998, Provisional)	●
E035 & E044	Whitby & Scalby (S&D: 1998. Provisional)	●
E040	Kirkby Stephen (S&D: 1997. Provisional)	■
E041	Richmond (S&D: 1997. Provisional)	■
E042	Northallerton (S&D: 1994)	●
E043	Egton (S&D: 1992. Provisional)	●
E044	see E035	●
E049	Kirkby Lonsdale (S: 1892 at 1:63,360)	●
E050	Hawes (S&D: 1997. Provisional)	■
E051	Masham (S&D and SwD: 1985)	■
E052	Thirsk (S&D and SwD: 1992)	●
E053	Pickering (S&D: 2001. Provisional)	●
E054	Scarborough (S&D: 1998. Provisional)	●
E055 & E065	Flamborough & Bridlington (S,D: 1986)	●
E059	Lancaster (S&D and SwD: 1995)	●
E060	Settle (S&D and S: 1991)	●■
E061	Pateley Bridge (S: 1889 at 1:63,360)	■
E062	Harrogate (S&D and SwD: 1987)	●
E063	York (S&D: 1983)	●
E064	Great Driffield (S&D: 1993. Provisional)	●
E065	see E055	●
E068	Clitheroe (SwD: 1960 at 1:63,360 and S&D: 1975)	●
E069	Bradford (S&D and S: 2000)	●
E070	Leeds (SwD: 1974 and S&D: 2003)	●
E071	Selby (S&D: 1973 and B&Sup: 2008)	●
E072	Beverley (S&D: 1995. Provisional)	●
E073	Hornsea (S&D: 1998. Provisional)	●
E076	Rochdale (S&D: 1974; S: 1992; B and B&Sup: 2008)	●
E077	Huddersfield (SwD: 1978 and S&D: 2003)	●
E078	Wakefield (SwD: 1978 and S&D: 1998)	●
E079	Goole (S&D: 1971 and SwD: 1972, both at 1:63,360)	●
E080	Kingston upon Hull (S&D and SwD: 1983)	●
E081 & E082	Patrington (S&D: 1991)	●
E082	see E081	●
E086	Glossop (SwD: 1981)	●
E087	Barnsley (S&D: 1976 and B&Sup: 2008)	●
E088	Doncaster (S&D and SwD: 1969, both at 1:63,360)	●
E099	Chapel en le Frith (SwD: 1975 and S&D: 1977)	●
E100	Sheffield (S&D: 1974)	●
E101	East Retford (S&D: 1967 at 1:63,360)	●
**	**Classical Area Map 1:25,000**	
SE30	Barnsley (1987)	

	Relevant Geological Maps of the UK and Continental Shelf areas (UTM series) 1:250,000.	
54N04W	Lake District	
54N02W	Tyne-Tees	
54N 00	California	
53N 04W	Liverpool Bay	
53N 02W	Humber-Trent	
53N 00	Spurn	

General Fossil reference works

Natural History Museum, 1975. *British Caenozoic Fossils*. 5th edition.

Natural History Museum, 1983. *British Mesozoic Fossils*. 6th edition.

Natural History Museum, 1975. *British Palaeozoic Fossils*. 4th edition.

Building Stones

Arkell, W. J. and Tomkeieff, S. I., 1953. *English Rock Terms chiefly as used by miners and quarrymen*. Oxord University Press.

Clifton-Taylor, A.,1972. *The pattern of English building*. Faber and Faber.

Dimes, F. G. and Murray, M., 2006. *The building stone heritage of Leeds*. The Leeds Philosophical and Literary Society.

Middleton, G. A. T., 1905. *Building Materials. Their nature, properties and manufacture*. Batsford.

INTRODUCTION

International Commission on Stratigraphy: www.stratigraphy.org

The British Geological Survey Lexicon on Named Rock Units: www.bgs.ac.uk/lexicon/home.cfm

ROOTED IN ROCK

Gray, H., 1991. *Yorkshire whys, wherefores, whats and whens*. Dalesman.

Morrell, J., 2005, *John Phillips and the business of Victorian science*. Ashgate.

Oxford Dictionary of National Biography. Oxford.

Pyrah, B. J., *The history of the Yorkshire Museum and its geological collections*. William Sessions.

Phillips, J., 1829. *Illustrations of the geology of Yorkshire; or, a description of the strata and organic remains; accompanied by a geological map, sections, and plates of the fossil plants and animals. The Yorkshire Coast*. York

Phillips, J., 1836. *Illustrations of the geology of Yorkshire; or, a description of the strata and organic remains; accompanied by a geological map, sections and diagrams, and figures of the fossils. Part 2. The Mountain Limestone District*. London.

Stephens, M. D. and Roderick, G. W., 1974. Nineteenth century educational finance. The literary and philosophical societies. *Annals of Science*, 31, 335-349.

Torrens, H. S., 2004, Scarborough's first geologist? The life and work of the Rev. Frederick Kendall (1790-1836). *Proceedings of the Yorkshire Geological Society*, 55, 119-129.

BORN OF FIRE

Cocks, L. R. M. and Torsvik, T. H., 2006. European geography in a global context from the Vendian to the end of the Palaeozoic, pp. 83-95 in Gee, D. G. and Stephenson, *European lithosphere dynamics*. Geological Society, London, Memoirs, 32.

McKerrow, W. S., MacNiocaill, C. and Dewey, J. F., 2000. The Caledonian Orogeny redefined. *Journal of the Geological Society*, 157, 1149-1154.

Millward, D., 2002. Early Palaeozoic magmatism in the English Lake District. *Proceedings of the Yorkshire Geological Society*, 54, 65-93.

Suthren, R. J., 1978. The Tempest Anderson collection of photographs at Yorkshire Museum. *GCG Newsletter*, 2, 68-79, pls 1A-11B.

FOUNDATIONS

Bott, M. H. P., Robinson, J. and Kohnstamm, M. A., 1978. Granite beneath Market Weighton, east Yorkshire. *Journal of the Geological Society*, 135, 535-543.

Bott, M. H. P., 1988. The Market Weighton gravity anomaly – granite or graben? *Proceedings of the Yorkshire Geological Society*, 47, 47-53.

Chadwick, R. A., and Evans, D. J., 2005. *A seismic atlas of southern Britain – images of subsurface structure*. British Geological Survey.

Dunham, K. C., Granite beneath the Pennines in North Yorkshire. *Proceedings of the Yorkshire Geological Society*, 40, 191-194.

Evans, D. J., Walker, A. S. D. and Chadwick, R. A., 2002. The Pennine Anticline, northern England – a continuing enigma. *Proceedings of the Yorkshire Geological Society*, 54, 17-34.

Wills, L. J., 1978, A Palaeogeological map of the Lower Palaeozoic floor below the cover of Upper Devonian, Carboniferous and later formations with inferred and speculative reconstructions of Lower Palaeozoic and Precambrian outcrops in adjacent areas. *Memoir of the Geological Society of London*, No. 8.

GLIMPSES OF THE PAST

King, W. B. R., 1932. A fossiliferous limestone associated with the Ingletonian beds at Horton-in-Ribblesdale, Yorkshire. *Quarterly Journal of the Geological Society of London*. 88, 100-111.

McCabe, P. J., 1972, The Wenlock and Lower Ludlow Strata of the Austwick and Horton-in-Ribblesdale Inlier of north-west England. *Proceedings of the Yorkshire*

Geological Society, 39, 167-174.

Soper, N. J. and Dunning, F. W., 2005. Structure and sequence of the Ingleton Group, basement to the central Pennines of northern England. *Proceedings of the Yorkshire Geological Society*, 55, 241-261.

Soper, N. J., Strachan, R. E., Holdsworth, R. E., Gayer, R. A. and Greiling, R. O., 1992. Sinistral transpression and the Silurian closure of Iapetus. *Journal of the Geological Society*, 149, 871-880.

Wilson, A. A. and Cornwell, J. D., 1982. The Institute of Geological Sciences borehole at Beckermonds Scar, North Yorkshire. *Proceedings of the Yorkshire Geological Society*, 44, 59-88.

WHITE MICA AND THE MISSING MILLIONS

Merriman, R. J., Rex, D. C., Soper, N. J. and Peacor, D. R., 1995. The age of Acadian cleavage in northern England, UKJ: K-Ar and TEM analysis of a Silurian metabentonite. *Proceedings of the Yorkshire Geological Society*, 50, 255-265.

Moseley, F. (Editor), 1978, *The geology of the Lake District*. Yorkshire Geological Society.

Romano, M. and Spears, D. A., 1991. Bentonites from the Horton Formation (Upper Silurian) of Ribblesdale, Yorkshire. *Proceedings of the Yorkshire Geological Society*, 48, 277-285.

Woodcock, N. H., Soper, N. J. and Stachan, R. A., 2007. A Rheic cause for the Acadian deformation in Europe. *Journal of the Geological Society*, 164, 1023-1036.

THE DROWNING

Brunton, C. H. C. and Mundy, D. J. C., 1988. Strophalosiacean and aulostegascean productoids (Brachiopoda) from the Craven Reef Belt (late Viséan) of North Yorkshire. *Proceedings of the Yorkshire Geological Society*, 47, 55-88.

Brunton, C. H. C. and Mundy, D. J. C., 1994. A new productoid from the late Visean Craven Reef Belt of North Yorkshire. *Proceedings of the Yorkshire Geological Society*, 50, 119-123.

Burgess, I. C. and Mitchell, M., 1976. Viséan lower Yoredale limestones on the Alston and Askrigg Blocks, and the base of the D_2 zone in northern England. *Proceedings of the Yorkshire Geological Society*, 40, 613-630.

Chapman, A. J., Rickards, R. B. and Grayson, R. F., 1993. The Carboniferous dendroid graptolites of Britain and Ireland. *Proceedings of the Yorkshire Geological Society*, 49, 295-319.

Leeder, M. R., 1982. Upper Palaeozoic basins of the British Isles – Caledonide inheritance versus Hercynian plate margin processes. *Journal of the Geological Society of London*, 139, 479-491.

Rigby, J. K. and Mundy, D. J. C., 2000. Lower Carboniferous sponges from the Craven Reef Belt of North Yorkshire. *Proceedings of the Yorkshire Geological Society*, 53, 119-128.

GREAT RIVERS, DELTAS AND SWAMPS

Clack, J. A., 1987. *Pholiderpeton scutigerum* Huxley, an amphibian from the Yorkshire Coal Measures. *Philosophical Transactions of the Royal Society of London*, Series B, Biological Sciences, 318, No. 1188, 1-107.

Cleal, C. J. and Thomas, B. A., 1994. Plant fossils of the British Coal Measures. *Palaeontological Association Field Guides to Fossils*: No. 6.

Fairbairn, R. A., 1999. Palaeocurrent direction and velocity in the Great/Main Limestone on the Alston and Askrigg blocks of northern England. *Proceedings of the Yorkshire Geological Society*, 52, 353-359.

Fairbairn, R. A., 2001. The stratigraphy of the Namurian Great/Main Limestone on the Alston Block, Stainmore Trough and Askrigg Block of northern England. *Proceedings of the Yorkshire Geological Society*, 53, 265-274.

Falcon, N. L. and Kent, P. E., 1960. Geological results of petroleum exploration in Britain 1945-1957. *Memoir of the Geological* Society, *London*, No. 2.

Ford, T. D., 1954. The Upper Carboniferous rocks of the Ingleton Coalfield. *Quarterly Journal of the Geological Society*, 110, 231-265.

Hallsworth, C. R. and Chisholm, J. I., 2000. Stratigraphic evolution of provenance characteristics in Westphalian sandstones of the Yorkshire Coalfield. *Proceedings of the Yorkshire Geological Society*, 53, 43-72.

Hodson, F., 1972. Edward William James Moore [Obituary, in The Annual Report of the Council of the Geologists' Association for the year 1971]. *Proceedings of the Geologists' Association*, 83, 115-117.

Huxley, T. H., 1869. On a new labyrinthodont from Bradford. *Quarterly Journal of the Geological Society*, 25, 309-311.

Kent, P. E., 1976. Hydrocarbons in Cleveland – an early proposal by P. F. Kendall. *Proceedings of the Yorkshire Geological Society*, 41, 141-144.

Langdon, J., 2004. Mills in the medieval economy: England 1300-1540. Oxford University Press.

Maynard, J. R. and Leeder, M. R., 1992. On the periodicity and magnitude of late Carboniferous glacio-eustatic sea-level changes. *Journal of the Geological Society*, 149, 303-311.

Morton, A. C. and Whitham, A. G., 2002. The Millstone Grit of northern England: a response to tectonic evolution of a northern sourceland. *Proceedings of the Yorkshire Geological Society*, 54, 47-56.

Scott, A. C., 1979. The ecology of Coal Measure floras from northern Britain. *Proceedings of the Geologists' Association*, 90, 97-116.

Sorby, H. C., 1875. On the remains of a fossil forest in the Coal Measures at Wadsley, near Sheffield. *Quarterly Journal of the Geological Society*, 31, 458-460.

Stewart, W. N. and Rothwell, G. W., 1993. *Paleobotany and the evolution of plants*. Cambridge University Press.

THE HEAT IS ON

Cann, J. R. and Banks, D. A., 2001. Constraints on the genesis of the mineralisation of the Alston Block, Northern Pennines Orefield, northern England. *Proceedings of the Yorkshire Geological Society*, 53, 187-196.

Delair, J. B. and Sarjeant, W. A. S., 1985. History and bibliography of the study of vertebrate footprints in the British Isles: Supplement 1973-1983. *Palaeogeography, Palaeoclimatology, Palaeoecology*, 49, 123-160.

Dunham, K. C., and Wilson, A. A., 1985. Geology of the Northern Pennine Orefield, Volume 2, Stainmore to Craven. HMSO.

Hawkins, T. R. W. and Saul, G. H., 2003. Complex extensional faulting of Triassic rocks north of York, North Yorkshire, UK. *Proceedings of the Yorkshire Geological Society*, 54, 257-267.

Holiday, D. W., 1993. Mesozoic cover over northern England: interpretation of apatite fission track data. *Journal of the Geological Society*, 150, 657-660.

Hsü, K., 2001. Gaia and the Mediterranean Sea. *Scientia Marina*, 65, 133-140.

Lott, G. K. and Richardson, C., 1997. Yorkshire stone for building the Houses of Parliament (1839-*c*.1852). *Proceedings of the Yorkshire Geological Society*. 51, 265-272.

Murphy, P. J., 2000. The karstification of the Permian strata east of Leeds. *Proceedings of the Yorkshire Geological Society*, 53, 25-30.

Rastrick, A., 1975, *The lead industry of Wensleydale and Swaledale, Vol. 1. The mines*. Moorland Publishing Co.

Small, A. T., 1982. New data on tetrahedrite, tennanite, chalcopyrite and pyromorphite from the Cumbrian and North Yorkshire Pennines. *Proceedings of the Yorkshire Geological Society*, 44, 153-158.

Smith, D. B., 1989. The late Pemian palaeogeography of north-east England. *Proceedings of the Yorkshire Geological Society*, 47, 285-312.

Swift, A. and Martill, D. M., 1999. Fossils of the Rhaetian Penarth Group. *Palaeontological Association Field Guides to Fossils*: No. 9.

Tucker, M. E., 1991. Sequence stratigraphy of carbonate-evaporite basins: models and application to the Upper Permian (Zechstein) of northeast England and adjoining North Sea. *Journal of the Geological Society*, 148, 1019-1036.

Wills, L. J., 1973. A Palaeogeological map of the Palaeozoic floor below the Permian and Mesozoic formations in England and Wales with inferred and speculative reconstructions of the Palaeozoic outcrops in adjacent areas as in Permo-Triassic times. *Memoir of the Geological Society of London*, No. 7.

Young, B., Livingstone, A. and Thomson, N., 1992. Fraipontite from Wensleydale, North Yorkshire. *Proceedings of the Yorkshire Geological Society*, 49, 25-127.

LIFE ON THE EDGE

Alexander, J., 1987. Synsedimentary and burial related deformation in the Middle Jurassic non-marine formations of the Yorkshire Basin, 315-324, in Jones, M. E. and Preston, M. F., (Editors), Deformation of sediments and sedimentary rocks. *Geological Society Special Publication*, No. 29.

Alexander, J., 1989. Delta or coastal plain? With an example of the controversy from the Middle Jurassic of Yorkshire, 11-19, in Whatley, M. K. G. and Pickering, K. T., (Editors), Deltas: sites and traps for fossil fuels. *Geological Society Special Publication*, No. 41.

Alexander, J., 1992. Nature and origin of a latertally extensive alluvial sandstone body in the Middle Jurassic Scalby Formation. *Journal of the Geological Society*, 149, 431-441.

Benton, M. J. and Taylor, M. A., 1984. Marine reptiles from the Upper Lias (Lower Toarcian, Lower Jurassic) of the Yorkshire coast. *Proceedings of the Yorkshire Geological Society*. 44, 399-429.

Clarke, D. V., Cowie, T. G., and Foxon, A., 1985. *Symbols of Power at the time of Stonehenge*. HMSO.

Fisher, M. J. and Hancock, N. J., 1985. The Scalby Formation (middle Jurassic, Ravenscar Group) of Yorkshire: reassessment of age and depositional environment [with discussion from Leeder, M. R. and Alexander, J.]. *Proceedings of the Yorkshire Geological Society*, 45, 293-298.

Glennie, K. W., (Editor), 1998. *Petroleum Geology of the North Sea. Basic concepts and recent advances.* Blackwell.

Gowland, S. and Riding, J. B., 1991. Stratigraphy, sedimentology and palaeontology of the Scarborough Formation (Middle Jurassic) at Hundale Point, North Yorkshire. *Proceedings of the Yorkshire Geological Society*, 48, 375-392.

Howard, A. S., 1985. Lithostratigraphy of the Staithes Sandstone and Cleveland Ironstone formations (Lower Jurassic) of north-east Yorkshire. *Proceedings of the Yorkshire Geological Society*, 45, 261-275.

Ivimey-Cook, H. C. and Powell, J. H., 1991. Late Triassic and early Jurassic biostratigraphy of the Felixkirk Borehole, North Yorkshire. *Proceedings of the Yorkshire Geological Society*, 48, 367-374.

Jeans, C. V., Wray, D. S., Mitchell, J. G. and Ditchfield, P., 2005. Correlation between the basal part of the Lower Cretaceous Speeton Clay Formation, Yorkshire, and the Purbeck Limestone Group, Dorset: a bentonite tie line. *Proceedings of the Yorkshire Geological Society*, 55, 183-197.

Kantorowicz, J. D., 1990. Lateral and vertical variations in pedogenesis and other early diagenetic phenomena, Middle Jurassic Ravenscar Group, Yorkshire. *Proceedings of the Yorkshire Geological Society*, 48, 61-74.

Kent, P. E., 1980. Subsidence and uplift in east Yorkshire and Lincolnshire: a double inversion. *Proceedings of the Yorkshire Geological Society*, 42, 505-524.

Knox, R. W. O'B., 1984. Lithostratigraphy and depositional history of the late Toarcian sequence at Ravenscar, Yorkshire. *Proceedings of the Yorkshire Geological Society*, 45, 99-108.

Knox, R. W. O'B., Howard, A. S., Powell, J.H. and Buchem, F. S. P. van, 1990. Lower and Middle Jurassic sediments of the Cleveland Basin N.E. England: shallow marine and paralic facies seen in their sequence stratigraphic context. 13th *International Sedimentological Congress Field Guide*, No. 5.

Lott, G. K. and Humphreys, B., 1992. The stratigraphy and petrology of Middle Jurassic (Ravenscar Group) sedimenst cored in boreholes from the north Yorkshire coast. *Proceedings of the Yorkshire Geological Society*, 49, 23-40.

Martill, D. M. and Hudson, J. D., 1991. Fossils of the Oxford Clay. *Palaeontological Association Field Guides to Fossils*: No. 4.

Mitchell, S. F. and Underwood, C. J., 1999. Lithological and faunal stratigraphy of the Aptian and Albian (Lower Cretaceous) of the type Speeton Clay, Speeton, north-east England. *Proceedings of the Yorkshire Geological Society*, 52, 277-296.

Morgans, H. S., 1999. Lower and Middle Jurassic woods of the Cleveland basin (North Yorkshire), England. *Palaeontology*, 42, 303-328.

Powell, J. H., 1984. Lithostratigraphical nomenclature of the Lias Group. *Proceedings of the Yorkshire Geological Society*, 45, 51-57.

Price, G. D., 1998. Isotopic variation in fossils and matrix of the Cretaceous Red Chalk at Speeton and South Ferriby, Yorkshire, England. *Proceedings of the Yorkshire Geological Society*, 52, 107-112.

Rawson, P. R., Greensmith, J. T. and Shalaby, S. E., 1983. Coarsening-upwards cycles in the uppermost Staithes and Cleveland Ironstone Formations (Lower Jurassic) of the Yorkshire coast, England. *Proceedings of the Geologists' Association*, 94, 91-93.

Romano, M. and Whyte, M. A., 2003. Jurassic dinosaur tracks of the Cleveland Basin, Yorkshire: preservation, diversity and distribution. *Proceedings of the Yorkshire Geological Society*, 54, 185-215.

Smith, A. B. and Batten, D. J., (Editors), 2002. Fossils of the Chalk. *Palaeontological Association Field Guides to Fossils*: No. 2.

Taylor, M. A., 1992. Taxonomy and taphonomy of *Rhomaleosaurus zetlandicus* (Plesiosauria, Reptilia) from the Toarcian (Lower Jurassic) of the Yorkshire coast. *Proceedings of the Yorkshire Geological Society*, 49, 49-55.

Taylor, P. D., (Editor), 1995. *Field Geology of the British Jurassic*. The Geological Society of London

Underwood, C. J., 2004, Barremian and Aptian (Cretaceous) sharks and rays from Speeton, Yorkshire, NE England. *Proceedings of the Yorkshire Geological*

Society, **55**, 107-118.

van Konijnenburg-van Cittert, J. H. A. and Morgans, H. S., 1999. The Jurassic Flora of Yorkshire. *Palaeontological Association Field Guides to Fossils*: No. 8.

van Konijnenburg-van Cittert, J. H. A., 2008. The Jurassic fossil plant record of the UK area. *Proceedings of the Geologists' Association*, **119**, 59-72.

Wray, D. S. and Wood, C. J., 1998. Distinction between detrital and volcanogenic clay-rich beds in Turonian-Coniacian chalks of eastern England. *Proceedings of the Yorkshire Geological Society*, **52**, 95-105.

Whitham, F., 1991. The stratigraphy of the Upper Cretaceous Ferriby, Welton and Burnham formations north of the Humber, north-east England. *Proceedings of the Yorkshire Geological Society*, **48**, 227-254.

Whitham, F., 1993. The stratigraphy of the Upper Cretaceous Flamborough Chalk Formation north of the Humber, north-east England. *Proceedings of the Yorkshire Geological Society*, **49**, 235-258.

Whyte, M. A. and Romano, M., 2001. A dinosaur ichnocoenosis from the Middle Jurassic of Yorkshire, UK. *Ichnos*, **8**, 223-234.

Wright, J. K., 1972. The stratigraphy of the Yorkshire Corallian. *Proceedings of the Yorkshire Geological Society*, **39**, 225-266 + 2 pls.

Wright, J. K., 1992. The depositional history of the Hackness Coral-Sponge Bed and its associated sediments within the Passage Beds Member of the Coralline Oolite Formation (Coralline Group; Oxfordian) of North Yorkshire. *Proceedings of the Yorkshire Geological Society*, **49**, 155-168.

Young, T. P. 1994. The Blea Wyke Sandstone Formation (Jurassic, Toarcian) of Rosedale, North Yorkshire, UK. *Proceedings of the Yorkshire Geological Society*, **50**, 129-142.

LANDSCAPE EVOLUTION

Cooper, R. G. and Halliwell, R. A., 1976. A relict karst feature in the Hambleton Hills, North Yorkshire. *Proceedings of the Yorkshire Geological Society*, **41**, 71-73.

Holiday, D. W., 1999. Palaeotemperatures, thermal modeling and depth of burial studies in northern and eastern England. *Proceedings of the Yorkshire Geological Society*, **52**, 337-352.

Macdonald, R., Wilson, L., Thorpe, R. S., and Martin, A., 1988. Emplacement of the Cleveland Dyke. Evidence from geochemistry, mineralogy, and physical modeling. *Journal of Petrology*, **29**, 559-583.

Milsom, J., Holdsworth, J., and Shorter, J., 2006. The eastern end of the Cleveland Dyke, North Yorkshire, UK. *Proceedings of the Yorkshire Geological Society*, **56**, 1-4.

Starmer, I. C., 1995. Deformation of the Upper Cretaceous Chalk at Selwicks Bay, Flamborough Head, Yorkshire: Its significance in the structural evolution of north-east England and the North Sea Basin. *Proceedings of the Yorkshire Geological Society*, **50**, 213-228.

ICE WORLDS AND THE YORKSHIRE UNDERGROUND

Boylan, P. J., 1981. A new revision of the Pleistocene mammalian fauna of Kirkdale Cave, Yorkshire. *Proceedings of the Yorkshire Geological Society*, **43**, 253-280.

Catt, J. A., 2007. The Pleistocene glaciations in eastern Yorkshire. *Proceedings of the Yorkshire Geological Society*, **56**, 177-207.

Gaunt, G. D., 1976. The Devensian ice limit in the Vale of York. *Proceedings of the Yorkshire Geological Society*, **40**, 631-637.

Goudie, A., 1990, *The landforms of England and Wales*. Basil Blackwell.

King, R. J., 1982. A new occurrence of scarbroite in Britain. *Journal of the Russell Society*, **1**, 9-18.

Lane, N. F., Watts, A. B. and Farrant, A. R., 2008. An analysis of Cotswold topography: insights into the landscape response to denudational isostasy. *Journal of the Geological Society, London*, **165**, 85-103.

Murphy, P., 2007, Cave development in the Yorkshire Dales. *Teaching Earth Sciences*, **32**, 23-26.

Waltham, Tony, 1987. *Yorkshire Dales: limestone country*. Constable, London.

Waltham, Tony, and Davies, Martin, 1987. Caves and karst of the Yorkshire Dales. British Cave Research Association, *Cave Studies Series*, Number 1.

YORKSHIRE WATER

Cooper, A. H. and Burgess, I. C., 1993. Geology of the Country around Harrogate. *Memoir of the Geological Survey*.

VISITORS FROM OUTER-SPACE

Hindley, K., 1979. Skylab isn't all that's falling. *Science News*, **115**, 426.

Index